✳ **HAESE MATHEMATICS**

Specialists in mathematics publishing

Mathematics

for the international student
Mathematics HL (Option):
Calculus

HL Topic 9
FM Topic 5

Catherine Quinn

Chris Sangwin

Robert Haese

Michael Haese

 or use with

B Diploma

Programme

D1511848

MATHEMATICS FOR THE INTERNATIONAL STUDENT
Mathematics HL (Option): Calculus

Catherine Quinn   B.Sc.(Hons), Grad.Dip.Ed., Ph.D.
Chris Sangwin   M.A., M.Sc., Ph.D.
Robert Haese   B.Sc.
Michael Haese   B.Sc.(Hons.), Ph.D.

Published by Haese Mathematics
152 Richmond Road, Marleston, SA 5033, AUSTRALIA
Telephone: +61 8 8210 4666, Fax: +61 8 8354 1238
Email: info@haesemathematics.com.au
Web: www.haesemathematics.com.au

National Library of Australia Card Number & ISBN 978-1-921972-33-1

© Haese & Harris Publications 2013

First Edition   2013
Reprinted   2013, 2015 (twice), 2017

Artwork by Brian Houston and Gregory Olesinski.

Cover design by Piotr Poturaj.

Computer software by Thomas Jansson, Troy Cruickshank, and Adrian Blackburn.

Typeset in Australia by Deanne Gallasch. Typeset in Times Roman $10\frac{1}{2}$.

Printed in China by Prolong Press Limited.

The textbook has been developed independently of the International Baccalaureate Organization (IBO). The textbook is in no way connected with, or endorsed by, the IBO.

Acknowledgements: While every attempt has been made to trace and acknowledge copyright, the authors and publishers apologise for any accidental infringement where copyright has proved untraceable. They would be pleased to come to a suitable agreement with the rightful owner.

Disclaimer: All the internet addresses (URLs) given in this book were valid at the time of printing. While the authors and publisher regret any inconvenience that changes of address may cause readers, no responsibility for any such changes can be accepted by either the authors or the publisher.

FOREWORD

Mathematics HL (Option): Calculus has been written as a companion book to the Mathematics HL (Core) textbook. Together, they aim to provide students and teachers with appropriate coverage of the two-year Mathematics HL Course, first examined in 2014.

This book covers all sub-topics set out in Mathematics HL Option Topic 9 and Further Mathematics HL Topic 5, Calculus.

The aim of this topic is to introduce students to the basic concepts and techniques of differential and integral calculus and their applications.

Detailed explanations and key facts are highlighted throughout the text. Each sub-topic contains numerous Worked Examples, highlighting each step necessary to reach the answer for that example.

Theory of Knowledge is a core requirement in the International Baccalaureate Diploma Programme, whereby students are encouraged to think critically and challenge the assumptions of knowledge. Discussion topics for Theory of Knowledge have been included on pages 129 and 140. These aim to help students discover and express their views on knowledge issues.

The accompanying online component includes online access to the full text and specially designed graphing software.

Graphics calculator instructions for Casio fx-9860G Plus, Casio fx-CG20, TI-84 Plus and TI-*n*spire are available from icons located throughout the book.

Fully worked solutions are provided at the back of the text, however students are encouraged to attempt each question before referring to the solution.

It is not our intention to define the course. Teachers are encouraged to use other resources. We have developed this book independently of the International Baccalaureate Organization (IBO) in consultation with experienced teachers of IB Mathematics. The Text is not endorsed by the IBO.

In this changing world of mathematics education, we believe that the contextual approach shown in this book, with associated use of technology, will enhance the student's understanding, knowledge and appreciation of mathematics and its universal applications.

We welcome your feedback.

Email: *info@haesemathematics.com.au*

Web: *www.haesemathematics.com.au*

CTQ   CS
RCH   PMH

ACKNOWLEDGEMENTS

The authors and publishers would like to thank all those teachers who offered advice and encouragement on this book, with particular mention to Peter Blythe.

ONLINE FEATURES

With the purchase of a new hard copy textbook, you will gain 27 months subscription to our online product. This subscription can be renewed for a small fee.

Students can revisit concepts taught in class and undertake their own revision and practice online.

By clicking on the relevant icon, a range of interactive features can be accessed:

- ◆ Graphics calculator instructions
- ◆ Interactive links to graphing software

Graphics calculator instructions: Detailed instructions are available online, as printable pages. Click on the icon throughout the book for Casio fx-9860G Plus, Casio fx-CG20, TI-84 Plus, or TI-nspire instructions.

COMPATIBILITY

For iPads, tablets, and other mobile devices, the interactive features may not work. However, the digital version of the textbook and additional pages can be viewed online using any of these devices.

REGISTERING

You will need to register to access the online features of this textbook.
Visit www.haesemathematics.com.au/register and follow the instructions. Once you have registered, you can:

- • activate your digital textbook
- • use your account to purchase additional digital products.

To activate your digital textbook, contact Haese Mathematics. On providing proof of purchase, your digital textbook will be activated. **It is important that you keep your receipt as proof of purchase.**

For general queries about registering and licence keys:

- • Visit our Snowflake help page: http://snowflake.haesemathematics.com.au/help

ONLINE VERSION OF THE TEXTBOOK

The entire text of the book can be viewed online, allowing you to leave your textbook at school.

TABLE OF CONTENTS

SYMBOLS AND NOTATION USED IN THIS BOOK

$\approx$	is approximately equal to
$>$	is greater than
$\geqslant$	is greater than or equal to
$<$	is less than
$\leqslant$	is less than or equal to
$\{\ldots\ldots\}$	the set of all elements ......
$\in$	is an element of
$\notin$	is not an element of
$\mathbb{N}$	the set of all natural numbers
$\mathbb{Z}$	the set of integers
$\mathbb{Q}$	the set of rational numbers
$\mathbb{R}$	the set of real numbers
$\mathbb{Z}^+$	the set of positive integers
$\subseteq$	is a subset of
$\subset$	is a proper subset of
$\Rightarrow$	implies that
$\not\Rightarrow$	does not imply that
$f:\ A \to B$	f is a function under which each element of set A has an image in set B
$f:\ x \mapsto y$	f is a function under which x is mapped to y
$f(x)$	the image of x under the function f
$f \circ g$	or $f(g(x))$ the composite function of f and g
$|x|$	the modulus or absolute value of x
$[a, b]$	the closed interval $\quad a \leqslant x \leqslant b$
$]a, b[$	the open interval $\quad a < x < b$
u_n	the nth term of a sequence or series
$\{u_n\}$	the sequence with nth term u_n
S_n	the sum of the first n terms of a sequence
S_∞	the sum to infinity of a series
$\displaystyle\sum_{i=1}^{n} u_i$	$u_1 + u_2 + u_3 + \ldots. + u_n$
$\displaystyle\prod_{i=1}^{n} u_i$	$u_1 \times u_2 \times u_3 \times \ldots. \times u_n$

$\displaystyle\lim_{x \to a} f(x)$	the limit of $f(x)$ as x tends to a
$\displaystyle\lim_{x \to a+} f(x)$	the limit of $f(x)$ as x tends to a from the positive side of a
$\displaystyle\lim_{x \to a-} f(x)$	the limit of $f(x)$ as x tends to a from the negative side of a
$\max\{a, b\}$	the maximum value of a or b
$\displaystyle\sum_{n=0}^{\infty} c_n x^n$	the power series whose terms have form $c_n x^n$
$\dfrac{dy}{dx}$	the derivative of y with respect to x
$f'(x)$	the derivative of $f(x)$ with respect to x
$\dfrac{d^2 y}{dx^2}$	the second derivative of y with respect to x
$f''(x)$	the second derivative of $f(x)$ with respect to x
$\dfrac{d^n y}{dx^n}$	the nth derivative of y with respect to x
$f^{(n)}(x)$	the nth derivative of $f(x)$ with respect to x
$\int y\, dx$	the indefinite integral of y with respect to x
$\int_a^b y\, dx$	the definite integral of y with respect to x between the limits $x = a$ and $x = b$
e^x	exponential function of x
$\ln x$	the natural logarithm of x
sin, cos, tan	the circular functions
csc, sec, cot	the reciprocal circular functions
arcsin, arccos, arctan	the inverse circular functions
$A(x, y)$	the point A in the plane with Cartesian coordinates x and y
[AB]	the line segment with end points A and B
AB	the length of [AB]
$\widehat{A}$	the angle at A
$\widehat{CAB}$ or $\angle CAB$	the angle between [CA] and [AB]
$\triangle ABC$	the triangle whose vertices are A, B, and C
$\parallel$	is parallel to
$\perp$	is perpendicular to

NUMBER PROPERTIES

IMPORTANT NUMBER SETS

You should be familiar with the following important number sets:

- $\mathbb{Z}^+ = \{1, 2, 3, ...\}$ is the set of **positive integers**.
- $\mathbb{N} = \{0, 1, 2, 3, ...\}$ is the set of **natural numbers**.
- $\mathbb{Z} = \{...., -2, -1, 0, 1, 2, ...\}$ is the set of **integers**.
- $\mathbb{Q}$ is the set of **rational numbers**. These are numbers which can be expressed in the form $\frac{p}{q}$ where $p, q \in \mathbb{Z}$, $q \neq 0$.
- $\mathbb{R}$ is the set of **real numbers** comprising the rational numbers $\mathbb{Q}$, and the irrational numbers which lie on the number line but cannot be expressed as a ratio of integers.

The number sets follow the hierarchy $\mathbb{Z}^+ \subset \mathbb{N} \subset \mathbb{Z} \subset \mathbb{Q} \subset \mathbb{R}$.

In this option topic we will be principally concerned with the set $\mathbb{R}$. Rigorous treatments of the algebraic and set theoretic properties of $\mathbb{R}$, such as the fact that $\mathbb{R}$ is a continuous set, are available in a variety of calculus and analysis books. However, we will outline here only those results of most immediate relevance to our work with limits, sequences, and series.

A **closed** interval consisting of all real numbers from a to b *inclusive* is denoted $[a, b]$.
$[a, b]$ is $\{x \mid a \leqslant x \leqslant b\}$.

An **open** interval consisting of all real numbers *between* a and b is denoted $]a, b[$.
$]a, b[$ is $\{x \mid a < x < b\}$.

THE ABSOLUTE VALUE FUNCTION

For any $a \in \mathbb{R}$, the **absolute value of** a, denoted by $|a|$, is defined by:

$$|a| = \begin{cases} a & \text{if } a \geqslant 0 \\ -a & \text{if } a < 0 \end{cases}$$

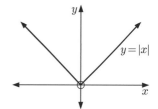

The absolute value $|a|$ of a number $a \in \mathbb{R}$ is the distance from a to the origin on the real number line. More generally, the distance between two numbers $a, b \in \mathbb{R}$ on the number line is given by $|a - b|$.

The absolute value function has the following properties:

1 $|a| \geqslant 0$ for all $a \in \mathbb{R}$.

2 $|-a| = |a|$ for all $a \in \mathbb{R}$.

3 $|ab| = |a| \, |b|$ for all $a, b \in \mathbb{R}$.

4 $a = |a|$ or $-|a|$, and hence $-|a| \leqslant a \leqslant |a|$ for all $a \in \mathbb{R}$.

5 If $c \geqslant 0$ then $|a| \leqslant c$ if and only if $-c \leqslant a \leqslant c$.

We will also need the property of real numbers that:

$$\text{If } \quad a \leqslant c \quad \text{and} \quad b \leqslant d, \quad \text{then} \quad a + b \leqslant c + d, \quad \text{for} \quad a, b, c, d \in \mathbb{R}.$$

Proof of Property 5:

$\Rightarrow$ Suppose that $|a| \leqslant c$.

     Since $a \leqslant |a|$ and $-a \leqslant |a|$, we find $a \leqslant |a| \leqslant c$ and $-a \leqslant |a| \leqslant c$

$$\therefore \quad a \leqslant c \quad \text{and} \quad -a \leqslant c.$$

     But $-a \leqslant c$ is equivalent to $-c \leqslant a$, so combining the two inequalities we have $-c \leqslant a \leqslant c$.

$\Leftarrow$ If $-c \leqslant a \leqslant c$, then $a \leqslant c$ and $-c \leqslant a$.

$$\therefore \quad -a \leqslant c.$$

$\therefore$ since $|a| = a$ or $-a$, $\quad |a| \leqslant c$.

For a proof "if and only if" we prove it one way $\Rightarrow$ and then the other $\Leftarrow$.

THE TRIANGLE INEQUALITY

The **Triangle Inequality** states:

$$\text{For any} \quad a, b \in \mathbb{R}, \quad |a + b| \leqslant |a| + |b|.$$

Proof:

From **Property 4** we have $\quad -|a| \leqslant a \leqslant |a| \quad$ and $\quad -|b| \leqslant b \leqslant |b| \quad$ for all $a, b \in \mathbb{R}$.

Adding these inequalities gives $\quad -(|a| + |b|) \leqslant a + b \leqslant |a| + |b|$.

Using **Property 5** with $c = |a| + |b|$, this is equivalent to $\quad |a + b| \leqslant |a| + |b|$.

Corollaries:

    1 $|a - b| \leqslant |a| + |b| \quad$ for all $\quad a, b \in \mathbb{R}$.

    2 $|a| - |b| \leqslant |a + b| \quad$ for all $\quad a, b \in \mathbb{R}$.

    3 $|a| - |b| \leqslant |a - b| \quad$ for all $\quad a, b \in \mathbb{R}$.

Proofs:

    1   By the Triangle Inequality, we have $\quad |a + c| \leqslant |a| + |c| \quad$ for all $\quad a, c \in \mathbb{R}$.

       $\therefore$ letting $c = -b$, we get $\quad |a - b| \leqslant |a| + |-b| \quad$ for all $\quad a, b \in \mathbb{R}$.

$$\therefore \quad |a - b| \leqslant |a| + |b|$$

    2 $|a| = |(a + b) + (-b)|$

      $\therefore$ $|a| \leqslant |a + b| + |-b| \quad$ for all $\quad a, b \in \mathbb{R} \quad$ by the Triangle Inequality.

        $\therefore$ $|a| - |b| \leqslant |a + b|$

    3 $|a| = |(a - b) + b|$

      $\therefore$ $|a| \leqslant |a - b| + |b| \quad$ for all $\quad a, b \in \mathbb{R} \quad$ by the Triangle Inequality.

        $\therefore$ $|a| - |b| \leqslant |a - b|$

EXERCISE A

1 Prove that $|a| \geqslant 0$ for all $a \in \mathbb{R}$.

2 Prove that $|-a| = |a|$ for all $a \in \mathbb{R}$.

3 Prove that $|a_1 + a_2 + \ldots + a_n| \leqslant |a_1| + |a_2| + \ldots + |a_n|$ for any $a_1, a_2, \ldots, a_n \in \mathbb{R}$.

4 If $a < x < b$ and $a < y < b$ show that $|x - y| < b - a$.
Interpret this result geometrically.

5 Prove that $|a - b| \leqslant |a - c| + |c - b|$.

6 Prove that if $|x - a| < \dfrac{a}{2}$ then $x > \dfrac{a}{2}$.

7 If $|x - a| < \varepsilon$ and $|y - b| < \varepsilon$ show that $|(x + y) - (a + b)| < 2\varepsilon$.

8 The **Archimedean Property** states that for each pair of positive real numbers a and b, there is a natural number n such that $na > b$.
Use the Archimedean Property to prove that for each positive number ε there is a natural number n such that $\dfrac{1}{n} < \varepsilon$.

> The properties of $\mathbb{R}$ in questions **8** and **9** are needed later in the course.

9 Prove the **Bernoulli Inequality** by mathematical induction:
If $x > -1$ then $(1 + x)^n \geqslant 1 + nx$ for all $n \in \mathbb{Z}^+$.

10 The Well-Ordering Principle states that every non-empty subset of $\mathbb{Z}^+$ has a least element.
Show that the Well-Ordering Principle does not apply to $\mathbb{R}^+$, the set of positive real numbers.

11 If $r \neq 0$ is rational and x is irrational, prove that $r + x$ and rx are irrational.

> For questions **10** and **11** you will need to write a **proof by contradiction**. For help with this, consult **Appendix A: Methods of proof**.

B   LIMITS

Consider a real function $f(x)$ whose domain D is a subset of $\mathbb{R}$. We can write $f : D \to \mathbb{R}$.

∞ is not a real number. $x \to \infty$ refers to positive values of x becoming increasingly large.

We wish to examine the behaviour of the function:

- as x approaches some particular finite value $a \in \mathbb{R}$, so $x \to a$
- as x tends to infinity or negative infinity, so $x \to \infty$ or $x \to -\infty$, when $D = \mathbb{R}$.

We shall work with the following *informal* definition of a limit of a function. For more information, consult **Appendix B: Formal definition of a limit**.

> Let $a \in \mathbb{R}$ be a fixed real number. Let f be a function defined in an open interval about $x = a$, except $f(a)$ need not be defined. We say the number l is the **limit of f as x approaches a**, provided $f(x)$ becomes as close as we like to l by choosing values of x close enough, but not equal to, the number a. We write $\lim\limits_{x \to a} f(x) = l$.

From this definition, we see that $f(x)$ gets closer and closer to l as x gets closer and closer to a, from either side of a.

If the function does not approach a finite value l, we say the limit **does not exist** (DNE).

If $f(x)$ gets closer and closer to l as x gets closer and closer to a from the right of a (where $x > a$), we say "x approaches a from the right", and write $\lim\limits_{x \to a^+} f(x) = l$.

If $f(x)$ gets closer and closer to l as x gets closer and closer to a from the left of a (where $x < a$), we say "x approaches a from the left", and write $\lim\limits_{x \to a^-} f(x) = l$.

> For $a \in \mathbb{R}$, $\lim\limits_{x \to a} f(x)$ exists if and only if both $\lim\limits_{x \to a^-} f(x)$ and $\lim\limits_{x \to a^+} f(x)$ *exist* and are *equal*.
> In this case $\lim\limits_{x \to a} f(x) = \lim\limits_{x \to a^-} f(x) = \lim\limits_{x \to a^+} f(x)$.

For example:

-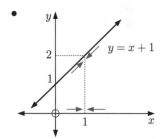

$$\lim_{x \to 1} (x + 1) = 2$$

In this case $f(1)$ can be evaluated directly, but we do not do this. Instead, when calculating limits we consider the behaviour of $f(x)$ for x *close to* 1.

- $y = \dfrac{x^2 - 1}{x - 1}$ is not defined at $x = 1$. This is not a

  problem, since in determining the limit as x approaches
  1, we never let x actually reach the value 1. But as we
  make x very, very close to value 1, we can make $f(x)$ as
  close as we like to value 2.

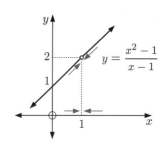

$$\lim_{x \to 1} \frac{x^2 - 1}{x - 1} = \lim_{x \to 1} \frac{(x - 1)(x + 1)}{(x - 1)} \quad \{\text{since } x \neq 1\}$$

$$= \lim_{x \to 1} x + 1$$

$$= 2$$

-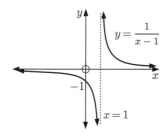

  As $x \to 1^-$, $f(x) \to -\infty$.

  As $x \to 1^+$, $f(x) \to \infty$.

  There is no finite real number that $f(x)$ approaches as x
  approaches value 1, so the limit of f as x approaches 1
  does not exist (DNE).

  So, $\displaystyle\lim_{x \to 1} \frac{1}{x - 1}$ DNE.

- Consider $f(x) = \begin{cases} x + 1, & x \leqslant 1 \\ x^2, & x > 1. \end{cases}$

  As $x \to 1^-$, $f(x) \to 2$ and so $\displaystyle\lim_{x \to 1^-} f(x) = 2$.

  As $x \to 1^+$, $f(x) \to 1$ and so $\displaystyle\lim_{x \to 1^+} f(x) = 1$.

  Since $\displaystyle\lim_{x \to 1^-} f(x) \neq \lim_{x \to 1^+} f(x)$,   there is no *unique*

  value which the function approaches as $x \to 1$.

  $\therefore$ $\displaystyle\lim_{x \to 1} f(x)$ DNE.

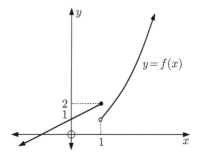

-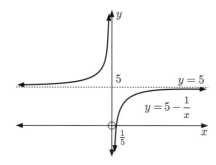

  We can make $f(x)$ as close as we like to value 5 by
  making x large enough.

  As $x \to \infty$, $f(x) \to 5$ from below.

  We write $\displaystyle\lim_{x \to \infty} f(x) = 5^-$.

  Similarly, as $x \to -\infty$, $f(x) \to 5$ from above.

  We write $\displaystyle\lim_{x \to -\infty} f(x) = 5^+$.

Example 1

By examining the graphs of $y = x$, $y = \dfrac{1}{x}$, and $y = \dfrac{1}{x^2}$, establish the following limits:

a $\displaystyle\lim_{x \to \infty} x$ DNE **b** $\displaystyle\lim_{x \to \infty} \dfrac{1}{x} = 0$ **c** $\displaystyle\lim_{x \to \infty} \dfrac{1}{x^2} = 0$ **d** $\displaystyle\lim_{x \to 0} \dfrac{1}{x}$ DNE

a

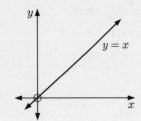

As $x \to \infty$, $y = x \to \infty$

$\therefore \displaystyle\lim_{x \to \infty} x$ DNE.

b

As $x \to \infty$, $\dfrac{1}{x} \to 0^+$

$\therefore \displaystyle\lim_{x \to \infty} \dfrac{1}{x} = 0$.

c

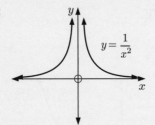

As $x \to \infty$, $\dfrac{1}{x^2} \to 0^+$

$\therefore \displaystyle\lim_{x \to \infty} \dfrac{1}{x^2} = 0$.

d

As $x \to 0^+$, $\dfrac{1}{x} \to \infty$

As $x \to 0^-$, $\dfrac{1}{x} \to -\infty$

$\therefore \displaystyle\lim_{x \to 0} \dfrac{1}{x}$ DNE.

EXERCISE B.1

1 By examining the graphs of $y = -x$, $y = -\dfrac{1}{x}$, and $y = -\dfrac{1}{x^2}$, establish the following limits:

a $\displaystyle\lim_{x \to \infty} (-x)$ DNE **b** $\displaystyle\lim_{x \to \infty} \left(-\dfrac{1}{x}\right) = 0$ **c** $\displaystyle\lim_{x \to \infty} \left(-\dfrac{1}{x^2}\right) = 0$ **d** $\displaystyle\lim_{x \to 0} \left(-\dfrac{1}{x}\right)$ DNE

2 Sketch each function and determine the existence or otherwise of $\displaystyle\lim_{x \to a} f(x)$.

a $f(x) = 3x + 2$, $a = -1$

b $f(x) = \dfrac{x^2 + x - 2}{x + 2}$, $a = -2$

3 **a** Sketch the function $f(x) = \begin{cases} \sin x, & x \geqslant \frac{\pi}{2} \\ \dfrac{2x}{\pi}, & x < \frac{\pi}{2}. \end{cases}$

b Hence determine $\displaystyle\lim_{x \to \frac{\pi}{2}^-} f(x)$ and $\displaystyle\lim_{x \to \frac{\pi}{2}^+} f(x)$.

    c Determine the existence or otherwise of $\lim\limits_{x\to\frac{\pi}{2}} f(x)$.

4   **a** Sketch the function $f(x) = \dfrac{x+1}{x-1}$.

    b Determine the existence or otherwise of:

      i $\lim\limits_{x\to-\infty} f(x)$ **ii** $\lim\limits_{x\to\infty} f(x)$ **iii** $\lim\limits_{x\to1} f(x)$

5 Let $f(x) = \begin{cases} x^2, & x > 3 \\ 5, & x = 3 \\ 3x, & x < 3. \end{cases}$

    a Sketch the graph of $y = f(x)$.   **b** Evaluate $\lim\limits_{x\to3^-} f(x)$ and $\lim\limits_{x\to3^+} f(x)$.

    c Does $\lim\limits_{x\to3} f(x)$ exist? Explain your answer.

6 Does $\lim\limits_{x\to0} \sqrt{x}$ exist? Explain your answer.

7 For each of the following functions, discuss the limits:

      i $\lim\limits_{x\to0^-} f(x)$ **ii** $\lim\limits_{x\to0^+} f(x)$ **iii** $\lim\limits_{x\to0} f(x)$

    a $f(x) = \begin{cases} (x-1)^3, & x \leqslant 0 \\ 1, & x > 0 \end{cases}$ **b** $f(x) = \begin{cases} \sin x, & x < 0 \\ \dfrac{x^2 - 3x + 5}{5}, & x > 0 \end{cases}$

    c $f(x) = \sin\left(\dfrac{1}{x}\right), \; x \neq 0$

THE LIMIT LAWS

We often define new functions using a sum, composition, or some other combination of simpler functions. The limit laws help us calculate limits for these new functions using what we already know about the simpler functions. For information about proving these laws, consult **Appendix B: Formal definition of a limit**.

> If $f(x) = c$ a constant, where $c \in \mathbb{R}$, then $\lim\limits_{x\to a} f(x) = \lim\limits_{x\to a} c = c$, for all $a \in \mathbb{R}$.

We can state the **limit laws** as follows:

> Consider real functions $f(x)$ and $g(x)$ for which $\lim\limits_{x\to a} f(x) = l$ and $\lim\limits_{x\to a} g(x) = m$, where $a, l, m \in \mathbb{R}$.
>
> - $\lim\limits_{x\to a} cf(x) = cl$ for any constant $c \in \mathbb{R}$
> - $\lim\limits_{x\to a} (f(x) \pm g(x)) = l \pm m$
> - $\lim\limits_{x\to a} f(x)\, g(x) = lm$
> - $\lim\limits_{x\to a} \left(\dfrac{f(x)}{g(x)}\right) = \dfrac{l}{m}$ provided $m \neq 0$
> - $\lim\limits_{x\to a} f(x)^n = l^n$ for all $n \in \mathbb{Z}^+$
> - $\lim\limits_{x\to a} \sqrt[n]{f(x)} = \sqrt[n]{l}$ for all $n \in \mathbb{Z}^+$ provided $l \geqslant 0$

From the first limit law we see that multiplying by the constant 1 will not change the value or existence of a limit. When evaluating many limits, it often helps to multiply by 1 in a well-chosen form. We will use this technique for rational functions.

RATIONAL FUNCTIONS

$f(x)$ is a **rational function** if it can be written in the form $f(x) = \dfrac{p(x)}{q(x)}$, where p, q are real polynomials.

Suppose x^m is the highest power of x present in either p or q.

To examine $\displaystyle\lim_{x \to \infty} \dfrac{p(x)}{q(x)}$ or $\displaystyle\lim_{x \to -\infty} \dfrac{p(x)}{q(x)}$, we divide all terms in the numerator and denominator by x^m.

$$\lim_{x \to \infty} \frac{p(x)}{q(x)} = \lim_{x \to \infty} \frac{p(x)}{q(x)} \times \frac{\frac{1}{x^m}}{\frac{1}{x^m}} \quad \text{since} \quad \frac{\frac{1}{x^m}}{\frac{1}{x^m}} = 1 \quad \text{for all} \quad x \neq 0 \quad \text{and multiplying by the constant 1}$$

does not change the value of the limit.

For rational functions, this allows us to make use of the known limits $\displaystyle\lim_{x \to \pm\infty} \frac{1}{x^m} = 0$ for all $m \in \mathbb{Z}^+$.

Example 2

Determine the existence or otherwise of the following limits:

a $\displaystyle\lim_{x \to \infty} \frac{x + 5}{-2x^2 + x + 1}$
  b $\displaystyle\lim_{x \to \infty} \frac{10x^2 - 5}{3x^2 + x + 2}$
  c $\displaystyle\lim_{x \to \infty} \frac{x^2 + x + 1}{x - 2}$

---

a
$$\lim_{x \to \infty} \frac{x + 5}{-2x^2 + x + 1}$$

$$= \lim_{x \to \infty} \frac{x + 5}{-2x^2 + x + 1} \times \frac{\frac{1}{x^2}}{\frac{1}{x^2}}$$

$$= \lim_{x \to \infty} \frac{\frac{1}{x} + \frac{5}{x^2}}{-2 + \frac{1}{x} + \frac{1}{x^2}}$$

$$= \frac{0}{-2} \quad \{\text{as } x \to \infty, \; \tfrac{1}{x} \to 0 \text{ and } \tfrac{1}{x^2} \to 0\}$$

$$= 0$$

b
$$\lim_{x \to \infty} \frac{10x^2 - 5}{3x^2 + x + 2}$$

$$= \lim_{x \to \infty} \frac{10x^2 - 5}{3x^2 + x + 2} \times \frac{\frac{1}{x^2}}{\frac{1}{x^2}}$$

$$= \lim_{x \to \infty} \frac{10 - \frac{5}{x^2}}{3 + \frac{1}{x} + \frac{2}{x^2}}$$

$$= \frac{10}{3}$$

c $\displaystyle\lim_{x \to \infty} \frac{x^2 + x + 1}{x - 2} = \lim_{x \to \infty} \frac{x^2 + x + 1}{x - 2} \times \frac{\frac{1}{x^2}}{\frac{1}{x^2}} = \lim_{x \to \infty} \frac{1 + \frac{1}{x} + \frac{1}{x^2}}{\frac{1}{x} - \frac{2}{x^2}}$

As $x \to \infty$, the numerator $\to 1$, but the denominator $\to 0$.

Hence as $x \to \infty$, $\dfrac{x^2 + x + 1}{x - 2} \to \infty$.

$\therefore \displaystyle\lim_{x \to \infty} \frac{x^2 + x + 1}{x - 2}$ DNE.

EXERCISE B.2

1 Evaluate the following limits, where possible:

a $\displaystyle\lim_{x \to 1} \frac{x + 1}{x^2 - 2x - 3}$
  b $\displaystyle\lim_{x \to -1} \frac{x + 1}{x^2 - 2x - 3}$
  c $\displaystyle\lim_{x \to 0} \frac{x^2 + 3x - 4}{x - 1}$

d $\displaystyle\lim_{x \to 1} \frac{x^2 + 3x - 4}{x - 1}$
  e $\displaystyle\lim_{y \to 2} \frac{1}{y - 5}\left(\frac{1}{y} - \frac{1}{5}\right)$
  f $\displaystyle\lim_{y \to 5} \frac{1}{y - 5}\left(\frac{1}{y} - \frac{1}{5}\right)$

2 Evaluate the following limits, where possible:

a $\displaystyle\lim_{x\to 2^-} \frac{\ln x}{\sqrt{2-x}}$

b $\displaystyle\lim_{x\to 0} \frac{\sin x}{e^x}$

c $\displaystyle\lim_{x\to\pi^-} \frac{\sin x}{1-\cos x}$

d $\displaystyle\lim_{\theta\to 0} \frac{\cos\theta}{\theta}$

e $\displaystyle\lim_{x\to\frac{\pi}{2}^-} \frac{\tan x}{\sec x}$

3 Evaluate the following limits, where possible:

a $\displaystyle\lim_{x\to\infty} \frac{3+x}{x+5}$

b $\displaystyle\lim_{x\to\infty} \frac{4x^2-5x+1}{x^2+x+1}$

c $\displaystyle\lim_{x\to\infty} \sqrt{\frac{x^2+3}{x}}$

d $\displaystyle\lim_{x\to\infty} \frac{1+x}{x^2+x+1}$

4 By first multiplying by $\dfrac{\sqrt{x^2+x}+x}{\sqrt{x^2+x}+x}$, find $\displaystyle\lim_{x\to\infty} \sqrt{x^2+x}-x$.

$$\frac{\sqrt{x^2+x}+x}{\sqrt{x^2+x}+x} = 1, \text{ for } x\neq 0.$$

5 Let f be a function with domain $\mathbb{R}$, and let $a, l \in \mathbb{R}$ be constants. Suppose $\displaystyle\lim_{x\to a} f(x)$ exists. Use the limit laws to prove that $\displaystyle\lim_{x\to a} f(x) = l$ if and only if $\displaystyle\lim_{x\to a} (f(x)-l) = 0$.

THE SQUEEZE THEOREM

The Squeeze Theorem shows us that inequalities between functions are preserved when we take limits.

> Let f, g, h be real functions and let $a, l \in \mathbb{R}$.
>
> Suppose that $f(x) \leqslant g(x) \leqslant h(x)$ for all $x \neq a$ in some open interval containing a.
>
> If $\displaystyle\lim_{x\to a} f(x) = l = \lim_{x\to a} h(x)$ then $\displaystyle\lim_{x\to a} g(x) = l$.

So, a function $g(x)$ is forced to have the same limit as f and h if g is squeezed between them.

Example 3

Use the Squeeze Theorem to evaluate $\displaystyle\lim_{x\to 0} x^2 \cos\left(\frac{9}{x}\right)$.

Since $-1 \leqslant \cos\left(\dfrac{9}{x}\right) \leqslant 1$ for all $x \in \mathbb{R}$,

$$-x^2 \leqslant x^2 \cos\left(\frac{9}{x}\right) \leqslant x^2$$

Now $\displaystyle\lim_{x\to 0} -x^2 = 0 = \lim_{x\to 0} x^2$.

$\therefore$ by the Squeeze Theorem, $\displaystyle\lim_{x\to 0} x^2 \cos\left(\frac{9}{x}\right) = 0$

Consider the limit $\lim_{x \to 0} \dfrac{\sin x}{x}$. Since $\lim_{x \to 0} \sin x = 0$ and $\lim_{x \to 0} x = 0$, we say this limit has **indeterminate**

form $\dfrac{0}{0}$. We cannot use the limit laws to determine whether or not this limit exists, or what its value might be. However, one way to evaluate the limit is to use the Squeeze Theorem.

The **Fundamental Trigonometric Limit** is $\lim_{\theta \to 0} \dfrac{\sin \theta}{\theta} = 1$.

Proof:

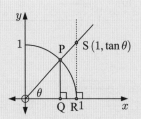

Consider the unit circle with angle $0 < \theta < \frac{\pi}{2}$, and also points $P(\cos \theta, \sin \theta)$, $Q(\cos \theta, 0)$, $R(1, 0)$, and $S(1, \tan \theta)$.

Clearly,   area of $\triangle OPQ$ < area of sector OPR < area of $\triangle ORS$

$\therefore$ $\frac{1}{2} \cos \theta \sin \theta < \frac{1}{2} \theta < \frac{1}{2} \dfrac{\sin \theta}{\cos \theta}$

Since $0 < \theta < \frac{\pi}{2}$, $\frac{1}{2} \sin \theta > 0$

$\therefore$ $\cos \theta < \dfrac{\theta}{\sin \theta} < \dfrac{1}{\cos \theta}$ {dividing by $\frac{1}{2} \sin \theta$}

$\therefore$ $\dfrac{1}{\cos \theta} > \dfrac{\sin \theta}{\theta} > \cos \theta$ {taking reciprocals}

$\therefore$ $\cos \theta < \dfrac{\sin \theta}{\theta} < \dfrac{1}{\cos \theta}$ {rearranging}

Let $f(\theta) = \cos \theta$, $g(\theta) = \dfrac{\sin \theta}{\theta}$, $h(\theta) = \dfrac{1}{\cos \theta}$.

Now $\lim_{\theta \to 0^+} f(\theta) = 1$ and $\lim_{\theta \to 0^+} \dfrac{1}{\cos \theta} = 1$

$\therefore$ $\lim_{\theta \to 0^+} \dfrac{\sin \theta}{\theta} = 1$ {Squeeze Theorem}

For $-\frac{\pi}{2} < \theta < 0$, $\sin(-\theta) = -\sin \theta$ and $\cos(-\theta) = \cos \theta$

$\therefore$ $\lim_{\theta \to 0^-} \dfrac{\sin \theta}{\theta} = \lim_{\theta \to 0^-} \dfrac{\sin(-|\theta|)}{-|\theta|}$

$= \lim_{\theta \to 0^+} \dfrac{-\sin(|\theta|)}{-|\theta|}$

$= \lim_{\theta \to 0^+} \dfrac{\sin \theta}{\theta}$

$= 1$

So, $\lim_{\theta \to 0^-} \dfrac{\sin \theta}{\theta} = 1 = \lim_{\theta \to 0^+} \dfrac{\sin \theta}{\theta}$

$\therefore$ $\lim_{\theta \to 0} \dfrac{\sin \theta}{\theta} = 1$ as required.

EXERCISE B.3

1 Use the Fundamental Trigonometric Limit $\displaystyle\lim_{\theta \to 0} \frac{\sin \theta}{\theta} = 1$ and the limit laws to determine the following limits:

a $\displaystyle\lim_{\theta \to 0} \frac{\sin^2 \theta}{\theta}$

b $\displaystyle\lim_{\theta \to 0} \frac{\sin 3\theta}{\theta}$

c $\displaystyle\lim_{\theta \to 0} \frac{\theta}{\tan \theta}$

d $\displaystyle\lim_{x \to 0} \frac{\sin 7x}{4x}$

e $\displaystyle\lim_{x \to 0} x \cot x$

f $\displaystyle\lim_{x \to 0} \frac{x^2 + x}{\sin 2x}$

g $\displaystyle\lim_{x \to 0^+} \frac{\sin x}{\sqrt{x}}$

2 Evaluate the following limits, where possible:

a $\displaystyle\lim_{x \to 0} \frac{x + \sin x}{x - \sin x}$ by multiplying by $\dfrac{\frac{1}{x}}{\frac{1}{x}}$

b $\displaystyle\lim_{h \to 0} \frac{\cos h - 1}{h}$ by multiplying by $\dfrac{\cos h + 1}{\cos h + 1}$

c $\displaystyle\lim_{x \to 0} \frac{1 - \cos x}{x^2}$ by multiplying by $\dfrac{1 + \cos x}{1 + \cos x}$.

3 Use the Squeeze Theorem to prove that $\displaystyle\lim_{x \to 0} g(x) = 0$ for:

a $g(x) = x^2 \cos \left(\frac{1}{x^2}\right)$

b $g(x) = x \sin \left(\frac{1}{x}\right)$

c $g(x) = \dfrac{|x|}{1 + x^4}$

4 **a** Use the Squeeze Theorem to prove that $\displaystyle\lim_{x \to 0^+} e^{\left(-\frac{1}{x}\right)} \sin x = 0$.

b Explain why $\displaystyle\lim_{x \to 0} e^{\left(-\frac{1}{x}\right)} \sin x$ does not exist.

C   CONTINUITY OF FUNCTIONS

We have seen that different functions define curves with particular properties:

- curves which continue indefinitely, such as polynomials, $y = e^x$, $y = \sqrt{x}$, $y = \ln x$, $y = \sin x$, $y = \cos x$

- curves with a break or 'hole' at a particular value, for example $y = \dfrac{x^2 - 1}{x - 1}$ has a 'hole' at $x = 1$

- curves with two or more branches which are not connected, for example $y = \dfrac{1}{x}$.

We now formalise this intuitive idea of a function being either continuous on its whole domain, or discontinuous at a particular value.

> Consider a real function f defined on an open interval containing the value a. We say that f is **continuous** at $x = a$ if $\lim\limits_{x \to a} f(x) = f(a)$.
>
> If f is continuous at $x = a$ for all $a \in \mathbb{R}$, we say **f is continuous on $\mathbb{R}$**.

Thus for a function f to be continuous at $x = a$, the following three conditions must be satisfied:

1 $f(a)$ needs to be defined

2 $\lim\limits_{x \to a} f(x)$ must exist, so $\lim\limits_{x \to a^-} f(x)$ and $\lim\limits_{x \to a^+} f(x)$ must both exist and be equal

3 $\lim\limits_{x \to a} f(x) = f(a)$.

If any of these three conditions fail, we say that   **f is not continuous at $x = a$,**

or   **f is discontinuous at $x = a$,**

or   **f has a discontinuity at $x = a$.**

Graphically, the points of discontinuity of a function f are points where the graph of $y = f(x)$ has a 'hole' such as a missing point, a 'jump' in the value of the function, or a 'break' such as a vertical asymptote.

> Suppose the function f is **discontinuous** at $x = a$.
>
> If $\lim\limits_{x \to a} f(x)$ exists, then f has a **removable discontinuity** at $x = a$.
>
> Otherwise, f has an **essential discontinuity** at $x = a$.

A removable discontinuity is "removed" by defining a new function based on f but which is continuous when $x = a$. In particular, when $x = a$ it takes the value $\lim\limits_{x \to a} f(x)$.

Essential discontinuities are characterised by 'jumps' or 'breaks' in the graph of the function which cannot be removed by simply redefining the value of the function there.

Example 4

Discuss the continuity of the following functions:

a $f(x) = \dfrac{1}{x-5}$

b $f(x) = \begin{cases} 1, & x \geqslant 0 \\ -1, & x < 0 \end{cases}$

a

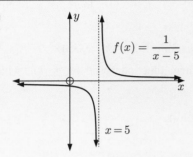

f is not defined at $x = 5$, and $\displaystyle\lim_{x \to 5} f(x)$ DNE.

f is continuous for all $x \in \mathbb{R}$, $x \neq 5$.

f has an essential discontinuity at $x = 5$.

b

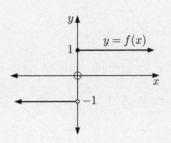

f is defined for all x, but there is a 'jump' discontinuity at $x = 0$.

$\displaystyle\lim_{x \to 0^-} f(x) = -1$ and $\displaystyle\lim_{x \to 0^+} f(x) = 1$

$\therefore \displaystyle\lim_{x \to 0} f(x)$ DNE.

f is continuous for all $x \in \mathbb{R}$, $x \neq 0$.

f has an essential discontinuity at $x = 0$.

Example 5

Discuss the continuity of the following functions. If there is a removable discontinuity, describe how this could be removed.

a $f(x) = \begin{cases} x^2, & x \neq 2 \\ 6, & x = 2 \end{cases}$

b $f(x) = \begin{cases} \dfrac{\sin x}{x}, & x \neq 0 \\ 0, & x = 0 \end{cases}$

a

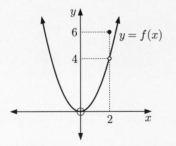

f is defined for all x, but there is a discontinuity at $x = 2$

$\displaystyle\lim_{x \to 2^-} f(x) = 4$ and $\displaystyle\lim_{x \to 2^+} f(x) = 4$

$\therefore \displaystyle\lim_{x \to 2} f(x) = 4$

But $\displaystyle\lim_{x \to 2} f(x) \neq f(2)$,   so there is a removable discontinuity when $x = 2$.

f is continuous for all $x \in \mathbb{R}$, $x \neq 2$.

The discontinuity can be removed by defining a new function based on f, but which is continuous at $x = 2$.

This is $g(x) = \begin{cases} x^2, & x \neq 2 \\ 4, & x = 2 \end{cases}$ which is actually just $g(x) = x^2$.

b

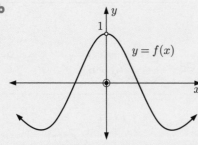

f is defined for all x, but there is a discontinuity at $x = 0$.

$$\lim_{x \to 0^-} f(x) = 1 \quad \text{and} \quad \lim_{x \to 0^+} f(x) = 1$$

$$\therefore \quad \lim_{x \to 0} f(x) = 1$$

But $\lim\limits_{x \to 0} f(x) \neq f(0)$, so there is a removable discontinuity when $x = 0$.

f is continuous for all $x \in \mathbb{R}$, $x \neq 0$.

The discontinuity can be removed by defining a new function based on f, but which is continuous at $x = 0$. This is $g(x) = \begin{cases} \dfrac{\sin x}{x}, & x \neq 0 \\ 1, & x = 0. \end{cases}$

EXERCISE C.1

1 Suppose f and g are functions which are continuous at $x = a$. Use the limit laws to prove that the following functions are also continuous at $x = a$:

   a $f(x)\,g(x)$ **b** $f(x) \pm g(x)$ **c** $\dfrac{f(x)}{g(x)}$, for $g(a) \neq 0$

   d $c\,f(x)$, for $c \in \mathbb{R}$ a constant   **e** $[f(x)]^n$, $n \in \mathbb{Z}^+$

2 Consider the function f with graph:

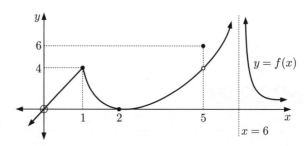

   a Complete the following:

     i f has an essential discontinuity at $x = $ ......

     ii f has a removable discontinuity at $x = $ ......

   b For which values of $x \in \mathbb{R}$ is f continuous?

3 Let $f(x) = \begin{cases} x, & x < -2 \\ x^2 - 6, & -2 \leqslant x < 0 \\ 5, & 0 \leqslant x < 3 \\ 6, & x = 3 \\ \dfrac{5}{4 - x}, & 3 < x < 4 \\ 2x, & x \geqslant 4. \end{cases}$

   a Sketch $y = f(x)$.

   b Discuss the continuity of f where:

     i $x = -2$ **ii** $x = 0$ **iii** $x = 3$ **iv** $x = 4$

4 Discuss the continuity of the following functions. If there is a removable discontinuity, describe how this could be removed.

   a $f(x) = \begin{cases} x^2, & x > 3 \\ 5, & x = 3 \\ 3x, & x < 3 \end{cases}$ **b** $g(x) = \begin{cases} x^2 - 10x + 7, & x \geqslant 3 \\ 5, & x < 3 \end{cases}$

5 Find, if possible, the value(s) of $k \in \mathbb{R}$ for which f is continuous on $\mathbb{R}$. Explain your working.

a $f(x) = \begin{cases} \dfrac{x^3 - 1}{x - 1}, & x \neq 1 \\ k, & x = 1 \end{cases}$

b $f(x) = \begin{cases} \dfrac{\sin 3x}{x}, & x \neq 0 \\ k, & x = 0 \end{cases}$

c $f(x) = \begin{cases} k + 1, & x < 2 \\ x^2, & x \geqslant 2 \end{cases}$

d $f(x) = \begin{cases} \dfrac{1}{x}, & x > 0 \\ k, & x \leqslant 0 \end{cases}$

e $f(x) = \begin{cases} kx, & x > 0 \\ 0, & x \leqslant 0 \end{cases}$

f $f(x) = \begin{cases} k + x, & x \geqslant 2 \\ |k + 2|, & x < 2 \end{cases}$

6 For a real function f with domain D, an alternative (equivalent) definition of continuity is as follows:

"f is continuous at $a \in D$ if, for any sequence $\{x_n\}$ of values in D such that
$\lim\limits_{n \to \infty} x_n = a$, then $\lim\limits_{n \to \infty} f(x_n) = f(a)$."

The **Dirichlet function** is defined by $g(x) = \begin{cases} 1, & x \in \mathbb{Q} \\ 0, & x \notin \mathbb{Q}. \end{cases}$

a Consider the sequence $x_n = a + \dfrac{\sqrt{2}}{n}$, $a \in \mathbb{Q}$, $n \in \mathbb{Z}^+$. Use the given definition of continuity to show that $g(x)$ is discontinuous at $x = a$.

b Now suppose $a \notin \mathbb{Q}$, and that x_n is the decimal expansion of a to n decimal places, $n \in \mathbb{Z}^+$. Use the given definition of continuity to show that $g(x)$ is discontinuous at $x = a$.

c Hence discuss the continuity of the Dirichlet function.

7 Consider two functions f, g and two values $a, l \in \mathbb{R}$. Suppose f is continuous on $\mathbb{R}$. If $l = g(a)$, you may assume the result:

"If g is continuous at a, and f is continuous at $g(a)$, then $f \circ g$ is continuous at a."

a If $\lim\limits_{x \to a} g(x) = l$, show that $\lim\limits_{x \to a} f(g(x)) = f(l)$.

b Show that $\lim\limits_{x \to a} f(g(x)) = f\left(\lim\limits_{x \to a} g(x) \right)$ whenever $\lim\limits_{x \to a} g(x)$ exists.

c Show that $\lim\limits_{x \to \infty} f(g(x)) = f\left(\lim\limits_{x \to \infty} g(x) \right)$ whenever $\lim\limits_{x \to \infty} g(x)$ exists.

8 **a** Show that $x^{\frac{1}{n}} = e^{\ln x^{\frac{1}{n}}}$ for $x > 0$, $x \in \mathbb{R}$.

b Use the fact that $f(x) = e^x$ is continuous on $\mathbb{R}$ to prove that $\lim\limits_{n \to \infty} x^{\frac{1}{n}} = 1$ for $x > 0$, $x \in \mathbb{R}$, $n \in \mathbb{Z}^+$.

THE INTERMEDIATE VALUE THEOREM (IVT)

A function f is **continuous on a closed interval** $[a, b]$, $a < b$, if f is continuous at x for all $x \in \,]a, b[$, and also $\lim\limits_{x \to a^+} f(x) = f(a)$ and $\lim\limits_{x \to b^-} f(x) = f(b)$.

The following theorem formalises the intuitive property that a function f which is continuous on a closed interval $[a, b]$ has no 'breaks' or 'holes' between $x = a$ and $x = b$, and will in fact take every value between $f(a)$ and $f(b)$ as we increase x from a to b.

The **Intermediate Value Theorem (IVT)** states that:

> Suppose a function f is continuous on a closed interval $[a,\ b]$. If k is any value between $f(a)$ and $f(b)$, then there exists $c \in [a,\ b]$ such that $f(c) = k$.

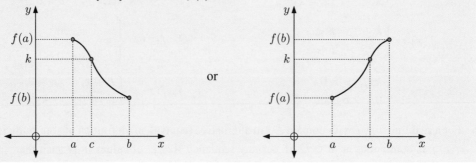

BOUNDED FUNCTIONS

A function f is **bounded** on $[a,\ b]$ if, for all $x \in [a,\ b]$, $|f(x)| \leqslant M$ for some $M \in \mathbb{R}$. In other words, a function is bounded on $[a,\ b]$ if it does not tend to infinity or negative infinity on the interval $[a,\ b]$.

> If a function f is continuous on $[a,\ b]$, then f is bounded on $[a,\ b]$.

It follows that if f is continuous on $[a,\ b]$, $a < b$, then:

- f has a maximum value M on the interval $[a,\ b]$ where $M = f(x_M)$ for some $x_M \in [a,\ b]$
- f has a minimum value m on the interval $[a,\ b]$ where $m = f(x_m)$ for some $x_m \in [a,\ b]$.

EXERCISE C.2

1 Using the IVT, explain why:

  a $f(x) = x^3 + x - 3$ has a real zero in the interval $[0,\ 2]$

  b $f(x) = \dfrac{4}{x - 2}$ does not have a real zero in the interval $[1,\ 3]$ even though $f(1) < 0$ and $f(3) > 0$.

2 Consider the function $f(x) = x^3 - 9x^2 + 24x - 10$ on the interval $[1,\ 5]$. Find:

  a the maximum value M of f on $[1,\ 5]$, and the values $x_M \in [1,\ 5]$ such that $f(x_M) = M$

  b the minimum value m of f on $[1,\ 5]$, and the values $x_m \in [1,\ 5]$ such that $f(x_m) = m$.

3 Suppose f is continuous on $[a,\ b]$, $a < b$, and suppose $f(a)$, $f(b)$ have opposite signs. Prove that f has at least one zero between a and b.

4   **a** Prove that for each constant $r \in \mathbb{R}$, $r > 0$, there exists a real value of x such that $\sin x = 1 - rx$.

     Hint: Let $f(x) = \sin x + rx - 1$ and apply the IVT to a suitable interval.

  b Suppose $r = 1$. Use your calculator to solve $\sin x = 1 - x$ on the domain $x \in]-2,\ 2[$.

5   **a** Use the IVT to prove that $f(x) = x^{15} + \dfrac{1}{1 + \sin^2 x + (r + 1)^2}$ has at least one zero on the interval $]-1,\ 1[$ for any constant $r \in \mathbb{R}$.

  b Let $r \in \mathbb{R}$, $r > 0$ be any constant. Can the IVT be used to prove the existence of a zero in $]-1,\ 1[$ of $g(x) = rx^{17} + \dfrac{1}{5x}$? Explain your answer.

D | DIFFERENTIABLE FUNCTIONS

Suppose f is a real function with domain D containing an open interval about $x = a$.

f is **differentiable** at $x = a$ if $\displaystyle\lim_{h \to 0} \frac{f(a+h) - f(a)}{h}$ exists. If this limit exists we denote it by

$f'(a)$, and $f'(a) = \displaystyle\lim_{h \to 0} \frac{f(a+h) - f(a)}{h}$ is the **derivative** of f at $x = a$.

If f is differentiable at a for all $a \in D$, then we say f is a **differentiable** function.

By letting $x = a + h$ in the definition of the derivative, and noting that as $h \to 0$, $x = a + h \to a$, we obtain the following alternative form for the derivative of f at $x = a$:

$$f'(x) = \lim_{x \to a} \frac{f(x) - f(a)}{x - a}.$$

Example 6

a Prove that $\displaystyle\lim_{h \to 0} \frac{\cos h - 1}{h} = 0$.

b Using the limit definition of the derivative, prove that if $f(x) = \sin x$ then $f'(x) = \cos x$.

a $\displaystyle\lim_{h \to 0} \frac{\cos h - 1}{h} = \lim_{h \to 0} \frac{\cos h - 1}{h} \times \frac{\cos h + 1}{\cos h + 1}$

$\displaystyle = \lim_{h \to 0} \frac{\cos^2 h - 1}{h(\cos h + 1)}$

$\displaystyle = \lim_{h \to 0} \frac{-\sin^2 h}{h(\cos h + 1)}$

$\displaystyle = \lim_{h \to 0} \frac{\sin h}{h} \times \frac{-\sin h}{\cos h + 1}$

$\displaystyle = \lim_{h \to 0} \frac{\sin h}{h} \times \lim_{h \to 0} \frac{-\sin h}{\cos h + 1}$ {by the limit laws since both limits exist}

$\displaystyle = 1 \times \frac{0}{2}$

$= 0$

b Let $f(x) = \sin x$. If $f'(x)$ exists, then it is given by

$f'(x) = \displaystyle\lim_{h \to 0} \frac{\sin(x + h) - \sin x}{h}$

$\displaystyle = \lim_{h \to 0} \frac{\sin x \cos h + \sin h \cos x - \sin x}{h}$

$\displaystyle = \lim_{h \to 0} \left[\sin x \left(\frac{\cos h - 1}{h} \right) + \frac{\sin h}{h} \times \cos x \right]$

$\displaystyle = \left(\lim_{h \to 0} \sin x \right) \left(\lim_{h \to 0} \frac{\cos h - 1}{h} \right) + \left(\lim_{h \to 0} \cos x \right) \left(\lim_{h \to 0} \frac{\sin h}{h} \right)$

{by the limit laws, since each of these limits exists}

$= \sin x \times 0 + \cos x \times 1$ {since x is independent of h}

$= \cos x$

DIFFERENTIABILITY AND CONTINUITY

If $f : D \to \mathbb{R}$ is differentiable at $x = a$, then f is continuous at $x = a$.

Proof:

$$\lim_{h \to 0} f(a+h) - f(a)$$

$$= \lim_{h \to 0} \frac{f(a+h) - f(a)}{h} \times h$$

$$= \lim_{h \to 0} \frac{f(a+h) - f(a)}{h} \times \lim_{h \to 0} h \qquad \text{\{by the limit laws since both limits exist\}}$$

$$= f'(a) \times 0$$

$$= 0$$

$$\therefore \quad \lim_{h \to 0} f(a+h) = f(a)$$

By letting $x = a + h$, and since h can take both positive and negative values, this is equivalent to $\lim_{x \to a} f(x) = f(a)$.

$\therefore$ f is continuous at $x = a$.

It follows that if a function is not continuous at $x = a$, then it is not differentiable at $x = a$.

The converse of this theorem is not true, however. If a function is continuous at $x = a$, it is not necessarily differentiable there.

The set of all differentiable functions is therefore a proper subset of the set of all continuous functions.

TESTING FOR DIFFERENTIABILITY

For functions which are defined by different expressions on separate intervals, we need a formal test to see whether the function is differentiable. To do this we first need to define:

- the **left-hand derivative** of f at $x = a$ is $f'_-(a) = \lim_{h \to 0^-} \dfrac{f(a+h) - f(a)}{h}$

- the **right-hand derivative** of f at $x = a$ is $f'_+(a) = \lim_{h \to 0^+} \dfrac{f(a+h) - f(a)}{h}$.

A function $f : D \to \mathbb{R}$ is differentiable at $x = a$, $a \in D$, if:

1 f is continuous at $x = a$,   and

2 $f'_-(a) = \lim_{h \to 0^-} \dfrac{f(a+h) - f(a)}{h}$ and $f'_+(a) = \lim_{h \to 0^+} \dfrac{f(a+h) - f(a)}{h}$ both exist and are equal.

Example 7

Prove that $f(x) = |x| = \begin{cases} x, & x \geqslant 0 \\ -x, & x < 0 \end{cases}$ is continuous but not differentiable at $x = 0$.

$f(0) = 0$, $\lim_{x \to 0^-} f(x) = \lim_{x \to 0^-} (-x) = 0$,

and $\lim_{x \to 0^+} f(x) = \lim_{x \to 0^+} x = 0$

$\therefore$ $\lim_{x \to 0} f(x) = f(0) = 0$

$\therefore$ f is continuous at $x = 0$.

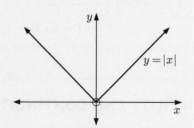

Now $f'(x) = \begin{cases} 1, & x > 0 \\ -1, & x < 0 \end{cases}$ since the derivative of f exists on the open interval $]-\infty, 0[$ and on the open inteval $]0, \infty[$.

$\therefore \quad f'_-(0) = -1$ and $f'_+(0) = 1$

$\therefore \quad f'_-(0) \neq f'_+(0)$

$\therefore \quad f$ is not differentiable at $x = 0$.

Example 8

Consider $f(x) = \begin{cases} \sin x, & x \geqslant 0 \\ x^2 + 5x, & x < 0 \end{cases}$ with domain $\mathbb{R}$.

a Prove that f is continuous but not differentiable at $x = 0$.

b Write down $f'(x)$ as a piecewise defined function.

a $f(0) = 0$ is defined.

$$\lim_{x \to 0^-} f(x) = \lim_{x \to 0^-} (x^2 + 5x) = 0$$

and $\lim_{x \to 0^+} f(x) = \lim_{x \to 0^+} \sin x = 0$

$\therefore \quad \lim_{x \to 0} f(x) = f(0) = 0$

$\therefore \quad f(x)$ is continuous at $x = 0$.

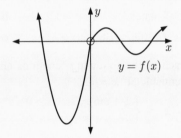

Using known derivatives for open intevals of $\mathbb{R}$, we have $f'(x) = \begin{cases} \cos x, & x > 0 \\ 2x + 5, & x < 0 \end{cases}$

$\therefore \quad f'_-(0) = \lim_{x \to 0^-} (2x + 5) = 2 \times 0 + 5 = 5$

and $f'_+(0) = \lim_{x \to 0^+} \cos x = \cos 0 = 1$

Since $f'_-(0) \neq f'_+(0)$, f is not differentiable at $x = 0$.

We observe on the graph of $y = f(x)$ that the curve does not have a unique tangent at $x = 0$.

b From **a** we have $f'(x) = \begin{cases} \cos x, & x > 0 \\ 2x + 5, & x < 0. \end{cases}$

DISCUSSION

There are functions which are continuous everywhere in their domain but which are differentiable nowhere!

Research and discuss the **Weierstrass** function.

EXERCISE D

1 Let $f(x) = \cos x$. Use the definition of the derivative to prove that $f'(x) = -\sin x$.

2 Prove that $f(x) = |x - 5| = \begin{cases} x - 5, & x \geqslant 5 \\ 5 - x, & x < 5 \end{cases}$ is continuous but not differentiable at $x = 5$.

3 Let $f(x) = \begin{cases} x + 2, & x \geqslant 0 \\ x^2 + 3x, & x < 0. \end{cases}$

Explain why $f(x)$ is not differentiable at $x = 0$.

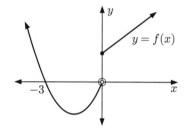

4 Let $f(x) = \begin{cases} -x^2 + 5x + 6, & x \geqslant 1 \\ 3x + 10, & x < 1. \end{cases}$

   a Sketch the function $y = f(x)$.

   b Calculate: **i** $f'_-(1)$ **ii** $f'_+(1)$

   c Is f differentiable at $x = 1$?   Explain your answer.

5 For each of the following functions and the given value of a, determine whether the function is differentiable at $x = a$.

   a $f(x) = \begin{cases} 1 + \sin x, & x \geqslant 0 \\ x^2 + x + 1, & x < 0 \end{cases}$, $a = 0$ **b** $f(x) = \begin{cases} \cos x, & x \geqslant 0 \\ x^3, & x < 0 \end{cases}$, $a = 0$

   c $f(x) = \begin{cases} 4x^2 - 3, & x \geqslant 2 \\ x^3 + 2x + 1, & x < 2 \end{cases}$, $a = 2$

6 Investigate the continuity and differentiability of f at $x = 0$ if

$f(x) = \begin{cases} k \sin x, & x \geqslant 0 \\ \tan x, & x < 0 \end{cases}$, where $k \in \mathbb{R}$ is any constant.

7 Find constants $c, d \in \mathbb{R}$ so that the given function is differentiable at $x = 1$.

   a $f(x) = \begin{cases} x^2, & x \leqslant 1 \\ cx + d, & x > 1 \end{cases}$ **b** $f(x) = \begin{cases} \sin(x - 1) + cx, & x \geqslant 1 \\ x^2 - x + d, & x < 1 \end{cases}$

8 Let $f(x) = \begin{cases} x^3 \sin\left(\frac{1}{x}\right), & x \neq 0 \\ 0, & x = 0. \end{cases}$

   a Prove that f is continuous and differentiable at $x = 0$.

   b Write down $f'(x)$ as a piecewise defined function.

   c Is $f'(x)$ continuous at $x = 0$?   Explain your answer.

E   L'HÔPITAL'S RULE

The limit laws do not help us to deal with limits which have *indeterminate forms*. These include:

Type	Description
$\frac{0}{0}$	$\displaystyle\lim_{x \to a} \frac{f(x)}{g(x)}$ where $\displaystyle\lim_{x \to a} f(x) = 0$ and $\displaystyle\lim_{x \to a} g(x) = 0$
$\frac{\infty}{\infty}$	$\displaystyle\lim_{x \to a} \frac{f(x)}{g(x)}$ where $f(x) \to \pm\infty$ and $g(x) \to \pm\infty$ when $x \to a$
$0 \times \infty$	$\displaystyle\lim_{x \to a} [f(x)\,g(x)]$ where $\displaystyle\lim_{x \to a} f(x) = 0$ and $g(x) \to \pm\infty$ when $x \to a$

For example, consider $\displaystyle\lim_{x \to 0} \frac{2^x - 1}{x}$.

Since $\displaystyle\lim_{x \to 0} (2^x - 1) = 0$ and $\displaystyle\lim_{x \to 0} (x) = 0$,   we have the indeterminate form $\frac{0}{0}$.

To address these types of limits, we use **l'Hôpital's Rule**:

Suppose $f(x)$ and $g(x)$ are differentiable and $g'(x) \neq 0$ on an open interval that contains the point $x = a$.

If $\displaystyle\lim_{x \to a} f(x) = 0$ and $\displaystyle\lim_{x \to a} g(x) = 0$,   or,   if as $x \to a$, $f(x) \to \pm\infty$ and $g(x) \to \pm\infty$,

then $\displaystyle\lim_{x \to a} \frac{f(x)}{g(x)} = \lim_{x \to a} \frac{f'(x)}{g'(x)}$ provided the limit on the right exists.

Proof of one case of l'Hôpital's Rule:

The derivative of a function $f(x)$ at a point $x = a$, denoted by $f'(a)$, is given by

$$f'(a) = \lim_{x \to a} \frac{f(x) - f(a)}{x - a}.$$

Using this definition of the derivative, we prove the case of l'Hôpital's Rule in which $f(a) = g(a) = 0$, $f'(x)$ and $g'(x)$ are continuous, and $g'(a) \neq 0$.

Under these conditions,

$$\lim_{x \to a} \frac{f(x)}{g(x)} = \lim_{x \to a} \frac{f(x) - f(a)}{g(x) - g(a)} \quad \{\text{since } f(a) = g(a) = 0\}$$

$$= \lim_{x \to a} \frac{\frac{f(x)-f(a)}{x-a}}{\frac{g(x)-g(a)}{x-a}} \quad \{\text{multiplying by } \frac{\frac{1}{x-a}}{\frac{1}{x-a}} = 1 \text{ since } x \neq a\}$$

$$= \frac{\displaystyle\lim_{x \to a} \frac{f(x)-f(a)}{x-a}}{\displaystyle\lim_{x \to a} \frac{g(x)-g(a)}{x-a}}$$

$$= \frac{f'(a)}{g'(a)}$$

$$= \frac{\displaystyle\lim_{x \to a} f'(x)}{\displaystyle\lim_{x \to a} g'(x)} \quad \{\text{since } f'(x) \text{ and } g'(x) \text{ are continuous}\}$$

$$= \lim_{x \to a} \frac{f'(x)}{g'(x)}$$

Example 9

Use l'Hôpital's Rule to evaluate:

a $\displaystyle\lim_{x\to 0} \frac{2^x - 1}{x}$ **b** $\displaystyle\lim_{x\to\infty} xe^{-x}$ **c** $\displaystyle\lim_{x\to\infty} \frac{\ln x}{x}$

a $\displaystyle\lim_{x\to 0}(2^x - 1) = 0$ and $\displaystyle\lim_{x\to 0} x = 0$, so we can use l'Hôpital's Rule if the resulting limit exists.

$$\therefore \quad \lim_{x\to 0} \frac{2^x - 1}{x}$$

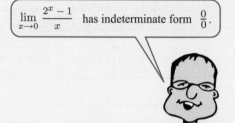

$$= \frac{\displaystyle\lim_{x\to 0} \frac{d}{dx}(2^x - 1)}{\displaystyle\lim_{x\to 0} \frac{d}{dx}(x)} \quad \{\text{l'Hôpital's Rule}\}$$

$$= \frac{\displaystyle\lim_{x\to 0} 2^x \ln 2}{\displaystyle\lim_{x\to 0} 1}$$

$$= \frac{\ln 2}{1}$$

$$= \ln 2$$

b As $x\to\infty$, $e^{-x}\to 0$, so we can use l'Hôpital's Rule.

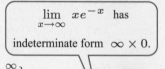

$$\therefore \quad \lim_{x\to\infty} xe^{-x}$$

$$= \lim_{x\to\infty} \frac{x}{e^x} \quad \{\text{convert limit to a quotient with the form } \tfrac{\infty}{\infty}\}$$

$$= \frac{\displaystyle\lim_{x\to\infty} \frac{d}{dx}(x)}{\displaystyle\lim_{x\to\infty} \frac{d}{dx}(e^x)} \quad \{\text{l'Hôpital's Rule}\}$$

$$= \frac{\displaystyle\lim_{x\to\infty} 1}{\displaystyle\lim_{x\to\infty}(e^x)}$$

$$= 0 \quad \{\text{since } \lim_{x\to\infty} 1 = 1 \text{ and as } x\to\infty,\ e^x\to\infty\}$$

c As $x\to\infty$, $\ln x\to\infty$ and $x\to\infty$, so we can use l'Hôpital's Rule.

$$\therefore \quad \lim_{x\to\infty} \frac{\ln x}{x}$$

$$= \frac{\displaystyle\lim_{x\to\infty} \frac{d}{dx}(\ln x)}{\displaystyle\lim_{x\to\infty} \frac{d}{dx}(x)} \quad \{\text{l'Hôpital's Rule}\}$$

$$= \frac{\displaystyle\lim_{x\to\infty}\left(\frac{1}{x}\right)}{\displaystyle\lim_{x\to\infty} 1}$$

$$= \frac{0}{1} \quad \{\text{since } \lim_{x\to\infty}\left(\frac{1}{x}\right) = 0\}$$

$$= 0$$

Important: A common error is to attempt to evaluate the Fundamental Trigonometric Limit $\displaystyle\lim_{x\to 0} \frac{\sin x}{x}$ using l'Hôpital's Rule. We cannot use l'Hôpital's Rule in this case as the derivative of $\sin x$ from first principles itself requires the use of $\displaystyle\lim_{x\to 0} \frac{\sin x}{x} = 1$, as shown in **Example 6**.

EXERCISE E

1   Evaluate, if possible, the following limits using l'Hôpital's Rule.

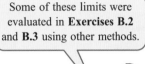

Some of these limits were evaluated in **Exercises B.2** and **B.3** using other methods.

a $\displaystyle\lim_{x\to 0} \frac{1-\cos x}{x^2}$

b $\displaystyle\lim_{x\to 0} \frac{e^x - 1 - x}{x^2}$

c $\displaystyle\lim_{x\to 1} \frac{\ln x}{x-1}$

d $\displaystyle\lim_{x\to\infty} \frac{e^x}{x}$

e $\displaystyle\lim_{x\to 0^+} x\ln x$

f $\displaystyle\lim_{x\to 0} \frac{\arctan x}{x}$

g $\displaystyle\lim_{x\to 0} \frac{x^2 + x}{\sin 2x}$

h $\displaystyle\lim_{x\to 0^+} \frac{\sin x}{\sqrt{x}}$

i $\displaystyle\lim_{x\to 0} \frac{x + \sin x}{x - \sin x}$

j $\displaystyle\lim_{x\to 0^+} x^2 \ln x$

k $\displaystyle\lim_{x\to 0} \frac{a^x - b^x}{\sin x}$,   where $a, b > 0$ are real constants.

2   Attempt to find $\displaystyle\lim_{x\to \frac{\pi}{2}^-} \frac{\tan x}{\sec x}$ using l'Hôpital's Rule.

3   Show that $\displaystyle\lim_{x\to 0} \frac{\frac{\pi}{2} - \arccos x - x}{x^3} = \frac{1}{6}$.

Example 10

Find $\displaystyle\lim_{x\to 0^+} \frac{\ln(\cos 3x)}{\ln(\cos 2x)}$.

$\displaystyle\lim_{x\to 0^+} \ln(\cos 3x) = 0$ and $\displaystyle\lim_{x\to 0^+} \ln(\cos 2x) = 0$,   so we can use l'Hôpital's Rule.

$\therefore \displaystyle\lim_{x\to 0^+} \frac{\ln(\cos 3x)}{\ln(\cos 2x)} = \lim_{x\to 0^+} \left(\frac{\frac{-3\sin 3x}{\cos 3x}}{\frac{-2\sin 2x}{\cos 2x}} \right)$ {l'Hôpital's Rule}

$\displaystyle = \lim_{x\to 0^+} \left(\frac{3\sin 3x \cos 2x}{2\sin 2x \cos 3x} \right)$

$\displaystyle = \left(\lim_{x\to 0^+} \frac{\sin 3x}{\sin 2x} \right) \times \left(\lim_{x\to 0^+} \frac{3\cos 2x}{2\cos 3x} \right)$

$\displaystyle = \left(\lim_{x\to 0^+} \frac{\sin 3x}{\sin 2x} \right) \times \frac{3}{2}$ $(*)$

At step $(*)$ we could have alternatively used the Fundamental Trigonometric Limit.

Now $\displaystyle\lim_{x\to 0^+} \sin 3x = 0$ and $\displaystyle\lim_{x\to 0^+} \sin 2x = 0$,

so we can use l'Hôpital's Rule again.

$\therefore \displaystyle\lim_{x\to 0^+} \frac{\ln(\cos 3x)}{\ln(\cos 2x)} = \left(\lim_{x\to 0^+} \frac{3\cos 3x}{2\cos 2x} \right) \times \frac{3}{2}$ {l'Hôpital's Rule}

$\displaystyle = \frac{3}{2} \times \frac{3}{2}$

$\displaystyle = \frac{9}{4}$

4 Evaluate:

a $\displaystyle\lim_{x\to 0^+}\frac{\ln(\cos 5x)}{\ln(\cos 3x)}$

b $\displaystyle\lim_{x\to\frac{\pi}{2}^-}\frac{\ln(\sin 2x)}{\ln(\sin 3x)}$

Example 11

Evaluate $\displaystyle\lim_{x\to\frac{\pi}{2}^-}(\sec x - \tan x)$.

As $x\to\dfrac{\pi}{2}^-$, both $\sec x\to\infty$ and $\tan x\to\infty$.

We therefore need to convert the difference $\sec x - \tan x$ into a quotient, and then apply l'Hôpital's Rule.

Now $\sec x - \tan x = \dfrac{1}{\cos x} - \dfrac{\sin x}{\cos x} = \dfrac{1 - \sin x}{\cos x}$

$\therefore\quad \displaystyle\lim_{x\to\frac{\pi}{2}^-}(\sec x - \tan x) = \lim_{x\to\frac{\pi}{2}^-}\left(\frac{1 - \sin x}{\cos x}\right)$

$\qquad\qquad$ where $\displaystyle\lim_{x\to\frac{\pi}{2}^-}(1 - \sin x) = 0$ and $\displaystyle\lim_{x\to\frac{\pi}{2}^-}\cos x = 0$

$\therefore\quad \displaystyle\lim_{x\to\frac{\pi}{2}^-}(\sec x - \tan x) = \frac{\displaystyle\lim_{x\to\frac{\pi}{2}^-}(-\cos x)}{\displaystyle\lim_{x\to\frac{\pi}{2}^-}(-\sin x)}$ {l'Hôpital's Rule}

$\qquad\qquad\qquad\qquad = \frac{0}{1} = 0$

---

5 Evaluate, if possible:

a $\displaystyle\lim_{x\to 0^+}\left(\frac{1}{x} - \frac{1}{\sin x}\right)$

b $\displaystyle\lim_{x\to 0^+}\left(\frac{1}{x} - \frac{1}{\sin 2x}\right)$

c $\displaystyle\lim_{x\to\frac{\pi}{2}^-}(\sec^2 x - \tan x)$

Example 12

Evaluate, if possible: $\displaystyle\lim_{x\to\infty}\frac{e^x}{x^n}$ where $n\in\mathbb{Z}^+$.

For all $n\in\mathbb{Z}^+$, as $x\to\infty$, $e^x\to\infty$ and $x^n\to\infty$, so we can use l'Hôpital's Rule.

$\therefore\quad \displaystyle\lim_{x\to\infty}\frac{e^x}{x^n} = \lim_{x\to\infty}\frac{e^x}{nx^{n-1}}$

$\qquad\qquad = \displaystyle\lim_{x\to\infty}\frac{e^x}{n(n-1)x^{n-2}}$

$\qquad\qquad\qquad\vdots$

$\qquad\qquad = \displaystyle\lim_{x\to\infty}\frac{e^x}{n!}$

$\qquad\qquad = \dfrac{1}{n!}\displaystyle\lim_{x\to\infty}e^x$

We use l'Hôpital's Rule n times.

As $x\to\infty$, $e^x\to\infty$, so the given limit DNE.

6   **a** Evaluate, if possible: $\lim\limits_{x\to\infty} \dfrac{x^k}{e^x}$, $k \in \mathbb{Z}^+$.

    b Hence explain why, as $x \to \infty$, the exponential function e^x increases more rapidly than any fixed positive power of x.

7 Prove that as $x \to \infty$, $\ln x$ increases more slowly than any fixed positive power of x.

8   **a** Prove that $\lim\limits_{x\to\infty} x \ln\left(1 + \dfrac{1}{x}\right) = 1$.

    b By writing $\left(1 + \dfrac{1}{x}\right)^x = e^{x \ln\left(1 + \frac{1}{x}\right)}$ and using the fact that $f(x) = e^x$ is continuous on $\mathbb{R}$,

    prove that $\lim\limits_{x\to\infty} \left(1 + \dfrac{1}{x}\right)^x = e$.

    c Prove that for $a \neq 0$, $\lim\limits_{x\to\infty} \left(1 + \dfrac{a}{x}\right)^x = e^a$.

9 By writing $x^{\sin x} = e^{\sin x \ln x}$ and using the fact that $f(x) = \ln x$ is continuous on $x \in \mathbb{R}$, $x > 0$, prove that $\lim\limits_{x\to 0^+} x^{\sin x} = 1$.

10 Prove that $\lim\limits_{x\to\infty} x^{\frac{1}{x}} = 1$.

F | ROLLE'S THEOREM AND THE MEAN VALUE THEOREM (MVT)

Suppose a real function f is defined on domain D.

$f : D \to \mathbb{R}$ is **continuous on a closed interval** $[a, b]$, $a < b$, if:

1 f is continuous at $x = c$ for all $c \in \,]a, b[$, and

2 $\lim_{x \to a^+} f(x) = f(a)$ and $\lim_{x \to b^-} f(x) = f(b)$

For a function $f : D \to \mathbb{R}$ we define:

f is **differentiable on an open interval** $]a, b[$, $a < b$ if f is differentiable at $x = c$ for all $c \in \,]a, b[$.

f is **differentiable on a closed interval** $[a, b]$, $a < b$, if:

1 f is differentiable on $]a, b[$, and

2 $f'_+(a)$ and $f'_-(b)$ both exist.

ROLLE'S THEOREM

Suppose function $f : D \to \mathbb{R}$ is continuous on the closed interval $[a, b]$, and differentiable on the open interval $]a, b[$.

If $f(a) = f(b)$, then there exists a value $c \in \,]a, b[$ such that $f'(c) = 0$.

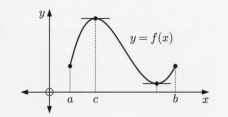

Proof of Rolle's theorem:

Since f is continuous on $[a, b]$, it attains both a maximum and minimum value on $[a, b]$. If f takes values greater than $f(a)$ on $[a, b]$, let $f(c)$ be the maximum of these.

Now $f(b) = f(a)$ and $f(c) > f(a)$, so $c \in \,]a, b[$.

Since f is differentiable at c, f must have a local maximum at $x = c$. $\therefore$ $f'(c) = 0$.

Similarly, if f takes values less than $f(a)$ on $[a, b]$, let the minimum of these be $f(c)$. It follows that f has a local minimum at $x = c$, and therefore $f'(c) = 0$.

Finally, if $f(x) = f(a)$ for all $x \in [a, b]$ then clearly $f'(c) = 0$ for all $c \in \,]a, b[$.

By taking $f(a) = f(b) = 0$, Rolle's theorem guarantees that between any two zeros of a differentiable function f there is *at least one* point at which the tangent line to the graph $y = f(x)$ is horizontal.

Rolle's theorem is a *lemma* used to prove the **Mean Value Theorem**.

A lemma is a proven proposition which leads on to a larger result.

THE MEAN VALUE THEOREM (MVT) (THE LAGRANGE FORM)

If f is a function continuous on $[a, b]$ and differentiable on $]a, b[$,
then $f(b) - f(a) = f'(c) \times (b - a)$ for some number $c \in]a, b[$.

The MVT tells us that for such a function f there exists *at least one* value $c \in]a, b[$ such that the tangent to the curve $y = f(x)$ at $x = c$ has gradient equal to the gradient of the chord through points $(a, f(a))$ and $(b, f(b))$.

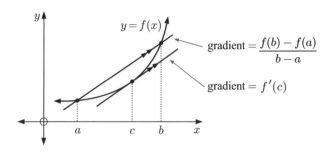

Proof of the MVT:

Let $h(x) = f(x) - \left[\dfrac{f(b) - f(a)}{b - a}\right](x - a) - f(a)$ for $x \in [a, b]$.

Since f is continuous on $[a, b]$ and differentiable on $]a, b[$, so is the function h.

Now, $h(a) = h(b) = 0$, so by Rolle's theorem there exists $c \in]a, b[$ such that $h'(c) = 0$.

But $h'(x) = f'(x) - \left(\dfrac{f(b) - f(a)}{b - a}\right)$ for $x \in]a, b[$

$\therefore \ h'(c) = f'(c) - \left(\dfrac{f(b) - f(a)}{b - a}\right) = 0$

$\therefore \ f'(c) = \dfrac{f(b) - f(a)}{b - a}$.

We have seen that the derivative of a constant function is zero. We can now prove the converse of this result, that if a continuous function f has derivative equal to zero, then f is a constant function.

FIRST COROLLARY OF THE MVT

Suppose the function f is continuous on $[a, b]$ and differentiable on $]a, b[$. If $f'(x) = 0$ for all $x \in]a, b[$, then $f(x)$ is a constant function on $[a, b]$.

Proof:

Let $x \in]a, b]$ and apply the MVT to f on the interval $[a, x]$.

Then $f(x) - f(a) = f'(c)(x - a)$ for some $c \in]a, x[$
$= 0 \times (x - a)$
$= 0$
$\therefore \ f(x) = f(a)$ for all $x \in]a, b]$
$\therefore \ f(x) = f(a)$ for all $x \in [a, b]$

A corollary is a result which follows directly from a theorem, and which is worth stating in its own right.

SECOND COROLLARY OF THE MVT

Suppose F and G are two functions continuous on $[a, b]$ and differentiable on $]a, b[$.
If $F'(x) = G'(x)$ for all $x \in]a, b[$, then $F(x) = G(x) + C$ for some constant C,
for all $x \in [a, b]$.

Proof: Let $H(x) = F(x) - G(x)$, for $x \in [a, b]$.

$\therefore$ H is differentiable on $]a, b[$ and $H'(x) = 0$ on $]a, b[$.

By the first corollary of the MVT, $H(x)$ is a constant for all $x \in [a, b]$.

Hence $F(x) = G(x) + C$ as required.

ANTIDERIVATIVES

A function f has an **antiderivative** G on $[a, b]$ if there exists a function G continuous on $[a, b]$ such
that $G'(x) = f(x)$ for all $x \in]a, b[$.

If a function f has an antiderivative G, then G is unique up to the addition of a constant.

Proof: Suppose f has two antiderivatives F, G on $[a, b]$.

By definition, $F'(x) = G'(x) = f(x)$ for all $x \in]a, b[$.

By the second corollary to the MVT, $F(x) = G(x) + C$, where C is a constant.

We define $\displaystyle\int f(x)\, dx = G(x) + C$ to be the **indefinite integral** of function f with respect to x. The
function f is called the **integrand** and the indefinite integral of f is thus the set of all antiderivatives
of f on $[a, b]$.

EXERCISE F

1   Determine whether or not Rolle's theorem applies to the function f on the given interval $[a, b]$.
    If Rolle's theorem does apply, find all values $c \in]a, b[$ for which $f'(c) = 0$.

   a $f(x) = 3x^3 + 5x^2 - 43x + 35$, $[a, b] = [-5, 2\frac{1}{3}]$

   b $f(x) = |x| - 5$, $[a, b] = [-5, 5]$

   c $f(x) = 2 - \dfrac{1}{x+1}$, $[a, b] = [-\frac{1}{2}, 7]$

   d $f(x) = \begin{cases} -2x - 5, & x < -1 \\ x^2 - 4, & x \geqslant -1 \end{cases}$, $[a, b] = [-2\frac{1}{2}, 2]$

2   For each of the following functions, find:

   i   the number of real zeros of the derivative $f'(x)$, as guaranteed by Rolle's theorem
   ii the exact number of real zeros of the derivative $f'(x)$.

   a $f(x) = (x-1)(x-2)(x-4)(x-5)$ b $f(x) = (x-1)^2(x^2 - 9)(x - 2)$
   c $f(x) = (x-1)^2(x^2 + 9)(x - 2)$

3 Show that the given function f satisfies the MVT on the given interval $[a, b]$. Find all values of c such that $f(b) - f(a) = f'(c) \times (b - a)$.

    a $f(x) = x^3$, $[a, b] = [-2, 2]$ **b** $f(x) = \sqrt{x - 2}$, $[a, b] = [3, 6]$

    c $f(x) = x + \dfrac{1}{x}$, $[a, b] = [1, 3]$

4 Let $f(x) = \sqrt{x}$.

    a Use the MVT to show there exists $c \in \,]49, 51[$ such that $\sqrt{51} - 7 = \dfrac{1}{\sqrt{c}}$.

    b Graph $y = \dfrac{1}{\sqrt{x}}$ on the interval $[49, 64]$.

    c Hence prove $\frac{1}{8} < \sqrt{51} - 7 < \frac{1}{7}$ without using decimal expansions.

G   RIEMANN SUMS

Let $y = f(x)$ be a function which is non-negative and continuous on the interval $[a, b]$, $a < b$.

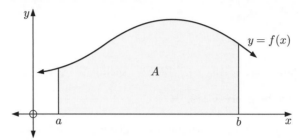

Let A denote the area under the curve $y = f(x)$ and above the x-axis for $a \leqslant x \leqslant b$.

Archimedes of Syracuse (c. 287 - 212 BC) developed the following method for approximating the area A using the sum of areas of rectangles:

A **partition** of the interval $[a, b]$ is a set of $n + 1$ points in $[a, b]$ which divide the interval into n subintervals $[x_0, x_1], [x_1, x_2], ..., [x_{n-1}, x_n]$, where $x_0 = a$, $x_n = b$, and $x_0 < x_1 < .... < x_{n-1} < x_n$.

We write partition $P = \{a = x_0, x_1, ..., x_n = b\}$.

The **length** of the ith subinterval $[x_{i-1}, x_i]$, $i = 1, ..., n$ is $\Delta x_i = x_i - x_{i-1}$.

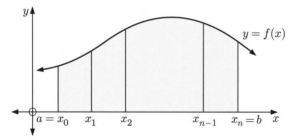

Let $x_i^* \in [x_{i-1}, x_i]$ be an *arbitrarily chosen* value in the ith subinterval, $i = 1, ..., n$.

Let $A_i =$ the area of the rectangle whose base is the width of the ith subinterval and with height equal to $f(x_i^*)$

$\therefore \ A_i = f(x_i^*) \times \Delta x_i$

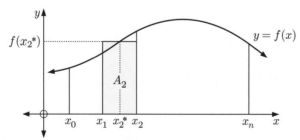

The area A can be approximated by $A \approx \sum\limits_{i=1}^{n} A_i = f(x_1^*)\Delta x_1 + ... + f(x_n^*)\Delta x_n$

$$= \sum\limits_{i=1}^{n} f(x_i^*)\Delta x_i$$

and this is called a **Riemann sum**.

LOWER AND UPPER RIEMANN SUMS

Suppose f is non-negative and continuous on $[a, b]$, and let partition $P = \{a = x_0, x_1, ..., x_n = b\}$.

If we choose the values $x_i^* \in [x_{i-1}, x_i]$, $i = 1, ..., n$ so that $f(x_i^*)$ is the minimum value of $f(x)$ on the interval $[x_{i-1}, x_i]$, then the Riemann Sum is called a **lower Riemann sum** and is denoted

$$L_n = \sum_{i=1}^{n} f(x_i^*) \Delta x_i.$$

If we choose the values $x_i^* \in [x_{i-1}, x_i]$, $i = 1, ..., n$ so that $f(x_i^*)$ is the maximum value of $f(x)$ on the interval $[x_{i-1}, x_i]$, then the Riemann Sum is called a **upper Riemann sum** and is denoted

$$U_n = \sum_{i=1}^{n} f(x_i^*) \Delta x_i.$$

REGULAR PARTITIONS

Partition P is **regular** if the n subintervals have equal length. In this case:

- $\Delta x = \dfrac{b - a}{n} = \Delta x_i$ for all $i = 1, ..., n$

- $x_i = a + \left(\dfrac{b - a}{n}\right) i$ for all $i = 0, ..., n$

- the Riemann sum is $\left(\dfrac{b - a}{n}\right) \sum_{i=1}^{n} f(x_i^*)$.

When evaluating Riemann sums, the following identities may be useful:

- $\displaystyle\sum_{i=1}^{n} c = cn$ for c a constant

- $\displaystyle\sum_{i=1}^{n} i = \dfrac{n(n + 1)}{2}$

- $\displaystyle\sum_{i=1}^{n} i^2 = \dfrac{n(n + 1)(2n + 1)}{6} = \dfrac{2n^3 + 3n^2 + n}{6}$

CALCULATING EXACT AREAS

For the function $f(x)$, the rectangles for the lower sum lie under the curve $y = f(x)$ and the rectangles for the upper sum lie above the curve. The exact area A under the curve and above the x-axis on $[a, b]$ therefore satisfies $L_n \leqslant A \leqslant U_n$ for all partitions of $[a, b]$ into n subintervals, $n \in \mathbb{Z}^+$.

For a regular partition, in the limit as $n \to \infty$, the width of each subinterval $\to 0$.

$$\lim_{n \to \infty} \Delta x = \lim_{n \to \infty} \frac{b - a}{n} = 0.$$

At the same time, the approximation for the area A is squeezed between the lower and upper Riemann sums.

$$\lim_{n \to \infty} L_n = \lim_{n \to \infty} A = \lim_{n \to \infty} U_n$$

For f a non-negative continuous function on $[a, b]$, $a < b$, the exact area A under the curve $y = f(x)$ and above the x-axis on $[a, b]$ is the unique value which satisfies $L_n \leqslant A \leqslant U_n$ for all regular partitions of $[a, b]$.

In particular, $\displaystyle\lim_{n \to \infty} L_n = A = \lim_{n \to \infty} U_n$.

Example 13

Suppose $f(x) = x^2$ on $[0, 1]$.

a Let P be a regular partition of $[0, 1]$ into n subintervals. Find Δx, and write x_i in terms of i and n.

b Show that the lower Riemann sum is given by $L_n = \dfrac{1}{3} - \dfrac{1}{2n} + \dfrac{1}{6n^2}$.

c Show that the upper Riemann sum is given by $U_n = \dfrac{1}{3} + \dfrac{1}{2n} + \dfrac{1}{6n^2}$.

d Hence find the area A under the curve $y = x^2$ and above the x-axis on $[0, 1]$.

a There are n subintervals from $x_0 = 0$ to $x_n = 1$.

$\therefore \quad \Delta x = \dfrac{1 - 0}{n} = \dfrac{1}{n}$

$\therefore \quad x_i = x_0 + i\Delta x$

$\qquad = \dfrac{i}{n}, \quad i = 1, \, ..., \, n.$

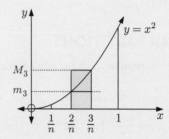

b The minimum value of $f(x)$ on $[x_{i-1}, x_i]$ is $m_i = f(x_{i-1}) = \left(\dfrac{i-1}{n}\right)^2$, $i = 1, \, ..., \, n$.

$\therefore$ the lower Riemann sum is

$L_n = \dfrac{1}{n} \displaystyle\sum_{i=1}^{n} m_i = \dfrac{1}{n} \sum_{i=1}^{n} \dfrac{(i-1)^2}{n^2}$

$\qquad = \dfrac{1}{n^3} \displaystyle\sum_{i=1}^{n} (i-1)^2$

$\qquad = \dfrac{1}{n^3} \displaystyle\sum_{i=0}^{n-1} i^2$

$\qquad = \dfrac{1}{n^3} \left(\dfrac{(n-1)(n)(2n-1)}{6}\right)$

$\qquad = \dfrac{1}{n^3} \left(\dfrac{2n^3 - 3n^2 + n}{6}\right)$

$\qquad = \dfrac{1}{3} - \dfrac{1}{2n} + \dfrac{1}{6n^2}$

c The maximum value of $f(x)$ on $[x_{i-1}, x_i]$ is $M_i = f(x_i) = \left(\dfrac{i}{n}\right)^2$, $i = 1, \, ..., \, n$.

$\therefore$ the upper Riemann sum is

$U_n = \dfrac{1}{n} \displaystyle\sum_{i=1}^{n} M_i = \dfrac{1}{n} \sum_{i=1}^{n} \dfrac{i^2}{n^2}$

$\qquad = \dfrac{1}{n^3} \displaystyle\sum_{i=1}^{n} i^2$

$\qquad = \dfrac{1}{n^3} \left(\dfrac{2n^3 + 3n^2 + n}{6}\right)$

$\qquad = \dfrac{1}{3} + \dfrac{1}{2n} + \dfrac{1}{6n^2}$

d The rectangles for the lower sum lie under the curve $y = x^2$ and the rectangles for the upper sum lie above the curve.

$\therefore$ the exact area A under the curve $y = x^2$ and above the x-axis on $[0, 1]$ satisfies $L_n \leqslant A \leqslant U_n$ for all regular partitions of $[0, 1]$ into n subintervals, $n \in \mathbb{Z}^+$.

$\therefore \quad \dfrac{1}{3} - \dfrac{1}{2n} + \dfrac{1}{6n^2} \leqslant A \leqslant \dfrac{1}{3} + \dfrac{1}{2n} + \dfrac{1}{6n^2}$ for all $n \in \mathbb{Z}^+$.

Now $\displaystyle\lim_{n \to \infty} \left(\dfrac{1}{3} - \dfrac{1}{2n} + \dfrac{1}{6n^2}\right) = \dfrac{1}{3} = \lim_{n \to \infty} \left(\dfrac{1}{3} + \dfrac{1}{2n} + \dfrac{1}{6n^2}\right)$

and $\displaystyle\lim_{n \to \infty} A = A$, since A is a constant.

$\therefore$ by the Squeeze Theorem, $A = \frac{1}{3}$ units^2.

EXERCISE G.1

1 Let $y = \sin x$ on $[0, \pi]$.

Let $P = \{0, \frac{\pi}{4}, \frac{\pi}{2}, \frac{3\pi}{4}, \pi\}$ be a regular partition of $[0, \pi]$.

Calculate L_4 and U_4 exactly, and sketch the corresponding areas on graphs of the function.

2 Suppose $f(x) = 2x$ on $[1, 4]$.

  a Let P be a regular partition of $[1, 4]$ into n subintervals. Find Δx, and write x_i in terms of i and n.

  b Write expressions for L_n and U_n.

  c Hence find the area A under the curve $f(x) = 2x$ and above the x-axis on $[1, 4]$.

3 Suppose $f(x) = x^2$ on $[1, 2]$.

  a Let P be a regular partition of $[1, 2]$ into n subintervals. Find Δx, and write x_i in terms of i and n.

  b Write expressions for L_n and U_n.

  c Hence show that the area A under the curve $f(x) = x^2$ and above the x-axis on $[1, 2]$ is $\frac{7}{3}$ units^2.

DEFINITE INTEGRALS

Let f, not necessarily non-negative or continuous, be *any* function defined on the interval $[a, b]$.

Let $P = \{a = x_0, x_1, ..., x_n = b\}$ be any partition of $[a, b]$.

If the values $x_i^* \in [x_{i-1}, x_i]$, $i = 1, ..., n$ are arbitrarily chosen then $R = \sum_{i=1}^{n} f(x_i^*)\Delta x_i$ where

$\Delta x_i = x_i - x_{i-1}$, $i = 1, ..., n$ is called the **Riemann sum** of f on $[a, b]$ for partition P and selection $\{x_1^*, x_2^*, ..., x_n^*\}$.

If P is a regular partition then $\Delta x = \dfrac{b-a}{n} = \Delta x_i$ for all $i = 1, ..., n$, and $R = \dfrac{(b-a)}{n} \sum_{i=1}^{n} f(x_i^*)$.

In the limit as $n \to \infty$, $\Delta x \to 0$ and $\displaystyle\lim_{n \to \infty} R = \lim_{n \to \infty} \frac{(b-a)}{n} \sum_{i=1}^{n} f(x_i^*)$.

If this limit exists, we say f is **integrable** on $[a, b]$. We denote the value of this limit by

$\displaystyle\int_{a}^{b} f(x)\,dx = \lim_{n \to \infty} \frac{(b-a)}{n} \sum_{i=1}^{n} f(x_i)$ and call this the **definite integral of function f from a to b.**

The function f is the **integrand**.

> If a function f is continuous on $[a, b]$, then f is integrable on $[a, b]$.

The interval $[a, b]$ is called the **domain of integration**. The values a and b are also called, respectively, the **lower** and **upper limits** of the integral.

INTERPRETING DEFINITE INTEGRALS AS AREAS

If f is an integrable function which takes negative values on $[a, b]$, we must take care when interpreting definite integrals as areas. We observe that:

- If $f(x) \geqslant 0$ on $[a, b]$, $a < b$, then

$$\int_a^b f(x)\,dx = A = \text{the area under the curve.}$$

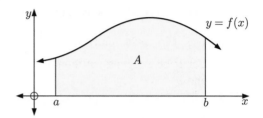

- If $f(x) \leqslant 0$ on $[a, b]$ with $a < b$, then

$$\int_a^b f(x)\,dx = -A = -(\text{the area between the curve and the } x\text{-axis})$$

In this case the values $f(x_i^*)$ in the corresponding Riemann sum will be negative.

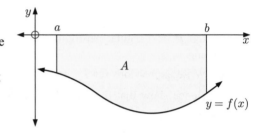

If we reverse the direction of integration we obtain $\displaystyle\int_a^b f(x)\,dx = -\int_b^a f(x)\,dx$ for f an integrable function on $[a, b]$ with $a < b$.

By interpreting definite integrals in terms of areas, the following results can be demonstrated:

For $f(x)$, $g(x)$ integrable functions on $[a, b]$:

- If f takes positive and negative values on $[a, b]$ then the area bounded by $y = f(x)$, the x-axis, and the lines $x = a$ and $x = b$ is given by

$$\int_a^b |f(x)|\,dx.$$

In this case,

$$\int_a^b f(x)\,dx = (\text{enclosed area above the } x\text{-axis})$$
$$- (\text{enclosed area below the } x\text{-axis})$$

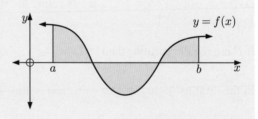

- $\displaystyle\int_a^a f(x)\,dx = 0$

- $\displaystyle\int_a^b f(x)\,dx = \int_a^c f(x)\,dx + \int_c^b f(x)\,dx$
  for all $c \in [a, b]$

- $\displaystyle\int_a^b (f(x) \pm g(x))\,dx = \int_a^b f(x)\,dx \pm \int_a^b g(x)\,dx$

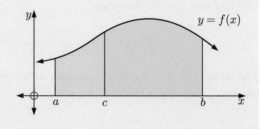

EXERCISE G.2

1 Suppose f is a function continuous on $\mathbb{R}$, and that $\displaystyle\int_1^3 f(x)\,dx = 2$, $\displaystyle\int_2^7 f(x)\,dx = \tfrac{1}{2}$,

$\displaystyle\int_2^5 f(x)\,dx = -\tfrac{1}{2}$, and $\displaystyle\int_3^6 f(x)\,dx = -2$.

a Find:

i $\displaystyle\int_1^6 f(x)\,dx$ **ii** $\displaystyle\int_5^7 f(x)\,dx$ **iii** $\displaystyle\int_7^5 f(x)\,dx$ **iv** $\displaystyle\int_4^4 f(x)\,dx$

v $\displaystyle\int_3^5 f(x)\,dx - \int_1^2 f(x)\,dx$ **vi** $\displaystyle\int_2^3 f(x)\,dx + \int_6^7 f(x)\,dx$

b Sketch a possible graph for $y = f(x)$ on $[1, 7]$.

2 Sketch the function $f(x) = \begin{cases} 3x, & 0 \leqslant x < 1 \\ 4, & x = 1 \\ 4 - 2x, & 1 < x \leqslant 3 \end{cases}$

Hence find   **a** $\displaystyle\int_0^3 f(x)\,dx$ **b** $\displaystyle\int_0^3 |f(x)|\,dx$

3 Use the limit definition of a definite integral to prove that, for integrable functions $f(x)$ and $g(x)$ on $[a,\,b]$:

a $\displaystyle\int_a^b f(x)\,dx = \int_a^c f(x)\,dx + \int_c^b f(x)\,dx$ for all $c \in [a,\,b]$

b $\displaystyle\int_a^b (f(x) + g(x))\,dx = \int_a^b f(x)\,dx + \int_a^b g(x)\,dx$

H THE FUNDAMENTAL THEOREM OF CALCULUS

Although Riemann sums and limits of Riemann sums are used to define the definite integral, we rarely use them to calculate the value of a definite integral.

In this section we prove the Fundamental Theorem of Calculus (FTOC). The FTOC links together the definite integral and the indefinite integral for integrable functions, which includes all continuous functions. It is this theorem we use when calculating definite integrals of continuous functions.

If f is integrable on $[a, b]$ with $a < b$ and if f is bounded on $[a, b]$ so that $m \leqslant f(x) \leqslant M$ for all $x \in [a, b]$ where $m, M \in \mathbb{R}$ are constants, then

$$m(b - a) \leqslant \int_a^b f(x)\,dx \leqslant M(b - a).$$

Proof: $m \leqslant f(x) \leqslant M$ for all $x \in [a, b]$

$\therefore$ for a regular partition P of $[a, b]$ with $\Delta x = \dfrac{b - a}{n}$, $n \in \mathbb{Z}^+$,

$\qquad m\Delta x \leqslant f(x)\,\Delta x \leqslant M\Delta x$

$\therefore$ $m\Delta x \leqslant f(x_i^*)\,\Delta x \leqslant M\Delta x$ for each $x_i^* \in [x_{i-1}, x_i]$, $i = 1, ..., n$.

By summing these n inequalities, and since $n\Delta x = \dfrac{n(b - a)}{n} = b - a$, we obtain:

$\qquad m(b - a) \leqslant \displaystyle\sum_{i=1}^n f(x_i^*)\,\Delta x \leqslant M(b - a)$

In the limit as $n \to \infty$, we obtain $m(b - a) \leqslant \displaystyle\int_a^b f(x)\,dx \leqslant M(b - a)$.

For the special case when f is non-negative and continuous on $[a, b]$, we observe in terms of area that

$m(b - a) \leqslant A \leqslant M(b - a)$ where $A = \displaystyle\int_a^b f(x)\,dx.$

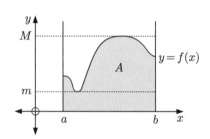

If f is continuous on $[a, b]$ with $a < b$, then there exists $c \in [a, b]$ such that

$$f(c) = \frac{1}{b - a} \int_a^b f(x)\,dx$$

which is called the **average value** of f on $[a, b]$.

Proof: If f is continuous on $[a, b]$ then f is bounded on $[a, b]$

$\therefore$ there exist constants $m, M \in \mathbb{R}$ such that $m \leqslant f(x) \leqslant M$ on $[a, b]$, where $m = f(x_m)$ is the minimum value of $f(x)$ on $[a, b]$ and $M = f(x_M)$ is the maximum value of $f(x)$ on $[a, b]$.

$$\therefore \; m(b-a) \leqslant \int_a^b f(x)\, dx \leqslant M(b-a) \quad \text{by the previous result.}$$

$$\therefore \; m \leqslant \frac{\int_a^b f(x)\, dx}{b-a} \leqslant M$$

By the Intermediate Value Theorem (IVT) applied to f on the interval $[x_m, x_M]$ or $[x_M, x_m]$, whichever is appropriate,

$$f(c) = \frac{\int_a^b f(x)\, dx}{b-a} \quad \text{for some} \;\; c \in [a, b].$$

Now let $f(x)$ be a continuous function on $[a, b]$, with $a < b$.

We define a new function $\;\; F(x) = \displaystyle\int_a^x f(t)\, dt \;\;$ for $x \in [a, b]$.

Since f is continuous on $[a, b]$, f is integrable on $[a, b]$, so function F is well defined for $x \in [a, b]$.

For the special case when f is also non-negative on $[a, b]$, we can interpret $F(x)$ as the area under the curve $y = f(t)$, above the t-axis, and between $t = a$ and $t = x$, as shown.

We prove that function $F(x)$ is an antiderivative of $f(x)$ on $[a, b]$.

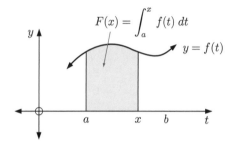

THE FUNDAMENTAL THEOREM OF CALCULUS (PART 1)

If $f(x)$ is continuous on $[a, b]$ with $a < b$ then $\;\; F(x) = \displaystyle\int_a^x f(t)\, dt \;\;$ is continuous on $[a, b]$, and $\;\; F'(x) = f(x) \;\;$ for all $\;\; x \in \,]a, b[$.

Proof:

Let $x \in \,]a, b[$, and let $h > 0$ be such that $x + h < b$.

Now $\;\; \dfrac{F(x+h) - F(x)}{h} = \dfrac{1}{h}\left(\displaystyle\int_a^{x+h} f(t)\, dt - \int_a^x f(t)\, dt \right)$

$$= \frac{1}{h} \int_x^{x+h} f(t)\, dt$$

$$= \frac{1}{(x+h)-x} \int_x^{x+h} f(t)\, dt$$

$$= f(c) \quad \text{for some} \;\; c \in [x, x+h], \;\; \text{since } f \text{ is continuous on } [a, b].$$

$$\therefore \quad \lim_{h \to 0^+} \frac{F(x+h) - F(x)}{h} = \lim_{h \to 0^+} f(c) = f(x) \quad \text{since } x \leqslant c \leqslant x + h$$
$$\text{and } f \text{ is continuous on } [a, b].$$

In the same way for $h < 0$, $x + h > a$, we find

$$\lim_{h \to 0^-} \frac{F(x+h) - F(x)}{h} = \lim_{h \to 0^-} f(c) = f(x) \quad \text{since } x + h \leqslant c \leqslant x$$
$$\text{and } f \text{ is continuous on } [a, b].$$

$$\therefore \quad F'(x) = f(x) \quad \text{as required.}$$

Since F is differentiable on $]a, b[$, F is continuous on $]a, b[$. We still need to show that F is continuous on $[a, b]$.

Since f is continuous on $[a, b]$, f is integrable on $[a, b]$

$$\therefore \quad F(a) = \int_a^a f(t) \, dt = 0 \quad \text{and} \quad F(b) = \int_a^b f(t) \, dt \qquad \text{are both defined.}$$

Now $\displaystyle \lim_{x \to a^+} F(x) = \lim_{x \to a^+} \int_a^x f(t) \, dt \qquad$ and $\qquad \displaystyle \lim_{x \to b^-} F(x) = \lim_{x \to b^-} \int_a^x f(t) \, dt$

$$= \int_a^a f(t) \, dt \qquad\qquad\qquad = \int_a^b f(t) \, dt$$
$$= 0 \qquad\qquad\qquad\qquad = F(b).$$
$$= F(a)$$

Thus $F(x)$ is continuous on $[a, b]$.

The FTOC (Part 1) can also be written as:

> If f is continuous on $[a, b]$ then $\dfrac{d}{dx}\left(\displaystyle\int_a^x f(t) \, dt \right) = f(x)$, for $x \in \,]a, b[$.

The FTOC (Part 1) guarantees that any function f continuous on $[a, b]$ has the antiderivative $F(x) = \displaystyle\int_a^x f(t) \, dt$ on $[a, b]$, even if we cannot write it down.

For example, $f(x) = \sin(x^3)$ has an antiderivative $F(x) = \displaystyle\int_0^x \sin(t^3) \, dt$ on $[0, \infty[$ even though we cannot write down an antiderivative of $\sin(x^3)$ explicitly as a function.

THE FUNDAMENTAL THEOREM OF CALCULUS (PART 2)

> If f is any function integrable on $[a, b]$ which has an antiderivative G on $[a, b]$,
> $$\int_a^b f(x) \, dx = [G(x)]_a^b = G(b) - G(a).$$

Proof:

Case: **If f is continuous on $[a, b]$ then f is integrable on $[a, b]$.**

By FTOC (Part 1) the function $F(x) = \int_a^x f(t)\, dt$ is an antiderivative of f on $[a, b]$.

By the second corollary to the MVT,

$$F(x) = G(x) + C \quad \text{where } C \text{ is a constant.}$$
$$\therefore \quad F(a) = G(a) + C$$
$$\therefore \quad \int_a^a f(t)\, dt = G(a) + C$$
$$\therefore \quad 0 = G(a) + C$$
$$\therefore \quad C = -G(a).$$

Hence $F(x) = G(x) - G(a)$
$$\therefore \quad F(b) = G(b) - G(a)$$
$$\therefore \quad \int_a^b f(t)\, dt = G(b) - G(a) \quad \text{as required.}$$

Case: **Suppose f is not continuous on $[a, b]$.** By the premise of the theorem, $\int_a^b f(x)\, dx$

exists, and G is a function continuous on $[a, b]$ such that $G'(x) = f(x)$ for $x \in\,]a, b[$.

Let $P = \{a = x_0,\, x_1,\, ...,\, x_n = b\}$ be a regular partition of $[a, b]$ with $n \in \mathbb{Z}^+$.

Consider the ith subinterval $[x_{i-1}, x_i]$, $i = 1, 2, ..., n$.

By the Mean Value Theorem, $\dfrac{G(x_i) - G(x_{i-1})}{x_i - x_{i-1}} = G'(x_i^*)$ for some $x_i^* \in [x_{i-1}, x_i]$.

Thus $G(x_i) - G(x_{i-1}) = G'(x_i^*)\Delta x$,   where $\Delta x = \dfrac{b-a}{n} = x_i - x_{i-1}$.

Summing over all subintervals in the partition we obtain

$$\sum_{i=1}^n G'(x_i^*)\Delta x = \sum_{i=1}^n \left(G(x_i) - G(x_{i-1}) \right)$$
$$= [G(x_1) - G(x_0)] + [G(x_2) - G(x_1)] + ... + [G(x_n) - G(x_{n-1})]$$
$$= G(x_n) - G(x_0)$$

$$\therefore \quad \sum_{i=1}^n f(x_i^*)\Delta x = G(b) - G(a), \quad \text{since} \quad G'(x_i^*) = f(x_i^*), \quad x_n = b, \text{ and } x_0 = a.$$

$$\therefore \quad \lim_{n \to \infty} \left[\sum_{i=1}^n f(x_i^*)\Delta x \right] = G(b) - G(a) \quad \text{which is a constant.}$$

$$\therefore \quad \int_a^b f(x)\, dx = G(b) - G(a) \quad \text{as required.}$$

If a function is integrable and has an explicitly defined antiderivative, then the FTOC (Part 2) allows us to calculate definite integrals easily.

For example, if $f(x) = x^2$ then $G(x) = \dfrac{x^3}{3}$ and therefore $\displaystyle\int_0^1 x^2\, dx = \left[\dfrac{x^3}{3} \right]_0^1 = \dfrac{1^3}{3} - \dfrac{0^3}{3} = \dfrac{1}{3}$.

DISCUSSION

Does the existence of an antiderivative guarantee that a function defined on $[a, b]$ is integrable on $[a, b]$?

Example 14

Find $F'(x)$ if: **a** $F(x) = \displaystyle\int_1^x \cos^3 t \, dt$ **b** $F(x) = \displaystyle\int_{x^2}^5 e^t \, dt$

a $F'(x)$

$= \dfrac{d}{dx} \left(\displaystyle\int_1^x \cos^3 t \, dt \right)$

$= \cos^3 x$

This is valid since
$f(t) = \cos^3 t$ is a
continuous function.

b $F'(x) = \dfrac{d}{dx} \left(\displaystyle\int_{x^2}^5 e^t \, dt \right)$

$= \dfrac{d}{dx} \left(-\displaystyle\int_5^{x^2} e^t \, dt \right)$

$= \dfrac{d}{dx} \left(-\displaystyle\int_5^{u(x)} e^t \, dt \right)$ where $u(x) = x^2$

$= \dfrac{d}{du} \left(-\displaystyle\int_5^u e^t \, dt \right) \times \dfrac{du}{dx}$ {Chain rule}

$= -e^u \times 2x$ {valid since $f(t) = e^t$ is continuous}

$= -2xe^{x^2}$

Example 15

Find $F'(x)$ if $F(x) = \displaystyle\int_x^{x^2} \dfrac{1}{t^2 + 3} \, dt$.

$F'(x) = \dfrac{d}{dx} \left(\displaystyle\int_x^{x^2} \dfrac{1}{t^2 + 3} \, dt \right)$

$= \dfrac{d}{dx} \left(\displaystyle\int_c^{x^2} \dfrac{1}{t^2 + 3} \, dt + \displaystyle\int_x^c \dfrac{1}{t^2 + 3} \, dt \right)$ where c is a constant

$= \dfrac{d}{dx} \left(\displaystyle\int_c^{x^2} \dfrac{1}{t^2 + 3} \, dt \right) + \dfrac{d}{dx} \left(-\displaystyle\int_c^x \dfrac{1}{t^2 + 3} \, dt \right)$

$= \dfrac{d}{dx} \left(\displaystyle\int_c^u \dfrac{1}{t^2 + 3} \, dt \right) - \dfrac{1}{x^2 + 3}$ {letting $u(x) = x^2$}

$= \dfrac{d}{du} \left(\displaystyle\int_c^u \dfrac{1}{t^2 + 3} \, dt \right) \times \dfrac{du}{dx} - \dfrac{1}{x^2 + 3}$ {Chain rule}

$= \dfrac{1}{u^2 + 3} \times 2x - \dfrac{1}{x^2 + 3}$ {valid since $f(t) = \dfrac{1}{t^2 + 3}$ is continuous}

$= \dfrac{2x}{x^4 + 3} - \dfrac{1}{x^2 + 3}$

EXERCISE H

1 Find $F'(x)$ if:

a $F(x) = \displaystyle\int_1^x \sin^4 t\, dt$

b $F(x) = \displaystyle\int_0^x \dfrac{dt}{(t^2+2)^{15}}$

c $F(x) = \displaystyle\int_x^4 e^{t^2}\, dt$

d $F(x) = \displaystyle\int_{-1}^{x^2} e^{\sin t}\, dt$

2 Explain what is wrong with the argument: $\displaystyle\int_{-1}^2 \dfrac{1}{x^2}\, dx = \left[\dfrac{-1}{x}\right]_{-1}^2$ {FTOC}

$$= -\tfrac{1}{2} - (1)$$
$$= -\tfrac{3}{2}$$

3 **a** Can $\dfrac{d}{dx}\left(\displaystyle\int_{-1}^x \dfrac{1}{t}\, dt \right)$ for $x \in \mathbb{R}$ be calculated using the Fundamental Theorem of Calculus? Explain your answer.

   b For which values of x can the derivative in **a** be calculated?

4 Calculate the following derivatives:

a $\dfrac{d}{dx}\left(\displaystyle\int_1^{2x} \dfrac{t}{\sqrt{1+t^4}}\, dt \right)$

b $\dfrac{d}{dx}\left(\displaystyle\int_x^{x^2} \sin(e^t)\, dt \right)$

c $\dfrac{d}{dx}\left(\displaystyle\int_{x^3}^{\sin x} \dfrac{1}{1+t^2}\, dt \right)$

5 Find $\displaystyle\int_{-3}^{10} |x|\, dx$.

6 Find $\displaystyle\int_0^5 f(x)\, dx$ for $f(x) = \begin{cases} \sin x, & 0 \leqslant x \leqslant \frac{\pi}{2} \\ 2x, & \frac{\pi}{2} < x \leqslant 3 \\ \dfrac{1}{x}, & 3 < x \leqslant 5 \end{cases}$

7 Find exactly the average value of each function on the given interval:

a $f(x) = \dfrac{1}{x^3}$ on $[2, 5]$

b $f(x) = \begin{cases} x^2, & -2 \leqslant x \leqslant 1 \\ e^x, & 1 < x \leqslant 5 \end{cases}$ on $[-2, 5]$

8 Let $F(x) = \displaystyle\int_1^x \cos(e^{t^2})\, dt$, $x > 1$. Find exactly:

a $F'(x)$ **b** $F'(2)$ **c** $F'\left(\sqrt{\ln \pi}\right)$ **d** $F''(x)$ **e** $F''(2)$

9 Let $y = f(t)$, $t \in [0, 4]$ be the function with the graph shown. Let $g(x) = \displaystyle\int_0^x f(t)\, dt$, $x \in [0, 4]$. Find exactly:

a $g(1)$ **b** $g(3)$ **c** $g'(1)$

d $g'(3)$ **e** $g''(3)$.

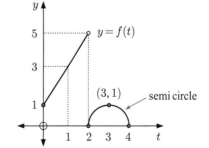

10 Suppose $g'(3) = 5$, $g(3) = 4$, $f(2) = -1$, and $F(x) = \displaystyle\int_1^{g(x)} f(t-2)\, dt$.

Find $F'(3)$, stating the assumptions about f and g necessary to make the calculation valid.

IMPROPER INTEGRALS OF THE FORM $\int_a^\infty f(x)\,dx$

An integral is described as **improper** if one of the following is true:

- the integrand approaches $+\infty$ or $-\infty$ for one or more points on the domain of integration,

  for example $\int_{-1}^{2} \frac{1}{x^2}\,dx$ is improper since $\frac{1}{x^2}$ is discontinuous at $x=0$ and as $x \to 0$, $f(x) \to \infty$

- it has the form $\int_a^\infty f(x)\,dx$, $\int_{-\infty}^{b} f(x)\,dx$, or $\int_{-\infty}^{\infty} f(x)\,dx$ where $a, b \in \mathbb{R}$ are any

  constants. We define, when these limits exist:

$$\int_a^\infty f(x)\,dx = \lim_{b \to \infty} \int_a^b f(x)\,dx$$

$$\int_{-\infty}^{b} f(x)\,dx = \lim_{a \to -\infty} \int_a^b f(x)\,dx$$

$$\text{and} \quad \int_{-\infty}^{\infty} f(x)\,dx = \int_{-\infty}^{a} f(x)\,dx + \int_a^\infty f(x)\,dx.$$

In this course we are only concerned with improper integrals of the form $\int_a^\infty f(x)\,dx$.

The improper integral $\int_a^\infty f(x)\,dx$ is said to be **convergent** if $\int_a^b f(x)\,dx$ exists for all b

where $a \leqslant b < \infty$, and if $\int_a^\infty f(x)\,dx = \lim_{b \to \infty} \int_a^b f(x)\,dx$ exists.

Otherwise the improper integral is **divergent**.

Example 16

Investigate the convergence of $\int_1^\infty \frac{1}{x^p}\,dx$ where $p \in \mathbb{R}$.

If $p = 1$, $\int_1^\infty \frac{1}{x^p}\,dx = \lim_{b \to \infty} \int_1^b \frac{1}{x}\,dx$

$\qquad\qquad\qquad\qquad = \lim_{b \to \infty} [\ln x]_1^b$

$\qquad\qquad\qquad\qquad = \lim_{b \to \infty} (\ln b)$ which DNE since as $b \to \infty$, $\ln b \to \infty$

$\qquad$ Hence $\int_1^\infty \frac{1}{x}\,dx$ is divergent.

If $p \neq 1$, $\int_1^\infty \frac{1}{x^p}\,dx = \lim_{b \to \infty} \int_1^b \frac{1}{x^p}\,dx$

$\qquad\qquad\qquad\qquad = \lim_{b \to \infty} \left[\frac{1}{(1-p)x^{p-1}} \right]_1^b$

$$\therefore \quad \int_1^\infty \frac{1}{x^p}\, dx = \lim_{b\to\infty} \left[\frac{1}{(1-p)x^{p-1}}\right]_1^b$$

$$= \frac{1}{1-p} \lim_{b\to\infty} \left[\left(\frac{1}{x}\right)^{p-1}\right]_1^b$$

$$= \frac{1}{1-p} \lim_{b\to\infty} \left[\left(\frac{1}{b}\right)^{p-1} - 1\right].$$

If $p > 1$ then $\dfrac{1}{1-p} \displaystyle\lim_{b\to\infty} \left[\left(\frac{1}{b}\right)^{p-1} - 1\right] = \dfrac{1}{p-1}$.

If $p < 1$, $\displaystyle\lim_{b\to\infty} \left(\frac{1}{b}\right)^{p-1}$ DNE as $b \to \infty$, $(b)^{1-p} \to \infty$.

Hence $\displaystyle\int_1^\infty \frac{1}{x^p}\, dx$ converges if $p > 1$ and diverges if $p \leqslant 1$.

From **Example 16** we conclude the important result:

$$\int_1^\infty \frac{1}{x^p}\, dx \quad \text{converges if } p > 1 \text{ and diverges if } p \leqslant 1.$$

THE COMPARISON TEST FOR IMPROPER INTEGRALS

Suppose $0 \leqslant f(x) \leqslant g(x)$ for all $x \geqslant a$.

- If $\displaystyle\int_a^\infty g(x)\, dx$ is convergent, then so is $\displaystyle\int_a^\infty f(x)\, dx$.

- If $\displaystyle\int_a^\infty f(x)\, dx$ is divergent, then so is $\displaystyle\int_a^\infty g(x)\, dx$.

Example 17

Determine whether $\displaystyle\int_2^\infty \frac{1}{\sqrt{x}-1}\, dx$ is convergent or divergent.

Now we know that $0 \leqslant \sqrt{x} - 1 \leqslant \sqrt{x}$ for all $x \geqslant 2$

so it follows that $0 \leqslant \dfrac{1}{\sqrt{x}} \leqslant \dfrac{1}{\sqrt{x}-1}$ for all $x \geqslant 2$.

Now $\displaystyle\int_2^\infty \frac{1}{\sqrt{x}}\, dx = \int_1^\infty \frac{1}{\sqrt{x}}\, dx - \int_1^2 \frac{1}{\sqrt{x}}\, dx$

where $\displaystyle\int_1^2 \frac{1}{\sqrt{x}}\, dx$ exists, but from **Example 16** $\displaystyle\int_1^\infty \frac{1}{\sqrt{x}}\, dx$ is divergent.

$\therefore \displaystyle\int_2^\infty \frac{1}{\sqrt{x}}\, dx$ is divergent, and so $\displaystyle\int_2^\infty \frac{1}{\sqrt{x}-1}\, dx$ is divergent by the Comparison Test.

If $\displaystyle\int_a^\infty |f(x)|\, dx$ converges then $\displaystyle\int_a^\infty f(x)\, dx$ converges.

Proof:

By definition, $-|f(x)| \leqslant f(x) \leqslant |f(x)|$

$$\therefore\ \ 0 \leqslant f(x) + |f(x)| \leqslant 2|f(x)|$$

$$\therefore\ \ 0 \leqslant \int_a^\infty f(x) + |f(x)|\, dx \leqslant 2\int_a^\infty |f(x)|\, dx$$

$\therefore$ by the Comparison Test, if $\displaystyle\int_a^\infty |f(x)|\, dx$ is convergent then so is $\displaystyle\int_a^\infty f(x) + |f(x)|\, dx$.

Supposing $\displaystyle\int_a^\infty |f(x)|\, dx = A$ and $\displaystyle\int_a^\infty f(x) + |f(x)|\, dx = B$ where $A,\, B \in \mathbb{R}$

then $\displaystyle\int_a^\infty f(x)\, dx = B - A.$

Hence $\displaystyle\int_a^\infty f(x)\, dx$ is convergent.

Example 18

Using integration by parts and the Comparison Test, prove that $\displaystyle\int_1^\infty \frac{\sin x}{x}\, dx$ is convergent.

$$\int_1^\infty \frac{\sin x}{x}\, dx = \lim_{b \to \infty} \int_1^b \frac{\sin x}{x}\, dx$$

$$= \lim_{b \to \infty} \left[-\frac{\cos x}{x} \right]_1^b - \lim_{b \to \infty} \int_1^b \frac{\cos x}{x^2}\, dx \qquad \{\text{integration by parts}\}$$

$$= \lim_{b \to \infty} \left(-\frac{\cos b}{b} + \cos 1 \right) - \int_1^\infty \frac{\cos x}{x^2}\, dx$$

$$= \cos 1 - \int_1^\infty \frac{\cos x}{x^2}\, dx$$

Now $0 \leqslant \left| \dfrac{\cos x}{x^2} \right| \leqslant \dfrac{1}{x^2}$ for all $x \geqslant 1$,

and we also know from **Example 16** that $\displaystyle\int_1^\infty \frac{1}{x^2}\, dx$ is convergent.

$\therefore\ \ \displaystyle\int_1^\infty \left| \frac{\cos x}{x^2} \right|\, dx$ is also convergent, and hence so is $\displaystyle\int_1^\infty \frac{\cos x}{x^2}\, dx.$

$\therefore\ \ \displaystyle\int_1^\infty \frac{\sin x}{x}\, dx$ converges.

EVALUATING IMPROPER INTEGRALS

When an improper integral is convergent, we may be able to evaluate it using a variety of techniques. These include use of the limit laws, l'Hôpital's Rule, integration by parts, and integration by substitution.

Example 19

Evaluate $\displaystyle\int_a^\infty xe^{-x}\,dx$, for any constant $a \in \mathbb{R}$.

$$\int_a^\infty xe^{-x}\,dx = \lim_{b\to\infty} \int_a^b xe^{-x}\,dx$$

$$= \lim_{b\to\infty} \left(\left[-xe^{-x}\right]_a^b - \int_a^b -e^{-x}\,dx \right) \qquad \{\text{integration by parts}\}$$

$$= \lim_{b\to\infty} \left(-be^{-b} + ae^{-a} - \left[e^{-x}\right]_a^b \right)$$

$$= \lim_{b\to\infty} \left(-be^{-b} + ae^{-a} - e^{-b} + e^{-a} \right)$$

$$= e^{-a}(a+1) + \lim_{b\to\infty} \left(e^{-b}(-1-b) \right)$$

$$= e^{-a}(a+1) + \lim_{b\to\infty} \left(\frac{-1-b}{e^b} \right)$$

Now as $b \to \infty$, $\ -1 - b \to -\infty\ $ and $\ e^b \to \infty$.

$$\therefore \int_a^\infty xe^{-x}\,dx = e^{-a}(a+1) + \lim_{b\to\infty} \frac{-1}{e^b} \qquad \{\text{l'Hôpital's Rule}\}$$

$$= e^{-a}(a+1)$$

EXERCISE I.1

1 Use the Comparison Test for improper integrals to test for convergence:

    a $\displaystyle\int_1^\infty \frac{x}{2x^5 + 3x^2 + 1}\,dx$
        b $\displaystyle\int_2^\infty \frac{x^2 - 1}{\sqrt{x^7 + 1}}\,dx$

2 Determine whether $\displaystyle\int_1^\infty \frac{\sin x}{x^3}\,dx$ is convergent.

3 Test for convergence:

    a $\displaystyle\int_1^\infty \frac{x^2 + 1}{x^4 + 1}\,dx$ **b** $\displaystyle\int_0^\infty e^{-x^2}\,dx$ **c** $\displaystyle\int_1^\infty \frac{\ln x}{x}\,dx$ **d** $\displaystyle\int_1^\infty e^{-x}\ln x\,dx$

4 Show that $\displaystyle\int_0^\infty e^{-x}\cos x\,dx$ is convergent.

5 Evaluate:

    a $\displaystyle\int_a^\infty \frac{dx}{x^2 + a^2}$
        b $\displaystyle\int_{\frac{1}{\pi}}^\infty \frac{1}{x^2}\sin\left(\frac{1}{x}\right)\,dx$

6 Evaluate $\displaystyle\int_a^\infty \frac{dx}{e^x + e^{-x}}$ using the substitution $u = e^x$.

7 Evaluate $\displaystyle\int_1^\infty \left(\frac{1}{\sqrt{x}} - \frac{1}{\sqrt{x+3}} \right) dx$.

8 Find the area in the first quadrant under the curve $y = \dfrac{1}{x^2 + 6x + 10}$.

9 Prove that $\displaystyle\int_e^\infty \frac{\ln x}{x^p}\, dx$ is divergent for $p \leqslant 1$.

10 **a** Evaluate the integral $\displaystyle\int_0^\infty x^n e^{-x}\, dx$ for $n = 0, 1, 2, 3$.

    b Predict the value of $\displaystyle\int_0^\infty x^n e^{-x}\, dx$ for $n \in \mathbb{Z}^+$.

    c Prove your prediction using mathematical induction.

APPROXIMATION TO THE IMPROPER INTEGRAL $\displaystyle\int_a^\infty f(x)\, dx,\ a \in \mathbb{Z}$

Suppose f is continuous and positive on $[a, \infty[$, $a \in \mathbb{Z}$. We consider the integral $\displaystyle\int_a^\infty f(x)\, dx$ in terms of area under the curve for $x \geqslant a$. Consider a regular partition $P = \{a, a+1, a+2, ...\}$ of $[a, \infty[$ with subintervals of length $\Delta x = 1$.

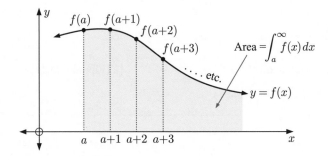

For each interval of length one along the x-axis, we can draw a rectangle of height equal to the value of the function on one side of the rectangle.

For example, using the left side of the rectangle, the rectangle from $x = a$ to $x = a+1$ would have height $f(a)$, the rectangle from $x = a+1$ to $x = a+2$ would have height $f(a+1)$, and so on.

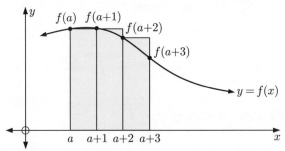

As with definite integrals approximated by Riemann sums, the improper integral $\displaystyle\int_a^\infty f(x)\, dx$ may be approximated by the corresponding sum of areas of these rectangles.

$$\int_a^\infty f(x)\, dx \approx \sum_{i=a}^\infty f(i) = \lim_{b \to \infty} \sum_{i=a}^b f(i) \quad \text{where} \quad \sum_{i=a}^\infty f(i) \quad \text{is also called an \textbf{infinite series}.}$$

DECREASING AND INCREASING FUNCTIONS

Suppose the function $f(x)$ is *decreasing* for all $x > a$.

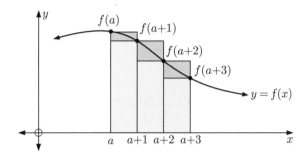

By taking the height of each rectangle to be the value of the function at the left endpoint of each subinterval, we obtain an upper sum U where

$$\int_a^\infty f(x)\,dx \leqslant \sum_{i=a}^\infty f(i) = U.$$

By taking the height of each rectangle to be the value of the function at the right endpoint of each subinterval, we obtain a lower sum L where

$$L = \sum_{i=a}^\infty f(i+1) \leqslant \int_a^\infty f(x)\,dx.$$

Hence, for a function which is **decreasing on** $[a, \infty[$,

$$L = \sum_{i=a}^\infty f(i+1) \leqslant \int_a^\infty f(x)\,dx \leqslant \sum_{i=a}^\infty f(i) = U.$$

Similarly, for any negative continuous function which is **increasing on** $[a, \infty[$,

$$L = \sum_{i=a}^\infty f(i) \leqslant \int_a^\infty f(x)\,dx \leqslant \sum_{i=a}^\infty f(i+1) = U.$$

Example 20

Write down a series which approximates $\displaystyle\int_0^\infty e^{-x^2}\,dx$.

$$\int_0^\infty e^{-x^2}\,dx \approx \sum_{i=0}^\infty e^{-i^2}$$

EXERCISE 1.2

1   Write down a series which approximates:

a $\displaystyle\int_0^\infty \frac{1}{\sqrt{x+1}}\,dx$

b $\displaystyle\int_4^\infty e^{-x}\,dx$

2 Consider the function $f(x) = e^{-x^2}$.

    a Show that $f(x)$ is decreasing for all $x > 0$.

    b Write upper and lower sums that approximate $\displaystyle\int_0^\infty f(x)\,dx$.

    c Write an inequality that relates the sums in **b** to the integral.

3 Consider the function $f(x) = -\dfrac{1}{x^2}$.

    a Show that $f(x)$ is increasing for all $x > 0$.

    b Write upper and lower sums that approximate $\displaystyle\int_1^\infty -\frac{1}{x^2}\,dx$.

    c Write an inequality that relates the sums in **b** to the integral.

J   SEQUENCES

A **sequence** is a list of numbers, called **terms**, in a definite order.

We write the sequence a_1, a_2, a_3, ... as $\{a_n\}$, where a_n is the nth term of the sequence.

The sequence is **infinite** if it contains an infinite number of terms, so $n \in \mathbb{Z}^+$.

The sequence is **finite** if it contains a finite number of terms, so $n \in \mathbb{Z}^+$, $n \leqslant N$.

For example, the sequence $\{a_n\}$, where $a_n = \dfrac{n}{n+1}$, $n \in \mathbb{Z}^+$, denotes the infinite set of discrete values

$\{\frac{1}{2},\ \frac{2}{3},\ \frac{3}{4},\ \frac{4}{5},\ \frac{5}{6},\ ....\}$ in this order.

We can plot a_n against n to give:

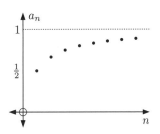

Consider the function $f(x) = \dfrac{x}{x+1}$, $x \in \mathbb{R}$, $x \neq -1$.

$$\lim_{x \to \infty} f(x) = \lim_{x \to \infty} \frac{x}{x+1} \times \frac{\frac{1}{x}}{\frac{1}{x}}$$

$$= \lim_{x \to \infty} \frac{1}{1 + \frac{1}{x}}$$

$$= \frac{1}{1+0} \qquad \{\text{since} \ \lim_{x \to \infty} \frac{1}{x} = 0\}$$

$$= 1$$

It follows that $\displaystyle\lim_{n \to \infty} \frac{n}{n+1} = 1$ for $n \in \mathbb{Z}^+$.

By considering n sufficiently large, the terms of the sequence will be as close as we like to value 1.

We say that $L = 1$ is the limit of the sequence $\{a_n\}$, where $a_n = \dfrac{n}{n+1}$, $n \in \mathbb{Z}^+$.

This is true even though the terms never actually reach the limit value 1.

A sequence $\{a_n\}$ has a **limit** L if for each $\varepsilon > 0$ there exists a positive integer N such that $|a_n - L| < \varepsilon$ for all terms a_n with $n > N$.

We write $\displaystyle\lim_{n \to \infty} a_n = L$.

If the limit of a sequence exists, then we say the sequence **converges**. Otherwise, the sequence **diverges**.

If a sequence converges, then its limit is unique.

Proof:

Suppose $\{a_n\}$ is a convergent sequence with two limits L_1, L_2 where $L_1 \neq L_2$.

If $\varepsilon = |L_1 - L_2|$, then $\varepsilon > 0$ since $L_1 \neq L_2$.

Since $\lim\limits_{n \to \infty} a_n = L_1$, there exists $N_1 \in \mathbb{Z}^+$ such that $n > N_1$ ensures $|a_n - L_1| < \dfrac{\varepsilon}{2}$.

Since $\lim\limits_{n \to \infty} a_n = L_2$, there exists $N_2 \in \mathbb{Z}^+$ such that $n > N_2$ ensures $|a_n - L_2| < \dfrac{\varepsilon}{2}$.

Suppose $n = \max(N_1, N_2)$ is the maximum of N_1 and N_2.

$$\therefore \ |L_1 - L_2| = |L_1 - a_n + a_n - L_2|$$
$$\leqslant |L_1 - a_n| + |a_n - L_2| \qquad \{\text{Triangle Inequality}\}$$
$$\leqslant |a_n - L_1| + |a_n - L_2|$$
$$< \frac{\varepsilon}{2} + \frac{\varepsilon}{2}$$
$$< \varepsilon$$

Thus for $n = \max(N_1, N_2)$ we have $|L_1 - L_2| < \varepsilon$ which is a contradiction since $|L_1 - L_2| = \varepsilon$.

Hence it is not possible for a sequence to have two distinct limits.

LIMIT THEOREMS FOR SEQUENCES

In this section we formally prove, in some cases very intuitive, limit results for some important sequences.

Archimedes of Syracuse stated that for any two line segments with lengths a and b, where $a < b$, it is possible to lay the shorter length a end to end a finite number of times to create a length greater than the longer length b.

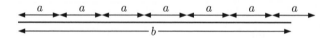

This is summarised in terms of real numbers as the **Archimedean property**:

Given any $\varepsilon > 0$, there exists $N \in \mathbb{Z}^+$ such that $N\varepsilon > 1$.

Result 1:   For any real constant c, $\lim\limits_{n \to \infty} c = c$.

Proof: Let $a_n = c$ for $n \in \mathbb{Z}^+$.

$\therefore \ |a_n - c| = |c - c| = 0 < \varepsilon$ for all $\varepsilon > 0$.

For any $\varepsilon > 0$ and for all $n > 0$ we have $|a_n - c| < \varepsilon$.

$\therefore$ by the definition of a limit of a sequence $\{a_n\}$, $\lim\limits_{n \to \infty} c = c$.

Result 2: $\lim\limits_{n \to \infty} \dfrac{1}{n} = 0.$

Proof:

Let $a_n = \dfrac{1}{n}$ for $n \in \mathbb{Z}^+$.

$\therefore$ $|a_n - 0| = \left| \dfrac{1}{n} - 0 \right| = \dfrac{1}{n}$.

For any $\varepsilon > 0$ there exists $N \in \mathbb{Z}^+$ such that $N\varepsilon > 1$ {Archimedean property}

$\therefore$ $\dfrac{1}{N} < \varepsilon$.

For $n > N$, $\dfrac{1}{n} < \dfrac{1}{N}$.

$\therefore$ for any $\varepsilon > 0$, there exists $N \in \mathbb{Z}^+$ such that for $n > N$,

$|a_n - 0| = \dfrac{1}{n} < \dfrac{1}{N} < \varepsilon$.

$\therefore$ by the definition of a limit of a sequence, $\displaystyle\lim_{n \to \infty} a_n = \lim_{n \to \infty} \dfrac{1}{n} = 0$.

Result 3:

If $p > 0$, then $\displaystyle\lim_{n \to \infty} \dfrac{1}{n^p} = 0$.

Proof:

Let $a_n = \dfrac{1}{n^p}$ for $n \in \mathbb{Z}^+$.

Suppose $\varepsilon > 0$ is given. Then $\varepsilon^{\frac{1}{p}} > 0$ and by the Archimedean property there exists

$N \in \mathbb{Z}^+$ such that $N\varepsilon^{\frac{1}{p}} > 1$.

$\therefore$ $\dfrac{1}{N} < \varepsilon^{\frac{1}{p}}$.

$\therefore$ since $y = x^p$, $p > 0$, is an increasing function, $\dfrac{1}{N^p} < (\varepsilon^{\frac{1}{p}})^p = \varepsilon$.

$\therefore$ for any $\varepsilon > 0$, there exists $N \in \mathbb{Z}^+$ such that for $n > N$,

$|a_n - 0| = \left| \dfrac{1}{n^p} - 0 \right| = \dfrac{1}{n^p} < \dfrac{1}{N^p} < \varepsilon$.

$\therefore$ by the definition of a limit of a sequence,

$\displaystyle\lim_{n \to \infty} a_n = \lim_{n \to \infty} \dfrac{1}{n^p} = 0$ for all $p > 0$.

Result 4:

Consider the sequence $\{c^n\}$, $c \in \mathbb{R}$.

If $0 \leqslant |c| < 1$, the sequence $\{c^n\}$ converges to 0, so $\displaystyle\lim_{n \to \infty} c^n = 0$.

If $|c| > 1$, the sequence $\{c^n\}$ diverges. As $n \to \infty$, $|c|^n \to \infty$.

Proof:

If $c = 0$ then $\displaystyle\lim_{n \to \infty} c^n = 0$. {Result 1}

Let $a_n = c^n$ for $n \in \mathbb{Z}^+$, where c is a constant such that $0 < |c| < 1$.

If we let $|c| = \dfrac{1}{1+d}$, then $d = \dfrac{1}{|c|} - 1 > 0$.

By the Bernoulli Inequality (see **Exercise A** question **9**), since $d > 0$,

$(1+d)^n \geqslant 1 + nd > 0$ for all $n \in \mathbb{Z}^+$.

$$\therefore \quad |c|^n = \frac{1}{(1+d)^n} \leqslant \frac{1}{1+nd} < \frac{1}{nd} \quad \text{for all} \quad n \in \mathbb{Z}^+.$$

Given $\varepsilon > 0,\ \varepsilon d > 0$, so by the Archimedean property there exists $N \in \mathbb{Z}^+$ such that $N\varepsilon d > 1$.

$$\therefore \quad \frac{1}{Nd} < \varepsilon.$$

$$\therefore \quad |a_n - 0| = |c^n - 0| = |c^n| = |c|^n < \frac{1}{nd} < \frac{1}{Nd} < \varepsilon \quad \text{for all integers} \quad n \geqslant N.$$

$\therefore$ by the definition of the limit of a sequence, $\lim\limits_{n \to \infty} a_n = \lim\limits_{n \to \infty} c^n = 0.$

If $|c| > 1$ then $|c| = 1 + \varepsilon$ for some $\varepsilon > 0$.

$|c|^n = (1+\varepsilon)^n \geqslant 1 + n\varepsilon$ by the Bernoulli Inequality.

Now $\{1 + n\varepsilon\}$ diverges to infinity as $n \to \infty$, so by comparison, $|c|^n \to \infty$.

THE SQUEEZE THEOREM FOR SEQUENCES

Suppose we have sequences of real numbers $\{a_n\}$, $\{b_n\}$, and $\{c_n\}$ where $a_n \leqslant b_n \leqslant c_n$ for all $n \in \mathbb{Z}^+$. If $\lim\limits_{n \to \infty} a_n = \lim\limits_{n \to \infty} c_n = L$ exists, then $\lim\limits_{n \to \infty} b_n = L$.

Proof: Suppose $L = \lim\limits_{n \to \infty} a_n = \lim\limits_{n \to \infty} c_n$.

Given $\varepsilon > 0$ there exists a natural number N such that if $n \geqslant N$ then
$$|a_n - L| < \varepsilon \quad \text{and} \qquad |c_n - L| < \varepsilon \quad \text{for all} \quad n \geqslant N$$
$$\therefore \quad -\varepsilon < a_n - L < \varepsilon \quad \text{and} \quad -\varepsilon < c_n - L < \varepsilon \quad \text{for all} \quad n \geqslant N.$$

Now $a_n \leqslant b_n \leqslant c_n$, so $a_n - L \leqslant b_n - L \leqslant c_n - L$.

$\therefore \quad -\varepsilon < b_n - L < \varepsilon \quad \text{for all} \quad n \geqslant N$

$\therefore \quad |b_n - L| < \varepsilon \quad \text{for all} \quad n \geqslant N.$

Hence $\lim\limits_{n \to \infty} b_n = L$.

The Squeeze Theorem still holds even if the condition $a_n \leqslant b_n \leqslant c_n$ only applies for every natural number from some point $n \geqslant k$. The finite number of sequence terms from $n = 1$ to $n = k$ does not affect the ultimate convergence (or divergence) of the sequence.

BOUNDED SEQUENCES

A sequence of real numbers $\{a_n\}$ is said to be **bounded** if there exists a real number $M > 0$ such that $|a_n| \leqslant M$ for all $n \in \mathbb{Z}^+$.

We can deduce that:

Every convergent sequence is bounded.

Proof: Let $\{a_n\}$ be a sequence where $\lim_{n \to \infty} a_n = a$.

If we let $\varepsilon = 1$, then by the definition of convergence there exists a natural number N such that $|a_n - a| < 1$ for all $n \geqslant N$.

But from Corollary **3** of the Triangle Inequality, $|a_n| - |a| \leqslant |a_n - a| < 1$ for all $n \geqslant N$

$$\therefore \quad |a_n| \leqslant 1 + |a| \quad \text{for all} \quad n \geqslant N.$$

If we define M as the maximum value in the set $\{1+|a|, |a_1|, ..., |a_{N-1}|\}$ then $|a_n| \leqslant M$ for all $n \in \mathbb{Z}^+$.

$\therefore$ the sequence $\{a_n\}$ is bounded.

ALGEBRA OF LIMITS THEOREMS

Suppose $\{a_n\}$ converges to a real number a and $\{b_n\}$ converges to a real number b.

1 $\quad \lim_{n \to \infty} (a_n + b_n) = \lim_{n \to \infty} a_n + \lim_{n \to \infty} b_n = a + b$

2 The sequence $\{a_n b_n\}$ converges and $\quad \lim_{n \to \infty} (a_n b_n) = \left(\lim_{n \to \infty} a_n \right) \left(\lim_{n \to \infty} b_n \right) = ab$.

3 If $b \neq 0$ then $\quad \lim_{n \to \infty} \left(\dfrac{a_n}{b_n} \right) = \dfrac{\lim_{n \to \infty} a_n}{\lim_{n \to \infty} b_n} = \dfrac{a}{b}$.

These results can be extended to finite sums and products of limits using mathematical induction.

Proof of 2:

For $n \in \mathbb{Z}^+$, we have $\quad a_n b_n - ab = a_n b_n - a_n b + a_n b - ab$
$$= a_n(b_n - b) + b(a_n - a).$$

By the Triangle Inequality, $\quad |a_n b_n - ab| \leqslant |a_n(b_n - b)| + |b(a_n - a)| = |a_n| |b_n - b| + |b| |a_n - a|$

Since $\{a_n\}$ and $\{b_n\}$ are convergent sequences, they are bounded and there exists $M_1, M_2 > 0$ such that $|a_n| \leqslant M_1$ and $|b_n| \leqslant M_2$ for all $n \in \mathbb{Z}^+$. If we let M be the greater of M_1 and M_2, then $|a_n b_n - ab| \leqslant M |b_n - b| + M |a_n - a|$ for all $n \in \mathbb{Z}^+$.

Since $\lim_{n \to \infty} a_n = a$ and $\lim_{n \to \infty} b_n = b$, for any given $\varepsilon > 0$ there exist positive integers N_1, N_2

such that $|a_n - a| < \dfrac{\varepsilon}{2M}$ for all $n > N_1$, and $|b_n - b| < \dfrac{\varepsilon}{2M}$ for all $n > N_2$.

Letting N be the greater of N_1 and N_2, then $|a_n b_n - ab| < M \left(\dfrac{\varepsilon}{2M} \right) + M \left(\dfrac{\varepsilon}{2M} \right) = \varepsilon$ for all $n > N$.

Hence $\lim_{n \to \infty} (a_n b_n) = ab$ from the definition of the limit of a sequence.

We have applied the formal definition of the limit of a sequence to rigorously establish some key results for sequences that can now be used to deal very efficiently with more general problems.

Example 21

Suppose $a_n = \left(\frac{4}{5}\right)^n + \frac{3}{n} - 9$ for all $n \in \mathbb{Z}^+$. Find $\lim\limits_{n \to \infty} a_n$.

By the generalised version of **1** of the Algebra of Limits Theorems,

$$\lim_{n \to \infty} \left[\left(\frac{4}{5}\right)^n + \frac{3}{n} - 9\right] = \lim_{n \to \infty} \left(\frac{4}{5}\right)^n + \lim_{n \to \infty} \frac{3}{n} + \lim_{n \to \infty} (-9)$$

provided each of these limits exist.

Now $\lim\limits_{n \to \infty} \left(\frac{4}{5}\right)^n = 0$ {since $0 < \frac{4}{5} < 1$}

$\lim\limits_{n \to \infty} \left(\frac{3}{n}\right) = \lim\limits_{n \to \infty} 3 \times \lim\limits_{n \to \infty} \frac{1}{n} = 3 \times 0 = 0$

$\lim\limits_{n \to \infty} (-9) = -9$

$\therefore \quad \lim\limits_{n \to \infty} \left[\left(\frac{4}{5}\right)^n + \frac{3}{n} - 9\right] = 0 + 0 - 9 = -9$

Example 22

Let $a_n = \dfrac{2n^2 + 4n - 3}{n^2 - 4\ln n}$ for all $n \in \mathbb{Z}^+$. Find $\lim\limits_{n \to \infty} a_n$.

Dividing the numerator and denominator by n^2, $\quad \dfrac{2n^2 + 4n - 3}{n^2 - 4\ln n} = \dfrac{2 + \dfrac{4}{n} - \dfrac{3}{n^2}}{1 - \dfrac{4\ln n}{n^2}}$

$$\therefore \quad \lim_{n \to \infty} a_n = \frac{\lim\limits_{n \to \infty} \left(2 + \dfrac{4}{n} - \dfrac{3}{n^2}\right)}{\lim\limits_{n \to \infty} \left(1 - \dfrac{4\ln n}{n^2}\right)}$$

GRAPHICS CALCULATOR INSTRUCTIONS

Using the limit laws, $\quad \lim\limits_{n \to \infty} \dfrac{1}{n^2} = 0$

$\therefore \quad \lim\limits_{n \to \infty} \left(2 + \dfrac{4}{n} - \dfrac{3}{n^2}\right) = \lim\limits_{n \to \infty} (2) + 4 \lim\limits_{n \to \infty} \left(\dfrac{1}{n}\right) - 3 \lim\limits_{n \to \infty} \left(\dfrac{1}{n^2}\right)$

You can use your calculator to check your answer.

$$= 2 + 0 + 0 = 2$$

Now $0 < \ln n < n$ for all $n \geqslant 1$

$\therefore \quad 0 < \dfrac{\ln n}{n^2} < \dfrac{1}{n}$

$\therefore \quad 0 < \dfrac{4\ln n}{n^2} < \dfrac{4}{n}$

Since $\lim\limits_{n \to \infty} 0 = 0 = \lim\limits_{n \to \infty} \dfrac{4}{n} = 4 \lim\limits_{n \to \infty} \dfrac{1}{n}$,

$\lim\limits_{n \to \infty} \dfrac{4\ln n}{n^2} = 0$ {Squeeze Theorem}

$\therefore$ using **3** of the Algebra of Limits Theorems $\quad \lim\limits_{n \to \infty} a_n = \dfrac{2}{1-0} = 2$

Example 23

If $a_n = \dfrac{\sin n}{n}$ for all $n \in \mathbb{Z}^+$, prove that $\lim\limits_{n \to \infty} a_n = 0$.

We cannot apply the $\lim\limits_{n \to \infty} \left(\dfrac{a_n}{b_n} \right) = \dfrac{a}{b}$ result as neither $\{\sin n\}$ nor $\{n\}$ are convergent sequences.

However, since $-1 \leqslant \sin n \leqslant 1$ for all $n \in \mathbb{Z}^+$,

$$-\frac{1}{n} \leqslant \frac{\sin n}{n} \leqslant \frac{1}{n} \quad \text{for all } n \in \mathbb{Z}^+.$$

Now $\lim\limits_{n \to \infty} \left(-\dfrac{1}{n} \right) = 0 = \lim\limits_{n \to \infty} \dfrac{1}{n}$.

$\therefore$ using the Squeeze Theorem, $\lim\limits_{n \to \infty} \left(\dfrac{\sin n}{n} \right) = 0$.

WRITING A SEQUENCE AS A FUNCTION

Consider a sequence $\{a_n\}$ which can be expressed as a real-valued function $f(x)$. We write $a_n = f(n)$, $n \in \mathbb{Z}^+$, for f a real-valued function.

The behaviour of $f(x)$ as $x \to \infty$ also describes how $\{a_n\}$ behaves as $n \to \infty$.

We can therefore use what we know about the limits of functions as $x \to \infty$ to help investigate the limit of a sequence:

1 Suppose $a_n = f(n)$, $n \in \mathbb{Z}^+$. If $\lim\limits_{x \to \infty} f(x) = L$ exists,

then $\lim\limits_{n \to \infty} a_n = L$.

2 If $\lim\limits_{n \to \infty} a_n = L$ exists and g is any function continuous

at $x = L$, then $\lim\limits_{n \to \infty} g(a_n) = g\left(\lim\limits_{n \to \infty} a_n \right) = g(L)$.

1 allows us to use l'Hôpital's Rule.

EXERCISE J.1

1 Using the appropriate Algebra of Limits Theorems, evaluate $\lim\limits_{n \to \infty} a_n$ when it exists:

a $a_n = \dfrac{1}{n + n^3}$, $n \in \mathbb{Z}^+$

b $a_n = \ln(1 + n) - \ln n$, $n \in \mathbb{Z}^+$

c $a_n = \dfrac{3n^2 - 5n}{5n^2 + 2n - 6}$, $n \in \mathbb{Z}^+$

d $a_n = \dfrac{n(n+2)}{n+1} - \dfrac{n^3}{n^2 + 1}$, $n \in \mathbb{Z}^+$

e $a_n = \sqrt{n+1} - \sqrt{n}$, $n \in \mathbb{Z}^+$

f $a_n = \left(\dfrac{2n - 3}{3n + 7} \right)^4$, $n \in \mathbb{Z}^+$

2 Determine whether the following sequences converge:

a $\left\{ \dfrac{n!}{(n+3)!} \right\}$

b $\left\{ \dfrac{1}{\sqrt{n^2 + 1} - n} \right\}$

c $\left\{ \dfrac{\sqrt{n} - 1}{\sqrt{n} + 1} \right\}$

d $\left\{ \dfrac{\cos^2 n}{2^n} \right\}$

e $\left\{ (-1)^n \sin \left(\dfrac{1}{n} \right) \right\}$

f $\left\{ \dfrac{\sqrt[3]{2n^5 - n^2 + 4}}{n^2 + 1} \right\}$

3 Find $\lim\limits_{n \to \infty} a_n$ where $a_n = \dfrac{1}{n^2} + \dfrac{2}{n^2} + \dfrac{3}{n^2} + \,....\, + \dfrac{n}{n^2}$.

4 If it exists, find $\lim\limits_{n \to \infty} a_n$ for:

    a $a_n = \left(\dfrac{1}{1+n} \right)^n, \ n \in \mathbb{Z}^+$
             b $a_n = \left(2 + \dfrac{1}{n} \right)^n, \ n \in \mathbb{Z}^+$

5 Prove part **1** of the Algebra of Limits Theorems:

If $\{a_n\}$ converges to a real number a and $\{b_n\}$ converges to a real number b, then
$$\lim_{n \to \infty} (a_n + b_n) = \lim_{n \to \infty} a_n + \lim_{n \to \infty} b_n = a + b.$$

6 Use the formal definition of a limit to prove that for $n \in \mathbb{Z}^+$, $\lim\limits_{n \to \infty} \left(\dfrac{3n+5}{7n-4} \right) = \dfrac{3}{7}$.

7 If $\lim\limits_{n \to \infty} a_n = a$, $\lim\limits_{n \to \infty} b_n = b$, and α and β are real constants, use the Algebra of Limits

Theorems to prove that $\lim\limits_{n \to \infty} (\alpha a_n + \beta b_n) = \alpha a + \beta b$.

Hence prove that $\lim\limits_{n \to \infty} (a_n - b_n) = a - b$.

MONOTONE SEQUENCES

A sequence $\{a_n\}$ is **monotone** (or **monotonic**) if $a_{n+1} \geqslant a_n$ or $a_{n+1} \leqslant a_n$ for all n.

To show that a sequence is monotone we show that either $a_{n+1} - a_n \geqslant 0$

                    or that $a_{n+1} - a_n \leqslant 0$ for all $n \in \mathbb{Z}^+$.

Alternatively, suppose a_n can be represented by a differentiable function $f(x)$, $x \in \mathbb{R}$, $x \geqslant 1$ such that $a_n = f(n)$ for all $n \in \mathbb{Z}^+$. If $f'(x) \geqslant 0$ for all $x \geqslant 1$, or if $f'(x) \leqslant 0$ for all $x \geqslant 1$, then $\{a_n\}$ is monotone.

THE MONOTONE CONVERGENCE THEOREM

A monotone sequence of real numbers is convergent if and only if it is bounded.

For example:

- The sequence $\{a_n\}$ where $a_n = n$, $n \in \mathbb{Z}^+$, is a monotone increasing sequence which is unbounded. Clearly $\{a_n\}$ diverges.

- The sequence $\{a_n\}$ where $a_n = 1 - \dfrac{1}{n}$, $n \in \mathbb{Z}^+$, is a monotone increasing sequence which is bounded since $|a_n| = \left| 1 - \dfrac{1}{n} \right| < 1$ for all $n \in \mathbb{Z}^+$.

We have shown previously that $\{a_n\}$ is convergent and $\lim\limits_{n \to \infty} a_n = 1$.

EXERCISE J.2

1 **a** Prove that the sequence $\{u_n\}$ with nth term $u_n = \dfrac{2n-7}{3n+2}$ is:

      i monotone increasing
                ii bounded.

  b Determine whether the following sequences are monotone and bounded, and calculate their limits if they exist:

      i $\left\{ \dfrac{3^n}{1 + 3^n} \right\}$
                ii $\left\{ \dfrac{1}{e^n - e^{-n}} \right\}$

2 Prove that the sequence $\left\{ \dfrac{1 \times 3 \times 5 \times .... \times (2n-1)}{2^n n!} \right\}$ is convergent.

3 The sequence $\{x_n\}$ is defined by $x_1 = 0$, $x_n = \sqrt{4 + 3x_{n-1}}$.

    a Use mathematical induction to show that $\{x_n\}$ is monotone increasing.

    b Evaluate x_1, x_2, x_3, ..., x_{11}, and hence suggest an upper bound for $\{x_n\}$.

    c Use mathematical induction to prove that $\{x_n\}$ is bounded.

    d Hence find $\lim\limits_{n\to\infty} x_n$.

4   **a** Find the values of $1 + \frac{1}{1}$, $1 + \dfrac{1}{1 + \frac{1}{1}}$, $1 + \dfrac{1}{1 + \dfrac{1}{1 + \frac{1}{1}}}$, $1 + \dfrac{1}{1 + \dfrac{1}{1 + \dfrac{1}{1 + \frac{1}{1}}}}$

    b Give a recursive definition for the sequence above in terms of u_n.

    c Show that $\{u_n\}$ is bounded but not monotone.

    d Given that $\{u_n\}$ converges, find the exact value of $\lim\limits_{n\to\infty} u_n$.

5   **a** Consider the sequence $\{u_n\}$ defined by $u_1 = a$ (a positive constant) and

      $u_{n+1} = \frac{1}{2}\left(u_n + \dfrac{2}{u_n}\right)$ for all $n \in \mathbb{Z}^+$.

      Use your calculator to find u_1, u_2, u_3, ..., u_8 when:

      i $a = 5$ **ii** $a = 1$ **iii** a of your choice.

    b Is $\{u_n\}$ monotone for all $a > 0$?

    c Do your experimental results in **a** suggest the existence of a limit L such that $\lim\limits_{n\to\infty} u_n = L$.

      If so, find L.

    d If $u_1 = a$ where $a > 0$ and $u_{n+1} = \frac{1}{2}\left(u_n + \dfrac{3}{u_n}\right)$, find $\lim\limits_{n\to\infty} u_n$ given that it exists.

    e State $\lim\limits_{n\to\infty} u_n$ given that $\{u_n\}$ is defined by $u_1 = 6$ and $u_{n+1} = \frac{1}{2}\left(u_n + \dfrac{k}{u_n}\right)$.

    f Suggest a recurrence relationship for generating values of $\sqrt[3]{k}$.

6   **a** Expand $\left(1 + \dfrac{1}{n}\right)^n$, $n \in \mathbb{Z}^+$, using the Binomial Theorem.

    b Define $\{e_n\}$ by $e_n = \left(1 + \dfrac{1}{n}\right)^n$ and show that e_n equals:

$$1 + 1 + \frac{1}{2!}\left(1 - \frac{1}{n}\right) + \frac{1}{3!}\left(1 - \frac{1}{n}\right)\left(1 - \frac{2}{n}\right) + ... + \frac{1}{n!}\left[\left(1 - \frac{1}{n}\right)\left(1 - \frac{2}{n}\right) .... \left(1 - \frac{n-1}{n}\right)\right]$$

    c **i** Show that $2 \leqslant e_n < e_{n+1}$ for all $n \in \mathbb{Z}^+$.

      ii Show that $e_n < 1 + 1 + \dfrac{1}{2!} + \dfrac{1}{3!} + ... + \dfrac{1}{n!} < 1 + 1 + \dfrac{1}{2} + \dfrac{1}{2^2} + ... + \dfrac{1}{2^{n-1}}$ for all

        $n \in \mathbb{Z}^+$.

      iii Hence show that $\{e_n\}$ is convergent.

    d **i** Given that $\lim\limits_{n\to\infty}\left(1 + \dfrac{1}{n}\right)^n = e \approx 2.718$, show that $\lim\limits_{n\to\infty}\left(1 - \dfrac{1}{n}\right)^n = e^{-1}$.

      ii Hence show that $\lim\limits_{n\to\infty}\left(\dfrac{n!}{n^n}\right) = 0$ using the Squeeze Theorem.

K   INFINITE SERIES

Let $\{u_1,\ u_2,\ u_3,\ ....\}$ be an infinite sequence.

We can form a new sequence $\{S_n\} = \{S_1,\ S_2,\ S_3,\ ....\}$ by letting

$$S_1 = u_1$$
$$S_2 = u_1 + u_2$$
$$\vdots$$
$$S_n = u_1 + u_2 + ... + u_n = \sum_{i=1}^{n} u_i.$$

The value S_n, which is the sum of the first n terms of $\{u_n\}$, is called the **nth partial sum**.

Each term of $\{S_n\}$ is a finite series.

If $\displaystyle\lim_{n\to\infty} S_n = \sum_{n=1}^{\infty} u_n$ exists and equals some finite value S, then the infinite series is **convergent**.

Otherwise it is **divergent**.

Example 24

Let $\{u_n\}$ be defined by $u_n = r^{n-1}$ where $r \in \mathbb{R}$, $r \neq 0$, $n \in \mathbb{Z}^+$.
Find an expression for S_n, the nth partial sum of $\{u_n\}$, which does not involve a summation.

$$S_n = \sum_{i=1}^{n} u_i = \sum_{i=1}^{n} r^{i-1} = 1 + r + r^2 + ... + r^{n-1}$$
$$\therefore \quad rS_n = r + r^2 + r^3 + ... + r^n$$
$$\therefore \quad rS_n - S_n = r^n - 1$$
$$\therefore \quad S_n = \frac{r^n - 1}{r - 1}$$

It is often important to know when $\displaystyle\lim_{n\to\infty} S_n = \sum_{n=1}^{\infty} u_n$ exists, and if so, what its value is. In general it is not possible to write S_n as an explicit expression as we did in **Example 24**. However, we shall see that more difficult functions can often be expressed as simpler infinite series. Great mathematicians such as **Euler** and **Newton** did much of their foundation work using infinite series representations of functions, though it was not until much later that other mathematicians such as **Cauchy** and **Lagrange** rigorously established when such representations were valid.

Since convergence of a series is in effect convergence of a sequence of partial sums, many of the sequence results apply. For example:

If $\displaystyle\sum_{n=1}^{\infty} a_n$ and $\displaystyle\sum_{n=1}^{\infty} b_n$ are convergent series, then

- $\displaystyle\sum_{n=1}^{\infty} c a_n = c \sum_{n=1}^{\infty} a_n$ where c is a constant, and

- $\displaystyle\sum_{n=1}^{\infty} (a_n \pm b_n) = \sum_{n=1}^{\infty} a_n \pm \sum_{n=1}^{\infty} b_n$ are also both convergent.

However, because the form of the sequence of partial sums is generally too unwieldy to deal with using our earlier methods, we need a special set of tests and conditions for determining when the limits of these partial sums exist.

We start with a useful result which can tell us something either about a series $\sum\limits_{n=1}^{\infty} a_n$ or its associated sequence of general terms $\{a_n\}$:

If the series $\sum\limits_{n=1}^{\infty} a_n$ is convergent then $\lim\limits_{n \to \infty} a_n = 0$.

Proof: Let $S_n = a_1 + a_2 + ... + a_n$

$\therefore \quad a_n = S_n - S_{n-1}$

Now $\sum\limits_{n=1}^{\infty} a_n$ is convergent, so $\{S_n\}$ is convergent (by definition).

Letting $\lim\limits_{n \to \infty} S_n = S, \quad \lim\limits_{n \to \infty} S_{n-1} = S$

$\therefore \quad \lim\limits_{n \to \infty} a_n = \lim\limits_{n \to \infty} (S_n - S_{n-1}) = S - S = 0$

We shall show later that even though $\lim\limits_{n \to \infty} \dfrac{1}{n} = 0$, $\sum\limits_{n=1}^{\infty} \dfrac{1}{n}$ diverges extremely slowly.

Therefore, the converse of the above theorem is not true.

However, we may establish the following **Test for Divergence**:

If $\lim\limits_{n \to \infty} a_n$ does not exist, or if $\lim\limits_{n \to \infty} a_n \neq 0$, then the series $\sum\limits_{n=1}^{\infty} a_n$ is divergent.

Example 25

Show that the series $\sum\limits_{n=1}^{\infty} \dfrac{n^2}{5n^2 + 4}$ diverges.

The nth term of the series is $a_n = \dfrac{n^2}{5n^2 + 4}$.

$\therefore \quad \lim\limits_{n \to \infty} a_n = \lim\limits_{n \to \infty} \dfrac{n^2}{5n^2 + 4}$

$= \lim\limits_{n \to \infty} \dfrac{1}{5 + \dfrac{4}{n^2}}$

$= \tfrac{1}{5}$

Since $\lim\limits_{n \to \infty} a_n \neq 0$, the series diverges.

The Test for Divergence puts no sign restriction on each term of $\{a_n\}$. However, all of the following series tests *only apply to series with positive terms*.

THE COMPARISON TEST FOR SERIES

Let $\{a_n\}$ be a **positive** sequence, so $a_n > 0$ for all n.

If there exists a convergent series $\sum_{n=1}^{\infty} b_n$ such that $a_n \leqslant b_n$, then $\sum_{n=1}^{\infty} a_n$ is also convergent.

Conversely, if $a_n \geqslant b_n$ and $\sum_{n=1}^{\infty} b_n$ diverges, then so does $\sum_{n=1}^{\infty} a_n$.

Proof of the first part:

Let $\{A_n\}$ and $\{B_n\}$ be the sequences of partial sums associated with a_n and b_n respectively.

Since $a_n, b_n > 0$, $\{A_n\}$ and $\{B_n\}$ are monotonic increasing.

Suppose $a_n \leqslant b_n$, and that $\{B_n\}$ is convergent with $\lim_{n \to \infty} B_n = B$.

$\therefore \quad 0 \leqslant A_n \leqslant B_n \leqslant B$.

$\therefore \quad A_n$ is also a bounded monotonic sequence, and therefore converges by the Monotone Convergence Theorem.

With a minor adjustment to the proof, the result can be shown to hold if $a_n \geqslant 0$ for all n.

However, the difficulty in using the Comparison Test is in finding a suitable $\sum_{n=1}^{\infty} b_n$.

An appropriate geometric series often tends to work. Indeed, convergent geometric series are used in the proofs of some of the most general and important convergence tests.

GEOMETRIC SERIES

A series $\sum_{k=1}^{\infty} a_k$ is a **geometric series** if there exists a constant r, called the **common ratio** of the series, such that $a_{k+1} = ra_k$ for all $k \in \mathbb{Z}^+$, and $a_1 = a$ is a constant.

In this case $\sum_{k=1}^{\infty} a_k = a + ar + ar^2 + ar^3 + \dots = \sum_{k=1}^{\infty} ar^{k-1}$.

The nth partial sum $S_n = \sum_{k=1}^{n} ar^{k-1} = a(1 + r + r^2 + \dots + r^{n-1})$.

Since $a \in \mathbb{R}$ is a constant it suffices to examine $\sum_{k=1}^{\infty} r^{k-1}$, or equivalently $\sum_{k=0}^{\infty} r^k$.

If $|r| < 1$, then the geometric series $\sum_{k=0}^{\infty} r^k$ converges with sum $S = \sum_{k=0}^{\infty} r^k = \dfrac{1}{1-r}$.

If $|r| \geqslant 1$ then the geometric series diverges.

Proof:

If $r = 1$ then $\sum_{k=1}^{\infty} 1^{k-1} = 1 + 1 + 1 + 1 + \dots$, and the nth partial sum is

$$S_n = \sum_{k=1}^{n} 1^{k-1} = \underbrace{1 + 1 + \dots + 1}_{n \text{ times}} = n.$$

Now $\lim_{n \to \infty} S_n = \lim_{n \to \infty} n$ DNE, so $\sum_{k=0}^{\infty} 1^k$ diverges.

If $r = -1$ then $\sum_{k=1}^{\infty} (-1)^{k-1} = 1 - 1 + 1 - 1 ....$ and the nth partial sum is $S_n = \begin{cases} 1, & n \text{ odd} \\ 0, & n \text{ even.} \end{cases}$

$\lim_{n \to \infty} S_n$ DNE as S_n alternates between constants 1 and 0 as $n \to \infty$.

If $|r| \neq 1$ then $S_n = \sum_{k=1}^{n} r^{k-1} = 1 + r + ... + r^{n-1}$

$$= \frac{r^n - 1}{r - 1} \quad \{\text{from } \textbf{Example 24}\}$$

$\therefore \lim_{n \to \infty} S_n = \lim_{n \to \infty} \frac{r^n - 1}{r - 1}$

By **Result 4** of the limit theorems for sequences, $\lim_{n \to \infty} r^n = 0$ for $|r| < 1$

and $\lim_{n \to \infty} r^n$ DNE for $|r| > 1$.

Hence for $|r| < 1$ $\lim_{n \to \infty} S_n = \frac{1}{1-r}$, and so $\sum_{k=0}^{\infty} r^k = \frac{1}{1-r}$ is convergent.

For $|r| > 1$, $\lim_{n \to \infty} S_n$ DNE and so $\sum_{k=0}^{\infty} r^k$ diverges.

Example 26

Test the series $\sum_{n=1}^{\infty} \frac{1}{2^n + 1}$ for convergence.

Now 2^n is positive for all n, and $2^n + 1 > 2^n$.

$\therefore \quad 0 < \frac{1}{2^n + 1} < \frac{1}{2^n} = \left(\frac{1}{2}\right)^n$ for all $n \in \mathbb{Z}^+$.

But $\sum_{n=1}^{\infty} \left(\frac{1}{2}\right)^n$ is a convergent geometric series and therefore,

by the Comparison Test, $\sum_{n=1}^{\infty} \frac{1}{2^n + 1}$ also converges.

We cannot use the Comparison Test in the same way as in **Example 26** to test the series $\sum_{n=1}^{\infty} \frac{1}{2^n - 1}$ for convergence. However, the following test may be useful when the Comparison Test cannot be applied directly.

THE LIMIT COMPARISON TEST

Suppose that $\sum_{n=1}^{\infty} a_n$ and $\sum_{n=1}^{\infty} b_n$ are series with positive terms.

1 If $\lim_{n \to \infty} \frac{a_n}{b_n} = c$, $c > 0$, then the series either both converge or both diverge.

2 If $\lim_{n \to \infty} \frac{a_n}{b_n} = 0$ and $\sum_{n=1}^{\infty} b_n$ converges, then $\sum_{n=1}^{\infty} a_n$ converges.

3 If $\frac{a_n}{b_n} \to \infty$ as $n \to \infty$ and $\sum_{n=1}^{\infty} b_n$ diverges, then $\sum_{n=1}^{\infty} a_n$ diverges.

Proof of 1:

Since $c > 0$, $0 < \varepsilon = \dfrac{c}{2}$.

Since $\lim\limits_{n \to \infty} \dfrac{a_n}{b_n} = c$, using the definition of a limit there exists $N \in \mathbb{Z}^+$ such that

$$\left| \frac{a_n}{b_n} - c \right| < \frac{c}{2} \quad \text{for all} \quad n > N$$

$$\therefore \quad -\frac{c}{2} < \frac{a_n}{b_n} - c < \frac{c}{2}$$

$$\therefore \quad \frac{c}{2} < \frac{a_n}{b_n} < \frac{3c}{2}$$

$$\therefore \quad b_n \left(\frac{c}{2} \right) < a_n < \left(\frac{3c}{2} \right) b_n \quad \text{for all} \quad n > N$$

Now if $\sum\limits_{n=1}^{\infty} b_n$ converges then so does $\sum\limits_{n=1}^{\infty} \left(\dfrac{3c}{2} \right) b_n$.

Hence by the Comparison Test, $\sum\limits_{n=1}^{\infty} a_n$ also converges.

However, if $\sum\limits_{n=1}^{\infty} b_n$ diverges then so does $\sum\limits_{n=1}^{\infty} \left(\dfrac{c}{2} \right) b_n$.

Hence by the Comparison Test, $\sum\limits_{n=1}^{\infty} a_n$ also diverges.

Example 27

Test the series $\sum\limits_{n=1}^{\infty} \dfrac{1}{2^n - 1}$ for convergence or divergence.

Let $a_n = \dfrac{1}{2^n - 1}$ and $b_n = \dfrac{1}{2^n}$.

$$\therefore \quad \lim_{n \to \infty} \frac{a_n}{b_n} = \lim_{n \to \infty} \frac{2^n}{2^n - 1}$$

$$= \lim_{n \to \infty} \frac{1}{1 - \left(\frac{1}{2} \right)^n}$$

$$= 1 \quad \left\{ \text{since} \quad \lim_{n \to \infty} \left(\tfrac{1}{2} \right)^n = 0 \right\}$$

Since $\sum\limits_{n=1}^{\infty} \dfrac{1}{2^n}$ is a convergent geometric series, $\sum\limits_{n=1}^{\infty} \dfrac{1}{2^n - 1}$ converges also.   {Limit Comparison Test **1**}

THE INTEGRAL TEST

The Integral Test links the sum of a series to the integral of a positive function.

We have seen that if a is an integer, $\sum\limits_{i=a}^{\infty} f(i) \approx \displaystyle\int_a^{\infty} f(x)\, dx$

In particular, when $a = 1$, $\sum\limits_{i=1}^{\infty} f(i) \approx \displaystyle\int_1^{\infty} f(x)\, dx$

The Integral Test is:

> Suppose that f is a continuous, positive, decreasing function on $[1, \infty[$.
> Let $a_n = f(n)$, $n \in \mathbb{Z}^+$, so that the terms in $\{a_n\}$ are all positive.
>
> **1** If $\displaystyle\int_1^\infty f(x)\,dx$ is convergent, then $\displaystyle\sum_{n=1}^\infty a_n$ is convergent.
>
> **2** If $\displaystyle\int_1^\infty f(x)\,dx$ is divergent, then $\displaystyle\sum_{n=1}^\infty a_n$ is divergent.

Clearly this test is only of practical use if $\displaystyle\int_1^\infty f(x)\,dx$ can be evaluated relatively easily.

Proof of 1:

If $f(x)$ is a continuous, positive, decreasing function, then we can approximate the integral $\displaystyle\int_1^\infty f(x)\,dx$ using lower and upper sums:

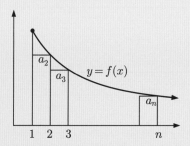
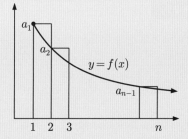

The lower sum

$$a_2 + a_3 + \ldots + a_n + \ldots \leqslant \int_1^\infty f(x)\,dx$$

$$\therefore \quad \sum_{n=1}^\infty a_n \leqslant a_1 + \int_1^\infty f(x)\,dx$$

The upper sum

$$a_1 + a_2 + \ldots + a_{n-1} + \ldots \geqslant \int_1^\infty f(x)\,dx$$

$$\therefore \quad \int_1^\infty f(x)\,dx \leqslant \sum_{n=1}^\infty a_n$$

Hence, $\displaystyle\int_1^\infty f(x)\,dx \leqslant \sum_{n=1}^\infty a_n \leqslant a_1 + \int_1^\infty f(x)\,dx$

If $\displaystyle\int_1^\infty f(x)\,dx$ converges then the sequence of partial sums $\{S_n\}$ of $\displaystyle\sum_{n=1}^\infty a_n$ is bounded and monotonic increasing, and hence convergent also.

From the proof we also gain the useful result:

> If $f(x)$ is a continuous, positive, decreasing function on $[1, \infty[$, then
> $$\int_1^\infty f(x)\,dx \leqslant \sum_{n=1}^\infty a_n \leqslant a_1 + \int_1^\infty f(x)\,dx.$$

Example 28

Test $\displaystyle\sum_{n=1}^{\infty} \frac{1}{n^2 + 1}$ for convergence.

$f(x) = \dfrac{1}{x^2 + 1}$ is continuous, positive, and decreasing for $x \geqslant 1$.

$\therefore$ the conditions to use the Integral Test are satisfied.

Now $\displaystyle\int_{1}^{\infty} \frac{1}{x^2 + 1}\,dx = \lim_{b \to \infty} \int_{1}^{b} \frac{1}{x^2 + 1}\,dx$

$\qquad\qquad = \displaystyle\lim_{b \to \infty} \left[\arctan x\right]_{1}^{b}$

$\qquad\qquad = \displaystyle\lim_{b \to \infty} \left(\arctan(b) - \frac{\pi}{4}\right)$

$\qquad\qquad = \dfrac{\pi}{2} - \dfrac{\pi}{4} = \dfrac{\pi}{4}$

GRAPHICS
CALCULATOR
INSTRUCTIONS

You can use your calculator to estimate $\displaystyle\int_{1}^{\infty} f(x)\,dx$

$\therefore \displaystyle\int_{1}^{\infty} f(x)\,dx$ is convergent, and so is $\displaystyle\sum_{n=1}^{\infty} \frac{1}{n^2 + 1}$.

Example 29

For what values of p is the series $\displaystyle\sum_{n=1}^{\infty} \frac{1}{n^p}$ convergent?

If $p < 0$ then $\displaystyle\lim_{n \to \infty} \frac{1}{n^p} = \lim_{n \to \infty} n^{|p|}$ which diverges, and **if $p = 0$** then $\displaystyle\lim_{n \to \infty} \frac{1}{n^p} = 1$.

In each of these cases, $\displaystyle\lim_{n \to \infty} \frac{1}{n^p} \neq 0$, so by the Test for Divergence, the series diverges.

If $p > 0$ then $\displaystyle\lim_{n \to \infty} \frac{1}{n^p} = 0$. Since the function $f(x) = \dfrac{1}{x^p}$ is continuous, positive, and decreasing for $x \geqslant 1$, we can apply the Integral Test:

$\displaystyle\int_{1}^{\infty} \frac{1}{x^p}\,dx = \lim_{b \to \infty} \int_{1}^{b} \frac{1}{x^p}\,dx$

$\qquad\qquad = \displaystyle\lim_{b \to \infty} \left[\frac{1}{1 - p} x^{1-p}\right]_{1}^{b}$ for $p \neq 1$

$\qquad\qquad = \dfrac{1}{1 - p} \displaystyle\lim_{b \to \infty} b^{1-p} - \frac{1}{1 - p}$

$\qquad\qquad = \begin{cases} -\dfrac{1}{1 - p} & \text{if } p > 1 \\ \text{DNE} & \text{if } 0 < p < 1 \end{cases}$

For $p = 1$, $\displaystyle\int_{1}^{\infty} \frac{1}{x}\,dx = \lim_{b \to \infty} \int_{1}^{b} \frac{1}{x}\,dx = \lim_{b \to \infty} \left[\ln |x|\right]_{1}^{b}$

$\qquad\qquad\qquad\qquad\qquad\qquad = \displaystyle\lim_{b \to \infty} (\ln b)$ which DNE

$\therefore$ by the Integral Test, the series $\displaystyle\sum_{n=1}^{\infty} \frac{1}{n^p}$ converges if $p > 1$ and diverges if $p \leqslant 1$.

p-SERIES

The series $\displaystyle\sum_{n=1}^{\infty} \frac{1}{n^p}$ is called the **p-series**, and can be used to rapidly test the convergence of series of this form.

As shown in **Example 29**:

> The p-series $\displaystyle\sum_{n=1}^{\infty} \frac{1}{n^p}$ converges if $p > 1$ and diverges if $p \leqslant 1$.

For example, the series $\displaystyle\sum_{n=1}^{\infty} \frac{1}{\sqrt{n}} = \sum_{n=1}^{\infty} \frac{1}{n^{0.5}}$ is divergent since $p = \frac{1}{2} < 1$.

The p-series with $p = 1$ is $\displaystyle\sum_{n=1}^{\infty} \frac{1}{n} = 1 + \frac{1}{2} + \frac{1}{3} + \frac{1}{4} + ...$ and is called the **harmonic series**.

This is an example of a series which is divergent even though $\displaystyle\lim_{n \to \infty} a_n = \lim_{n \to \infty} \frac{1}{n} = 0$.

Example 30

Test for convergence or divergence $\displaystyle\sum_{n=1}^{\infty} \sin\left(\frac{1}{n}\right)$.

Let $x = \dfrac{1}{n}$.

$\therefore\ \displaystyle\lim_{n \to \infty} \frac{\sin\left(\frac{1}{n}\right)}{\frac{1}{n}} = \lim_{x \to 0} \frac{\sin(x)}{x} = 1$ by the Fundamental Trigonometric Limit.

$\therefore$ by the Limit Comparison Test $\displaystyle\sum_{n=1}^{\infty} \sin\left(\frac{1}{n}\right)$ and $\displaystyle\sum_{n=1}^{\infty} \frac{1}{n}$ either both converge or both diverge.

Since the harmonic series $\displaystyle\sum_{n=1}^{\infty} \frac{1}{n}$ diverges, $\displaystyle\sum_{n=1}^{\infty} \sin\left(\frac{1}{n}\right)$ also diverges.

EXERCISE K.1

1 Determine whether the following series converge or diverge using an appropriate geometric series, the Comparison Test, or the Test for Divergence.

   a $\displaystyle\sum_{n=1}^{\infty} \frac{1}{e^{2n}}$
   b $\displaystyle\sum_{n=1}^{\infty} \frac{n^2}{3(n+1)(n+2)}$
   c $\displaystyle\sum_{n=1}^{\infty} \frac{3^n + 2^n}{6^n}$
   d $\displaystyle\sum_{n=1}^{\infty} \left(\frac{1}{n} - \frac{1}{n^2}\right)$

2 Use the Limit Comparison Test with $b_n = \dfrac{2}{\sqrt{n^3}}$ to show that the series $\displaystyle\sum_{n=1}^{\infty} \frac{2n^2 + 3n}{\sqrt{5 + n^7}}$ is convergent.

3 Determine whether $\displaystyle\sum_{n=1}^{\infty} \frac{1}{n^n}$ and $\displaystyle\sum_{n=1}^{\infty} \frac{1}{n!}$ are convergent using the Comparison Test.

4 Determine whether the following series converge or diverge using the Comparison Test or Limit Comparison Test.

   a $\displaystyle\sum_{n=1}^{\infty} \frac{1}{\sqrt{n(n+1)(n+2)}}$
   b $\displaystyle\sum_{n=2}^{\infty} \frac{1}{\sqrt[3]{n(n+1)(n-1)}}$
   c $\displaystyle\sum_{n=1}^{\infty} \frac{\sin^2 n}{n\sqrt{n}}$

   d $\displaystyle\sum_{n=2}^{\infty} \frac{\sqrt{n}}{n-1}$
   e $\displaystyle\sum_{n=1}^{\infty} \frac{1 + 2^n}{1 + 3^n}$
   f $\displaystyle\sum_{n=2}^{\infty} \frac{1}{\ln n}$

5 Find all the values of $x \in [0, 2\pi]$ for which the series $\displaystyle\sum_{n=0}^{\infty} 2^n |\sin^n x|$ converges.

6 Find c if $\displaystyle\sum_{n=2}^{\infty} (1+c)^{-n} = 2$.

7 Use the Integral Test to determine whether the following series converge:

a $\displaystyle\sum_{n=1}^{\infty} \frac{n}{n^2 + 1}$

b $\displaystyle\sum_{n=1}^{\infty} ne^{-n^2}$

c $\displaystyle\sum_{n=1}^{\infty} \frac{\ln n}{n}$

d $\displaystyle\sum_{n=2}^{\infty} \frac{1}{n \ln n}$

8 Show that $\dfrac{\pi}{4} < \displaystyle\sum_{n=1}^{\infty} \frac{1}{n^2 + 1} < \frac{1}{2} + \frac{\pi}{4}$.

9 Determine the values of p for which the series $\displaystyle\sum_{n=2}^{\infty} \frac{1}{n^p \ln n}$ converges.

10 Suppose $\displaystyle\sum_{n=1}^{\infty} a_n$ is convergent, where $a_n \neq 0$ for all $n \in \mathbb{Z}^+$. Prove that $\displaystyle\sum_{n=1}^{\infty} \frac{1}{a_n}$ is divergent.

11 Consider the p-series $\displaystyle\sum_{n=1}^{\infty} \frac{1}{\sqrt{n}}$ with $p = \frac{1}{2}$. Let $S_n = \displaystyle\sum_{i=1}^{n} \frac{1}{\sqrt{i}}$ be the nth partial sum.

a Find $\displaystyle\lim_{n\to\infty} \frac{1}{\sqrt{n}}$.

b Show that $S_n \geqslant \dfrac{1}{\sqrt{n}} + \dfrac{1}{\sqrt{n}} + \dots + \dfrac{1}{\sqrt{n}} = \dfrac{n}{\sqrt{n}}$.

c Hence prove that the sequence $\{S_n\}$ of partial sums diverges.

d Does $\displaystyle\sum_{n=1}^{\infty} \frac{1}{\sqrt{n}}$ converge or diverge? Explain your answer.

12 Consider the series $\displaystyle\sum_{n=1}^{\infty} \frac{n^2}{3^n}$.

a Use induction to prove that the nth partial sum is $S_n = \displaystyle\sum_{i=1}^{n} \frac{i^2}{3^i} = \frac{3 - 3^{-n}(n^2 + 3n + 3)}{2}$.

b Find $\displaystyle\lim_{n\to\infty} S_n$.

c Does the series $\displaystyle\sum_{n=1}^{\infty} \frac{n^2}{3^n}$ converge? If not, explain why. If so, find the value of the sum of the series.

APPROXIMATING BY TRUNCATING AN INFINITE SERIES

The tests for infinite series can help us determine whether a series is convergent or divergent.

However, even if we prove an infinite series is convergent, we do not in general have techniques to determine the value of the limit $S = \displaystyle\sum_{n=1}^{\infty} a_n$. It is only in special cases such as geometric series that we can do this.

Instead, we can *approximate* the sum S of a convergent infinite series using a partial sum S_k.

Suppose we approximate the sum of a convergent series $S = \sum\limits_{n=1}^{\infty} a_n$ by the sum S_k of its first k terms:

$$\sum_{n=1}^{\infty} a_n \approx \sum_{n=1}^{k} a_n = a_1 + a_2 + \dots. + a_k \quad \text{for some } k \in \mathbb{Z}^+.$$

If f is a continuous, positive, decreasing function on $[k, \infty[$, then we can apply the Integral Test.

The **error** in the approximation is $R_k = S - S_k = \sum\limits_{n=k+1}^{\infty} a_n$ and the error satisfies

$$\int_{k+1}^{\infty} f(x)\,dx < R_k < \int_{k}^{\infty} f(x)\,dx.$$

Example 31

Suppose we can use the Integral Test to show that $\sum\limits_{n=1}^{\infty} a_n$ is convergent, where $a_n = f(n)$.

a Show that the error R_k in approximating $\sum\limits_{n=1}^{\infty} a_n$ by $a_1 + a_2 + \dots. + a_k$ for some $k \in \mathbb{Z}^+$

satisfies $\int_{k+1}^{\infty} f(x)\,dx < R_k < \int_{k}^{\infty} f(x)\,dx$.

b Hence determine the number of terms necessary to approximate $\sum\limits_{n=1}^{\infty} \dfrac{1}{n^3}$ correct to two decimal places.

a The error $R_k = S - S_k = \sum\limits_{n=1}^{\infty} a_n - \sum\limits_{n=1}^{k} a_n$

$= a_{k+1} + a_{k+2} + a_{k+3} + \dots.$

From the areas of lower rectangles, we deduce

$$R_k = a_{k+1} + a_{k+2} + a_{k+3} + \dots. < \int_{k}^{\infty} f(x)\,dx.$$

Using the upper rectangles from $x = k+1$ onwards, we deduce

$$R_k = a_{k+1} + a_{k+2} + a_{k+3} + \dots. > \int_{k+1}^{\infty} f(x)\,dx$$

Hence $\int_{k+1}^{\infty} f(x)\,dx < R_k < \int_{k}^{\infty} f(x)\,dx$ as required.

b For the sum $\sum\limits_{n=1}^{\infty} \dfrac{1}{n^3}$, we have $f(x) = \dfrac{1}{x^3}$.

Hence $R_k < \int_{k}^{\infty} \dfrac{1}{x^3}\,dx = \lim\limits_{b \to \infty} \left[-\dfrac{1}{2x^2} \right]_{k}^{b} = \lim\limits_{b \to \infty} \left(-\dfrac{1}{2b^2} + \dfrac{1}{2k^2} \right) = \dfrac{1}{2k^2}$

To approximate correctly to two decimal places, we require $R_k < 0.005 = \dfrac{1}{200}$

$\therefore \quad \dfrac{1}{2k^2} < \dfrac{1}{200}$

$\therefore \quad k^2 > 100$

$\therefore \quad k > 10 \quad \{\text{as } k > 0\}$

Hence we require 11 terms to correctly approximate $\sum\limits_{n=1}^{\infty} \dfrac{1}{n^3}$ to 2 decimal places.

EXERCISE K.2

1 **a** Estimate the error when $\sum\limits_{n=1}^{\infty} \dfrac{1}{5n^2}$ is approximated by its first 12 terms.

   b How many terms are necessary to approximate $\sum\limits_{n=1}^{\infty} \dfrac{1}{n^4}$ correct to 6 decimal places?

2 The nth partial sum of a series $\sum\limits_{n=1}^{\infty} a_n$ is $S_n = \dfrac{n-1}{n+1}$.

   a Find a_n. **b** Write $\sum\limits_{n=1}^{\infty} a_n$ in expanded form and find its sum.

3 **a** Use your calculator to evaluate the partial sums S_1, S_2, S_3, S_4, S_5, and S_6 for $\sum\limits_{n=1}^{\infty} \dfrac{n}{(n+1)!}$. Give your answers in rational form.

GRAPHICS CALCULATOR INSTRUCTIONS

   b Conjecture a formula for S_n.

   c Use mathematical induction to prove your conjecture.

   d Hence find $\sum\limits_{n=1}^{\infty} \dfrac{n}{(n+1)!}$.

4 The harmonic series is defined by $\sum\limits_{n=1}^{\infty} \dfrac{1}{n} = 1 + \frac{1}{2} + \frac{1}{3} + \frac{1}{4} + \dots$.

Consider the following sequence of partial sums for the harmonic series:

$$S_1 = 1$$
$$S_2 = 1 + \tfrac{1}{2}$$
$$S_4 = 1 + \tfrac{1}{2} + \left(\tfrac{1}{3} + \tfrac{1}{4}\right)$$
$$> 1 + \tfrac{1}{2} + \left(\tfrac{1}{4} + \tfrac{1}{4}\right) = 1 + \tfrac{2}{2}$$
$$S_8 = 1 + \tfrac{1}{2} + \left(\tfrac{1}{3} + \tfrac{1}{4}\right) + \left(\tfrac{1}{5} + \tfrac{1}{6} + \tfrac{1}{7} + \tfrac{1}{8}\right)$$
$$> 1 + \tfrac{1}{2} + \left(\tfrac{1}{4} + \tfrac{1}{4}\right) + \left(\tfrac{1}{8} + \tfrac{1}{8} + \tfrac{1}{8} + \tfrac{1}{8}\right) = 1 + \tfrac{3}{2}$$

> In **Example 29** we saw the most efficient proof that the Harmonic series is divergent. This is an alternative proof.

   a Use the same method to find an inequality involving S_{16}.

   b Conjecture an inequality involving S_{2^m}, $m \in \mathbb{Z}^+$.
   Use mathematical induction to prove your conjecture.

   c Show that $S_{2^m} \to \infty$ as $m \to \infty$ and hence prove that $\{S_n\}$ is divergent.

ALTERNATING SERIES

Thus far, we have dealt with series with only positive terms.

An **alternating series** is one whose terms are alternately positive and negative.

For example, $1 - \frac{1}{2} + \frac{1}{4} - \frac{1}{8} + \frac{1}{16} - \frac{1}{32} + \dots$.

THE ALTERNATING SERIES TEST

If the alternating series $\sum\limits_{n=1}^{\infty} (-1)^{n-1} b_n = b_1 - b_2 + b_3 - \dots$ satisfies $0 \leqslant b_{n+1} \leqslant b_n$

for all $n \in \mathbb{Z}^+$, and if $\lim\limits_{n \to \infty} b_n = 0$, then the series is convergent.

The theorem also applies if the first term is negative, since we can multiply through by constant -1 and proceed as above.

Proof:

The $(2n+2)$th partial sum of the series is $S_{2n+2} = b_1 - b_2 + ... - b_{2n} + b_{2n+1} - b_{2n+2}$, where the b_i are all non-negative and non-increasing.

We therefore find that $S_{2n+1} = S_{2n} + b_{2n+1}$

$$S_{2n+2} = S_{2n} + b_{2n+1} - b_{2n+2}$$

$$S_{2n+3} = S_{2n+1} - b_{2n+2} + b_{2n+3}$$

$$= S_{2n+2} + b_{2n+3}$$

Since $b_{2n+1} \geqslant b_{2n+2} \geqslant b_{2n+3}$,   we find $S_{2n+1} \geqslant S_{2n+3} \geqslant S_{2n+2} \geqslant S_{2n}$.

Also, $S_{2n+2} = (b_1 - b_2) + (b_3 - b_4) + ... + (b_{2n+1} - b_{2n+2})$.

Because the b_i are non-increasing, each expression in brackets is $\geqslant 0$.

Hence $S_n \geqslant 0$ for any even n, and since $S_{2n+1} \geqslant S_{2n+2}$, $S_n \geqslant 0$ for all n.

Finally, since $S_{2n+1} \leqslant b_1$,   we conclude that $b_1 \geqslant S_{2n+1} \geqslant S_{2n+3} \geqslant S_{2n+2} \geqslant S_{2n} \geqslant 0$.

Hence the even partial sums S_{2n} and the odd partial sums S_{2n+1} are bounded. The S_{2n} are monotonically non-decreasing, while the odd sums S_{2n+1} are monotonically non-increasing. Thus the even and odd series both converge.

Since $S_{2n+1} - S_{2n} = b_{2n+1}$,   the sums converge to the same limit if and only if $\lim\limits_{n\to\infty} b_n = 0$.

The convergence process is illustrated in the following diagram.

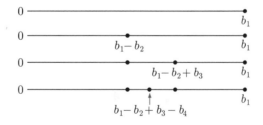

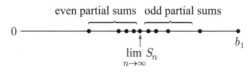

If $0 \leqslant b_{n+1} \leqslant b_n$ for all $n \in \mathbb{Z}^+$ but $\lim\limits_{n\to\infty} b_n \neq 0$,   then the series will eventually oscillate between the two values $\lim\limits_{n\to\infty} S_{2n}$ and $\lim\limits_{n\to\infty} S_{2n+1}$.

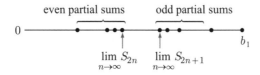

Example 32

Show that $1 - \frac{1}{2} + \frac{1}{3} - \frac{1}{4} + ... = \sum_{n=1}^{\infty} \frac{(-1)^{n-1}}{n}$ converges.

Compare this with the harmonic series which diverges!

This is an alternating series of the form $\sum_{n=1}^{\infty} (-1)^{n-1} b_n$,

where $b_n = \frac{1}{n}$.

Since $\frac{1}{n+1} < \frac{1}{n}$,   the series satisfies $0 < b_{n+1} < b_n$ for all $n \in \mathbb{Z}^+$.

Also, $\lim_{n \to \infty} b_n = \lim_{n \to \infty} \frac{1}{n} = 0$

$\therefore \sum_{n=1}^{\infty} \frac{(-1)^{n-1}}{n}$ converges by the Alternating Series Test.

Suppose a convergent infinite series converges to a sum S.

If the nth partial sum S_n is used to estimate the sum S, the **truncation error** is defined by $R_n = |S - S_n|$.

THE ALTERNATING SERIES ESTIMATION THEOREM

Suppose $S = \sum_{n=1}^{\infty} (-1)^{n-1} b_n$ is the sum of a convergent alternating series,

so $0 \leqslant b_{n+1} \leqslant b_n$ for all $n \in \mathbb{Z}^+$ and $\lim_{n \to \infty} b_n = 0$.

The truncation error $R_n = |S - S_n| \leqslant b_{n+1}$.

Proof:

$$S - S_n = \sum_{k=1}^{\infty} (-1)^{k-1} b_k - \sum_{k=1}^{n} (-1)^{k-1} b_k$$

$$= (-1)^n b_{n+1} + (-1)^{n+1} b_{n+2} + ...$$

$$= (-1)^n [(b_{n+1} - b_{n+2}) + (b_{n+3} - b_{n+4}) + ...]$$

Since $b_r \geqslant b_{r+1}$ for all $r \in \mathbb{Z}^+$, $b_{n+r} \geqslant b_{n+r+1}$ for all $r \in \mathbb{Z}^+$.

$\therefore (b_{n+1} - b_{n+2}) + (b_{n+3} - b_{n+4}) + ... \geqslant 0$

$\therefore R_n = |S - S_n| = (b_{n+1} - b_{n+2}) + (b_{n+3} - b_{n+4}) + ...$

$$= b_{n+1} - (b_{n+2} - b_{n+3}) - (b_{n+4} - b_{n+5}) - ....$$

$$= b_{n+1} - [(b_{n+2} - b_{n+3}) + (b_{n+4} - b_{n+5}) + ...]$$

$\leqslant b_{n+1}$ since $[(b_{n+2} - b_{n+3}) + (b_{n+4} - b_{n+5}) + ...] \geqslant 0$

Example 33

Find the sum of $\displaystyle\sum_{n=1}^{\infty} \frac{(-1)^{n-1}}{n!}$ correct to 3 decimal places.

This is an alternating series of the form $\displaystyle\sum_{n=1}^{\infty} (-1)^{n-1} b_n$, where $b_n = \dfrac{1}{n!}$.

Now $0 < \dfrac{1}{(n+1)!} < \dfrac{1}{n!}$, so $0 < b_{n+1} < b_n$ for all $n \in \mathbb{Z}^+$.

Also, $0 < \dfrac{1}{n!} < \dfrac{1}{n}$

$\therefore$ since $\displaystyle\lim_{n \to \infty} \frac{1}{n} = 0$, $\displaystyle\lim_{n \to \infty} \frac{1}{n!} = \lim_{n \to \infty} b_n = 0$ {Squeeze Theorem}

$\therefore$ the series converges by the Alternating Series Test.

Now $S = 1 - \frac{1}{2} + \frac{1}{6} - \frac{1}{24} + \frac{1}{120} - \frac{1}{720} + \frac{1}{5040} + \dots.$

Notice that $b_7 = \frac{1}{5040} < \frac{1}{2000} = 0.0005$

and $S_6 = 1 - \frac{1}{2} + \frac{1}{6} - \frac{1}{24} + \frac{1}{120} - \frac{1}{720} = 0.631\,944$

Now by the Estimation Theorem, $|S - S_6| \leqslant b_7$,

$\qquad \therefore \quad -b_7 \leqslant S - S_6 \leqslant b_7$

$\qquad \therefore \quad S_6 - b_7 \leqslant S \leqslant S_6 + b_7$

$\therefore \quad 0.631\,944 - \frac{1}{5040} \leqslant S \leqslant 0.631\,944 + \frac{1}{5040}$

$\qquad \therefore \quad 0.631\,745\,6 \leqslant S \leqslant 0.632\,142\,4$

$\qquad\qquad \therefore \quad S \approx 0.632$

ABSOLUTE AND CONDITIONAL CONVERGENCE

Given any series $\displaystyle\sum_{n=1}^{\infty} a_n$ we can consider the corresponding series $\displaystyle\sum_{n=1}^{\infty} |a_n| = |a_1| + |a_2| + \dots.$ whose terms are the absolute values of the terms of the original series.

A series $\displaystyle\sum_{n=1}^{\infty} a_n$ is **absolutely convergent** if the series of absolute values $\displaystyle\sum_{n=1}^{\infty} |a_n|$ is convergent.

Clearly if $a_n \geqslant 0$ for all n, absolute convergence is the same as convergence.

A series such as $\displaystyle\sum_{n=1}^{\infty} \frac{(-1)^{n-1}}{n}$ which is convergent but not absolutely convergent, is called **conditionally convergent**.

So what is important about absolute and conditional convergence?

We all know that the addition of scalars is commutative, so $a + b = b + a$. Furthermore, if we have a finite sum $\displaystyle\sum_{n=1}^{N} a_n$, then we can also reorder the terms without affecting the total sum. Infinite series which are absolutely convergent behave like finite series, in that we can reorder the terms of the series without affecting the sum. However, the same is *not* true for conditionally convergent series!

For example, let $\quad S = 1 - \frac{1}{2} + \frac{1}{3} - \frac{1}{4} + \frac{1}{5} - \frac{1}{6} + \frac{1}{7} - \frac{1}{8} + ...$ (1)

$$\therefore \quad \tfrac{1}{2}S = \tfrac{1}{2} - \tfrac{1}{4} + \tfrac{1}{6} - \tfrac{1}{8} + ...$$

$$\therefore \quad \tfrac{1}{2}S = 0 + \tfrac{1}{2} + 0 - \tfrac{1}{4} + 0 + \tfrac{1}{6} + 0 - \tfrac{1}{8} + ...$$ (2)

Adding (1) and (2) gives $\quad \tfrac{3}{2}S = 1 + 0 + \tfrac{1}{3} - \tfrac{1}{2} + \tfrac{1}{5} + 0 + \tfrac{1}{7} - \tfrac{1}{4} + ...$

$$\therefore \quad \tfrac{3}{2}S = 1 + \tfrac{1}{3} - \tfrac{1}{2} + \tfrac{1}{5} + \tfrac{1}{7} - \tfrac{1}{4} + ...$$

We thus obtain a rearrangement of the original series, but with a different sum! In fact, Riemann showed that by taking groups of sufficiently large numbers of negative or positive terms, it is possible to rearrange a conditionally convergent series so it adds up to any arbitrary real value.

THEOREM OF ABSOLUTE CONVERGENCE

If a series $\displaystyle\sum_{n=1}^{\infty} a_n$ is absolutely convergent then it is convergent.

Proof: By the definition of absolute value, $\quad -|a_n| \leqslant a_n \leqslant |a_n|$

$$\therefore \quad 0 \leqslant a_n + |a_n| \leqslant 2|a_n|$$

Now if $\displaystyle\sum_{n=1}^{\infty} a_n$ is absolutely convergent then $\displaystyle 2\sum_{n=1}^{\infty} |a_n|$ is convergent.

$\therefore$ by the Comparison Test, $\displaystyle\sum_{n=1}^{\infty} (a_n + |a_n|)$ is convergent.

But $\displaystyle\sum_{n=1}^{\infty} a_n = \sum_{n=1}^{\infty} (a_n + |a_n|) - \sum_{n=1}^{\infty} |a_n|$ since the series is absolutely convergent.

$\therefore$ since $\displaystyle\sum_{n=1}^{\infty} (a_n + |a_n|)$ and $\displaystyle\sum_{n=1}^{\infty} |a_n|$ are both convergent, $\displaystyle\sum_{n=1}^{\infty} a_n$ is convergent.

Example 34

Show that $\displaystyle\sum_{n=1}^{\infty} \frac{\cos n}{n^2}$ is convergent.

$\displaystyle\sum_{n=1}^{\infty} \frac{\cos n}{n^2} = \frac{\cos 1}{1^2} + \frac{\cos 2}{2^2} + ...$ has terms with different signs, but is not an alternating series.

However, $\left| \dfrac{\cos n}{n^2} \right| \leqslant \dfrac{1}{n^2}$ for all $n \in \mathbb{R}$, and $\displaystyle\sum_{n=1}^{\infty} \frac{1}{n^2}$ is convergent.

$\therefore$ by the Comparison Test, $\displaystyle\sum_{n=1}^{\infty} \left| \frac{\cos n}{n^2} \right|$ is convergent.

$\therefore$ by the Theorem of Absolute Convergence, $\displaystyle\sum_{n=1}^{\infty} \frac{\cos n}{n^2}$ is also convergent.

THE RATIO TEST

The **Ratio Test** can be used to determine whether a general series is absolutely convergent, and hence convergent:

> **1** If $\displaystyle\lim_{n\to\infty}\left|\dfrac{a_{n+1}}{a_n}\right| < 1$, then $\displaystyle\sum_{n=1}^{\infty} a_n$ is absolutely convergent.
>
> **2** If $\displaystyle\lim_{n\to\infty}\left|\dfrac{a_{n+1}}{a_n}\right| > 1$, then $\displaystyle\sum_{n=1}^{\infty} a_n$ is divergent.
>
> **3** If $\displaystyle\lim_{n\to\infty}\left|\dfrac{a_{n+1}}{a_n}\right| = 1$, the Ratio Test is inconclusive.

Proof of 1:

Let $u_n = |a_n|$, with $a_n \neq 0$ for all $n \in \mathbb{Z}^+$.

Suppose that $\displaystyle\lim_{n\to\infty}\dfrac{u_{n+1}}{u_n} = L < 1$, so given $\varepsilon > 0$ there exists a positive integer N such that $\left|\dfrac{u_{n+1}}{u_n} - L\right| < \varepsilon$ for all $n \geqslant N$.

In particular, as $L < 1$ we can choose r such that $L < r < 1$ and let $\varepsilon = r - L > 0$.

$$\text{Now} \quad \left|\frac{u_{n+1}}{u_n} - L\right| < \varepsilon$$

$$\therefore \quad \frac{u_{n+1}}{u_n} - L < \varepsilon$$

$$\therefore \quad \frac{u_{n+1}}{u_n} < \varepsilon + L$$

$$\therefore \quad \frac{u_{n+1}}{u_n} < r$$

$$\therefore \quad \text{since} \quad n \geqslant N, \quad u_{N+1} < r u_N$$

$$u_{N+2} < r u_{N+1} < r^2 u_N$$

$$u_{N+3} < r u_{N+2} < r^3 u_N, \quad \text{and so on}$$

$$\therefore \quad u_{N+1} + u_{N+2} + u_{N+3} + \dots < u_N(r + r^2 + r^3 + \dots)$$

Since $0 < r < 1$, $r + r^2 + r^3 + \dots$ is a convergent geometric series.

$\therefore$ by the Comparison Test, $u_{N+1} + u_{N+2} + u_{N+3} + \dots$ is also convergent.

$\therefore$ since $u_1 + u_2 + u_3 + \dots + u_N$ is finite, $\displaystyle\sum_{n=1}^{\infty} u_n = \sum_{n=1}^{\infty} |a_n|$ is convergent.

Proof of 2:

If $\displaystyle\lim_{n\to\infty}\left|\dfrac{a_{n+1}}{a_n}\right| = L > 1$, we let $\varepsilon = L - 1$.

$\therefore$ there exists $N \in \mathbb{Z}^+$ such that $\left|\dfrac{|a_{n+1}|}{|a_n|} - L\right| < \varepsilon$ for all $n > N$

$$\therefore \quad -\varepsilon < \frac{|a_{n+1}|}{|a_n|} - L < \varepsilon$$

$$\therefore \quad L - \varepsilon < \frac{|a_{n+1}|}{|a_n|} < \varepsilon + L$$

$$\therefore \quad 1 < \frac{|a_{n+1}|}{|a_n|}$$

Thus $0 \leqslant |a_n| < |a_{n+1}|$ for all $n > N$, $n \in \mathbb{Z}^+$.

Thus $\lim\limits_{n \to \infty} a_n \neq 0$ and hence $\sum\limits_{n=1}^{\infty} a_n$ diverges.

Example 35

Test $a_n = (-1)^n \dfrac{n^3}{3^n}$ for absolute convergence.

Using the Ratio Test, $\left| \dfrac{a_{n+1}}{a_n} \right| = \left| \dfrac{\frac{(n+1)^3}{3^{n+1}}}{\frac{n^3}{3^n}} \right| = \dfrac{(n+1)^3}{3^{n+1}} \times \dfrac{3^n}{n^3}$

$= \dfrac{1}{3} \left(\dfrac{n+1}{n} \right)^3$

$= \dfrac{1}{3} \left(1 + \dfrac{1}{n} \right)^3$

Now $\lim\limits_{n \to \infty} \dfrac{1}{3} \left(1 + \dfrac{1}{n} \right)^3 = \dfrac{1}{3} < 1$

$\therefore \quad \sum\limits_{n=1}^{\infty} (-1)^n \dfrac{n^3}{3^n}$ is absolutely convergent.

Using the Ratio Test we can prove the useful result: $\lim\limits_{n \to \infty} \dfrac{k^n}{n!} = 0$ for any $k \in \mathbb{R}$

Proof: If $a_n = \dfrac{k^n}{n!}$ then $\lim\limits_{n \to \infty} \left| \dfrac{a_{n+1}}{a_n} \right| = \lim\limits_{n \to \infty} \left| \dfrac{k^{n+1}}{(n+1)!} \times \dfrac{n!}{k^n} \right|$

$= \lim\limits_{n \to \infty} \dfrac{|k|}{n+1} \qquad \{ \text{for } k \text{ any constant} \}$

$= 0$

$\therefore \quad \sum\limits_{n=1}^{\infty} a_n$ is convergent   {Ratio Test}

$\therefore \quad \lim\limits_{n \to \infty} a_n = 0$

EXERCISE K.3

1 Show that:

a $\sum\limits_{n=1}^{\infty} \dfrac{1-n}{n^2}$ diverges

b $\sum\limits_{n=1}^{\infty} \dfrac{1}{n} - \sum\limits_{n=1}^{\infty} \dfrac{1-n}{n^2}$ diverges

c $\sum\limits_{n=1}^{\infty} \dfrac{1}{n} - \sum\limits_{n=1}^{\infty} \dfrac{n-1}{n^2}$ converges.

2 Test these series for convergence or divergence:

a $\dfrac{1}{\ln 2} - \dfrac{1}{\ln 3} + \dfrac{1}{\ln 4} - \dfrac{1}{\ln 5} + \dots$

b $\sum\limits_{n=1}^{\infty} (-1)^{n-1} \dfrac{\sqrt{n}}{n+4}$

3 Test these series for convergence or divergence:

a $\displaystyle\sum_{n=1}^{\infty} (-1)^n \frac{n^n}{n!}$

b $\displaystyle\sum_{n=1}^{\infty} (-1)^n \sin\left(\frac{\pi}{n}\right)$

c $\displaystyle\sum_{n=2}^{\infty} \frac{(-1)^{n-1}}{\sqrt[3]{\ln n}}$

d $\displaystyle\sum_{n=1}^{\infty} \frac{\sin\left(\frac{n\pi}{2}\right)}{n!}$

e $\displaystyle\sum_{n=0}^{\infty} \frac{(-1)^n}{2^n n!}$

f $\displaystyle\sum_{n=1}^{\infty} (-1)^{n+1} \frac{n^2}{n^3 + 1}$

4 Approximate the sum of each series to the indicated level of accuracy:

a $\displaystyle\sum_{n=1}^{\infty} \frac{(-1)^{n+1}}{n!}$ to error < 0.01

b $\displaystyle\sum_{n=1}^{\infty} \frac{(-1)^{n-1}}{(2n-1)!}$ to 4 decimal places

c $\displaystyle\sum_{n=0}^{\infty} \frac{(-1)^n}{2^n n!}$ to 4 decimal places.

**GRAPHICS
CALCULATOR
INSTRUCTIONS**

5 Use technology to find the first 10 partial sums of the series $\displaystyle\sum_{n=1}^{\infty} \frac{(-1)^{n-1}}{n^3}$.

Estimate the error in using the 10th partial sum to approximate the total sum.

6 Consider the alternating series $\displaystyle\sum_{n=1}^{\infty} (-1)^{n-1} b_n$ where

$0 \leqslant b_{n+1} \leqslant b_n$ for all $n \in \mathbb{Z}^+$ and $\displaystyle\lim_{n\to\infty} b_n = 0$.

> In this question we prove
> the Alternating Series Test.

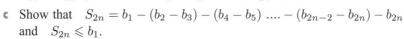

a Explain why $S_2 = b_1 - b_2 \geqslant 0$.

b Show that $S_4 \geqslant S_2$. Hence prove that in general,
   $S_{2n} \geqslant S_{2n-2}$ and $0 \leqslant S_2 \leqslant S_4 \leqslant .... \leqslant S_{2n} \leqslant .....$

c Show that $S_{2n} = b_1 - (b_2 - b_3) - (b_4 - b_5) .... - (b_{2n-2} - b_{2n}) - b_{2n}$
   and $S_{2n} \leqslant b_1$.

d Hence prove that S_{2n} is convergent. Let $\displaystyle\lim_{n\to\infty} S_{2n} = S$.

e Show that $S_{2n+1} = S_{2n} + b_{2n+1}$.

f Show that if $\displaystyle\lim_{n\to\infty} b_n = 0$ then $\displaystyle\lim_{n\to\infty} S_{2n+1} = S$ and hence $\displaystyle\lim_{n\to\infty} S_n = S$.

7 Determine whether these series are absolutely convergent, conditionally convergent, or divergent:

a $\displaystyle\sum_{n=1}^{\infty} \frac{(-3)^n}{n!}$

b $\displaystyle\sum_{n=1}^{\infty} (-1)^n \frac{2^n}{n^2 + 1}$

c $\displaystyle\sum_{n=1}^{\infty} (-1)^n \frac{\arctan n}{n^3}$

d $\displaystyle\sum_{n=1}^{\infty} \left(\frac{1-3n}{3+4n}\right)^n$

e $\displaystyle\sum_{n=1}^{\infty} \frac{(-1)^{n-1} \ln n}{n}$

f $\displaystyle\sum_{n=2}^{\infty} \frac{(-1)^n}{n \ln n}$

g $\displaystyle\sum_{r=0}^{\infty} (-1)^{r-1} \left(\sqrt{r+1} - \sqrt{r}\right)$

8 **a** Show that $\displaystyle\sum_{n=0}^{\infty} \frac{x^n}{n!}$ converges for all $x \in \mathbb{R}$.

b Deduce that $\displaystyle\lim_{n\to\infty} \frac{x^n}{n!} = 0$ for all $x \in \mathbb{R}$.

9 Test these series for convergence or divergence:

a $\displaystyle\sum_{n=0}^{\infty} \frac{10^n}{n!}$

b $\displaystyle\sum_{n=1}^{\infty} \frac{1}{\sqrt{n(n+1)}}$

c $\displaystyle\sum_{n=1}^{\infty} \frac{2n}{8n-5}$

d $\displaystyle\sum_{n=1}^{\infty} \frac{\cos\left(\frac{n}{2}\right)}{n^2 + 4n}$

e $\displaystyle\sum_{n=2}^{\infty} \frac{n^3 + 1}{n^4 - 1}$

f $\displaystyle\sum_{n=0}^{\infty} \frac{n!}{2 \times 5 \times 8 \times .... \times (3n+2)}$

10 Test the series $\displaystyle\sum_{n=1}^{\infty} \frac{1}{n^2}$ and $\displaystyle\sum_{n=1}^{\infty} \frac{1}{n}$ for absolute convergence using the Ratio Test.

Hence explain why the Ratio Test is inconclusive when $\displaystyle\lim_{n\to\infty} \left|\frac{a_{n+1}}{a_n}\right| = 1.$

POWER SERIES

A **power series** is a series of the form $\displaystyle\sum_{n=0}^{\infty} c_n x^n = c_0 + c_1 x + c_2 x^2 + \dots$

or more generally $\displaystyle\sum_{n=0}^{\infty} c_n (x - a)^n = c_0 + c_1 (x - a) + c_2 (x - a)^2 + \dots$

The convergence of a power series will often, but not always, depend on the value of x.

For example, consider the power series $\displaystyle\sum_{n=0}^{\infty} c_n x^n$ where $c_n = 1$ for all n. This is in fact the

geometric series $1 + x + x^2 + x^3 + x^4 + \dots$, which converges for all $|x| < 1$.

We use the Ratio Test to determine the convergence of a power series.

Example 36

For what values of x is $\displaystyle\sum_{n=1}^{\infty} \frac{(x-3)^n}{n}$ convergent?

If $a_n = \dfrac{(x-3)^n}{n}$ then $\left|\dfrac{a_{n+1}}{a_n}\right| = \left|\dfrac{(x-3)^{n+1}}{n+1} \times \dfrac{n}{(x-3)^n}\right|$

$$= \left|\dfrac{(x-3)n}{n+1}\right|$$

$$= \left|\dfrac{(x-3)}{1+\frac{1}{n}}\right|$$

$$\therefore \quad \lim_{n\to\infty} \left|\dfrac{a_{n+1}}{a_n}\right| = |x-3|$$

By the Ratio Test, $\displaystyle\sum_{n=1}^{\infty} a_n$ is divergent if $|x-3| > 1$, but is absolutely convergent and hence convergent if $|x-3| < 1$

$$\therefore \quad -1 < x - 3 < 1$$
$$\therefore \quad 2 < x < 4$$

For $|x-3| = 1$, the Ratio Test is inconclusive, so we consider the $x = 2$ and $x = 4$ cases separately:

For $x = 2$, $\displaystyle\sum_{n=1}^{\infty} a_n = \sum_{n=1}^{\infty} \frac{(-1)^n}{n}$, which is conditionally convergent. {**Example 32**}

For $x = 4$, $\displaystyle\sum_{n=1}^{\infty} a_n = \sum_{n=1}^{\infty} \frac{1}{n}$, which is the harmonic series, which is divergent.
{**Example 29**, p-series with $p = 1$}

So, $\displaystyle\sum_{n=1}^{\infty} a_n$ converges for $2 \leqslant x < 4$.

If a power series $\sum_{n=0}^{\infty} a_n x^n$ is absolutely convergent when $x = b$, $b \neq 0$, then it is convergent whenever $0 \leqslant |x| < |b|$.

Proof: Suppose $0 \leqslant |x| < |b|$. Then $|a_n x^n| = \left| \dfrac{a_n b^n x^n}{b^n} \right|$

$$= |a_n b^n| \times \left| \left(\frac{x}{b} \right)^n \right|$$

$$< |a_n b^n| \quad \text{since} \quad |x| < |b|$$

But $\sum_{n=0}^{\infty} |a_n b^n|$ is convergent, so $\sum_{n=0}^{\infty} |a_n x^n|$ is also convergent. {Comparison Test}

$\therefore \sum_{n=0}^{\infty} a_n x^n$ is absolutely convergent, and hence convergent.

For a power series $\sum_{n=0}^{\infty} c_n (x - a)^n$, there exist only three possibilities for convergence:

- the series converges only when $x = a$
- the series converges for all $x \in \mathbb{R}$
- there exists $R \in \mathbb{R}^+$ such that the series converges if $|x - a| < R$ and diverges if $|x - a| > R$.

The power series $\sum_{n=0}^{\infty} c_n (x - a)^n$ has **radius of convergence** R if R is the greatest number such that the series converges for all $x \in \mathbb{R}$ such that $|x - a| < R$ and diverges for all $x \in \mathbb{R}$ such that $|x - a| > R$.

If the series converges only when $x = a$, we say $R = 0$.

If the series converges for all $x \in \mathbb{R}$, we say R is infinite.

The **interval of convergence** I is the set of all points x for which the power series converges.

Most of the interval of convergence may be deduced from the radius of convergence. However, we need to consider convergence for the cases $|x - a| = R$ separately.

For instance, we saw in **Example 36**, that $\sum_{n=1}^{\infty} \dfrac{(x - 3)^n}{n}$ converges for $2 \leqslant x < 4$. In this case $R = 1$.

Example 37

Find the radius and interval of convergence for $\displaystyle\sum_{n=0}^{\infty} \frac{(-3)^n x^n}{\sqrt{n+1}}$.

If $\quad a_n = \dfrac{(-3)^n x^n}{\sqrt{n+1}} \quad$ then $\quad \left| \dfrac{a_{n+1}}{a_n} \right| = \left| \dfrac{(-3)^{n+1} x^{n+1}}{\sqrt{n+2}} \times \dfrac{\sqrt{n+1}}{(-3)^n x^n} \right|$

$$= 3\,|x|\,\sqrt{\frac{n+1}{n+2}}$$

$$= 3\,|x|\,\sqrt{\frac{1+\frac{1}{n}}{1+\frac{2}{n}}}$$

$$\therefore \quad \lim_{n \to \infty} \left| \frac{a_{n+1}}{a_n} \right| = 3\,|x|$$

By the Ratio Test, $\displaystyle\sum_{n=0}^{\infty} a_n$ converges if $|x| < \frac{1}{3}$ and diverges if $|x| > \frac{1}{3}$.

$\therefore$ the radius of convergence is $R = \frac{1}{3}$.

To determine the interval of convergence, we must consider what happens when $x = \pm\frac{1}{3}$.

If $\quad x = -\frac{1}{3}, \quad \displaystyle\sum_{n=0}^{\infty} a_n = \sum_{n=0}^{\infty} \frac{(-3)^n \left(-\frac{1}{3}\right)^n}{\sqrt{n+1}} = \sum_{n=0}^{\infty} \frac{1}{\sqrt{n+1}}$

$\qquad$ Letting $\quad r = n+1, \quad \displaystyle\sum_{n=0}^{\infty} a_n = \sum_{r=1}^{\infty} \frac{1}{r^{0.5}} \quad$ which is a divergent p-series.

If $\quad x = \frac{1}{3}, \quad \displaystyle\sum_{n=0}^{\infty} a_n = \sum_{n=0}^{\infty} \frac{(-3)^n \left(\frac{1}{3}\right)^n}{\sqrt{n+1}}$

$$= \sum_{n=0}^{\infty} \frac{(-1)^n}{\sqrt{n+1}} \quad \text{which converges by the Alternating Series Test.}$$

So, the interval of convergence of $\displaystyle\sum_{n=0}^{\infty} a_n$ is $\left]-\frac{1}{3}, \frac{1}{3}\right]$.

Example 38

a Find the radius of convergence and interval of convergence for $\displaystyle\sum_{n=0}^{\infty} \frac{x^n}{n!}$, where $x \in \mathbb{R}$.

b Hence show that $\displaystyle\lim_{n \to \infty} \frac{x^n}{n!} = 0$ for all $x \in \mathbb{R}$.

a If $\quad a_n = \dfrac{x^n}{n!} \quad$ then $\quad \displaystyle\lim_{n \to \infty} \left| \frac{a_{n+1}}{a_n} \right| = \lim_{n \to \infty} \left| \frac{x^{n+1}}{(n+1)!} \times \frac{n!}{x^n} \right|$

$$= \lim_{n \to \infty} \frac{|x|}{n+1}$$

$$= 0 \quad \text{for any constant } x \in \mathbb{R}$$

$\qquad \therefore$ by the Ratio Test the series has an infinite radius of convergence, and its interval of convergence is $\mathbb{R}$.

b Since $\displaystyle\sum_{n=0}^{\infty} \frac{x^n}{n!}$ converges for all $x \in \mathbb{R}$, $\displaystyle\lim_{n \to \infty} \frac{x^n}{n!} = 0$ for all $x \in \mathbb{R}$.

DIFFERENTIATION AND INTEGRATION OF POWER SERIES

A power series can be differentiated or integrated term by term over an interval contained entirely within its interval of convergence. In the case of differentiation, an open interval is required.

If $f(x) = \sum\limits_{n=0}^{\infty} c_n x^n$ then $f'(x) = \sum\limits_{n=1}^{\infty} n c_n x^{n-1}$ and $\int f(x)\,dx = \sum\limits_{n=0}^{\infty} \dfrac{c_n}{n+1} x^{n+1}$.

Example 39

Find $\displaystyle\int_0^{0.1} \left(\sum_{n=0}^{\infty} \frac{(-3)^n x^n}{\sqrt{n+1}} \right) dx$.

From **Example 37**, the series $\displaystyle\sum_{n=0}^{\infty} \frac{(-3)^n x^n}{\sqrt{n+1}}$ has interval of convergence $\left] -\frac{1}{3}, \frac{1}{3} \right]$.

$\therefore$ since $[0, 0.1]$ lies entirely within the interval of convergence,

$$\int_0^{0.1} \left(\sum_{n=0}^{\infty} \frac{(-3)^n x^n}{\sqrt{n+1}} \right) dx = \sum_{n=0}^{\infty} \left(\int_0^{0.1} \frac{(-3)^n x^n}{\sqrt{n+1}}\,dx \right)$$

$$= \sum_{n=0}^{\infty} \frac{(-3)^n}{\sqrt{n+1}} \left[\frac{x^{n+1}}{n+1} \right]_0^{0.1}$$

$$= \sum_{n=0}^{\infty} \frac{(-3)^n (0.1)^{n+1}}{(n+1)^{\frac{3}{2}}}$$

EXERCISE K.4

1 Use the geometric series to write a formula for each of the following. In each case find the corresponding radius of convergence and interval of convergence.

   a $\displaystyle\sum_{n=0}^{\infty} x^{3n}$
   b $\displaystyle\sum_{n=0}^{\infty} (2-x)^n$
   c $\displaystyle\sum_{n=0}^{\infty} (-1)^n x^{4n}$

2 Find the interval of convergence of $\displaystyle\sum_{n=0}^{\infty} \frac{1}{x^{2n}}$.

3 Find the radius and interval of convergence for each of the following series:

   a $\displaystyle\sum_{n=1}^{\infty} n5^n x^n$
   b $\displaystyle\sum_{n=0}^{\infty} \frac{3^n x^n}{(n+1)^2}$
   c $\displaystyle\sum_{n=1}^{\infty} \frac{(-1)^n x^{2n-1}}{(2n-1)!}$
   d $\displaystyle\sum_{n=2}^{\infty} (-1)^n \frac{(2x+3)^n}{n \ln n}$

4 Find the radius and interval of convergence of $\displaystyle\sum_{n=1}^{\infty} \frac{2 \times 4 \times 6 \times \dots \times (2n) x^n}{1 \times 3 \times 5 \times \dots \times (2n-1)}$.

5 A function f is defined by $f(x) = 1 + 2x + x^2 + 2x^3 + x^4 + \dots$, so f is a power series with $c_{2n-1} = 2$ and $c_{2n} = 1$ for all $n \in \mathbb{Z}^+$.

   a Find the interval of convergence for the series.

   b Write an explicit formula for $f(x)$.

6 Suppose that the radius of convergence of a power series $\sum\limits_{n=0}^{\infty} c_n x^n$ is R.

Find the radius of convergence of the power series $\sum\limits_{n=0}^{\infty} c_n x^{2n}$.

7 Suppose the series $\sum\limits_{n=0}^{\infty} c_n x^n$ has radius of convergence 2 and the series $\sum\limits_{n=0}^{\infty} d_n x^n$ has radius of convergence 3.

What can you say about the radius of convergence of the series $\sum\limits_{n=0}^{\infty} (c_n + d_n) x^n$?

8 Show that the power series $\sum\limits_{n=1}^{\infty} \dfrac{x^n}{n^2 3^n}$ and the series of derivatives $\sum\limits_{n=1}^{\infty} \dfrac{n x^{n-1}}{n^2 3^n}$ have the same radius of convergence, but not the same interval of convergence.

9 Find $\dfrac{d}{dx}\left(\sum\limits_{n=1}^{\infty} \dfrac{x^n}{n!}\right)$ and $\displaystyle\int_0^x \left(\sum\limits_{n=0}^{\infty} \dfrac{t^n}{n!}\right) dt$. For what values of x do these series converge?

10 Find:

a $\displaystyle\int_0^{0.1} \left(\sum\limits_{n=1}^{\infty} \dfrac{x^{n-1}}{(n-1)!}\right) dx$ **b** $\displaystyle\int_{-2}^{-1.5} \left(\sum\limits_{n=0}^{\infty} \dfrac{(-1)^n}{x^{2n}}\right) dx$ **c** $\displaystyle\int_0^{\frac{1}{2}} \left(\sum\limits_{n=0}^{\infty} x^{2n}\right) dx$

11 Is $\displaystyle\int_0^2 \left(\sum\limits_{n=0}^{\infty} x^{2n}\right) dx$ defined? Explain your answer.

L   TAYLOR AND MACLAURIN SERIES

Let $\sum_{n=0}^{\infty} c_n(x - a)^n$ be a power series with radius of convergence $R > 0$, and interval of convergence I.

For each x with $|x - a| < R$, the series $\sum_{n=0}^{\infty} c_n(x - a)^n$ converges to a finite value. The series may therefore define a function $f(x) = \sum_{n=0}^{\infty} c_n(x - a)^n$ with domain I.

Functions defined in this way may look awkward. However, as we have seen, convergent power series can be added, differentiated, and integrated just like ordinary polynomials. They are very useful because we can express many different functions as power series expansions.

TAYLOR SERIES EXPANSIONS

Suppose $f(x) = \sum_{n=0}^{\infty} c_n(x - a)^n$
$$= c_0 + c_1(x - a) + c_2(x - a)^2 + ... \quad \text{where} \quad |x - a| < R.$$

Since we can differentiate the power series on an open interval contained in I,

$$f'(x) = c_1 + 2c_2(x - a) + 3c_3(x - a)^2 + ...$$
$$f''(x) = 2c_2 + 6c_3(x - a) + ...$$
$$\vdots$$
$$f^{(n)}(x) = n!\,c_n + (n + 1)!\,c_{n+1}(x - a) + ...$$

Using the above formulae, we find that: $f(a) = c_0$
$$f'(a) = c_1$$
$$f''(a) = 2c_2 = 2!c_2$$
$$\vdots$$
$$f^{(n)}(a) = n!c_n$$

Hence $c_n = \dfrac{f^{(n)}(a)}{n!}$ where $0! = 1$ and $f^{(0)}(x) = f(x)$.

We can use this information to reconstruct the function f in terms of the values of its derivatives evaluated at $x = a$:

For such a function f, the **Taylor series expansion of $f(x)$ about $x = a$** is

$$f(x) = f(a) + \frac{f'(a)}{1!}(x - a) + \frac{f''(a)}{2!}(x - a)^2 + \frac{f'''(a)}{3!}(x - a)^3 .... = \sum_{k=0}^{\infty} \frac{f^{(k)}(a)}{k!}(x - a)^k.$$

When $a = 0$, this is also called the **Maclaurin series expansion of $f(x)$.** This is

$$f(x) = f(0) + xf'(0) + \frac{x^2}{2!}f''(0) + \frac{x^3}{3!}f'''(0) + ... = \sum_{k=0}^{\infty} \frac{f^{(k)}(0)x^k}{k!}$$

We have shown for a function $f(x)$ with domain I, that if:

1 f has a convergent power series representation for $x \in I$,   and

2 the derivatives of f of all orders exist on I, or I with its endpoints removed if I is closed,

then f has a Taylor series representation and this is the only power series representation of f.

However, we still need to consider the conditions under which the power series representation of f will converge.

TAYLOR POLYNOMIALS

If $f^{(k)}(x)$ exists at $x = a$ for $k = 0, 1, ..., n$, then the **nth degree Taylor polynomial** approximation to $f(x)$ **about** $x = a$ is

$$T_n(x) = f(a) + f'(a)(x - a) + ... + \frac{f^{(n)}(a)}{n!}(x - a)^n$$

$$= \sum_{k=0}^{n} \frac{(x-a)^k}{k!} f^{(k)}(a)$$

When $a = 0$, this is also called the **nth degree Maclaurin polynomial** $\sum_{k=0}^{n} \frac{x^k}{k!} f^{(k)}(0)$.

Consider the function $f(x) = e^x$.

$f^{(n)}(x) = e^x$ exists for all $n \in \mathbb{Z}^+$ and $x \in \mathbb{R}$, and $f^{(n)}(0) = e^0 = 1$ for all $n \in \mathbb{Z}^+$.

The nth degree Taylor approximation to e^x about 0 is $T_n(x) = 1 + \frac{x}{1!} + \frac{x^2}{2!} + ... + \frac{x^n}{n!}$.

Graphs of $f(x) = e^x$, $T_1(x) = 1 + x$,

$T_2(x) = 1 + x + \dfrac{x^2}{2!}$,   and

$T_5(x) = 1 + x + \dfrac{x^2}{2!} + \dfrac{x^3}{3!} + \dfrac{x^4}{4!} + \dfrac{x^5}{5!}$

are shown alongside:

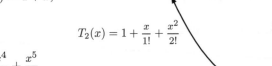

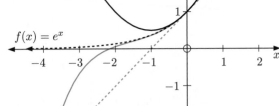

Note that $T_n(x) \approx f(x)$ when x is close to 0. As n increases, $T_n(x)$ approximates $f(x) = e^x$ closely for an increasingly large subset of $I = \mathbb{R}$.

If we denote $R_n(x : a)$ to be the error involved in using $T_n(x)$ to approximate $f(x)$ about $x = a$ on I, then $f(x) = T_n(x) + R_n(x : a)$.

The graphs for the case of $f(x) = e^x$ expanded about $x = 0$ suggest that as n increases, $R_n(x : 0)$ decreases and $T_n(x)$ becomes closer to $f(x)$.

Consider a function f with domain I containing $x = a$ (not at an endpoint of I). Suppose $f^{(n+1)}(x)$ exists on I, or I with its endpoints removed if I is closed.

For $x \in I$, **Taylor's formula with remainder** is $f(x) = T_n(x) + R_n(x : a)$

where $T_n(x) = \displaystyle\sum_{k=0}^{n} \frac{f^{(k)}(a)(x-a)^k}{k!}$

and $R_n(x : a) = \dfrac{f^{(n+1)}(c)(x-a)^{n+1}}{(n+1)!}$

where c is between x and a, so either $c \in\ ]a,\ x[$ or $c \in\ ]x,\ a[$, depending on the values of a and x.

This formula for $R_n(x : a)$ is called the **Lagrange form** of the error term.

Proof of Taylor's Formula:

Consider an interval $[a,\ b] \subseteq I$.

We define a new function

$$h(x) = f(b) - f(x) - f'(x)(b-x) - \frac{f''(x)}{2!}(b-x)^2 - \ .... \ - \frac{f^{(n)}(x)}{n!}(b-x)^n - K(b-x)^{n+1}$$

where K is the constant found by solving $h(a) = 0$.   Note that $h(b) = 0$.

Since f and its $n + 1$ derivatives exist on $[a,\ b]$, h is continuous on $[a,\ b]$ and differentiable on $]a,\ b[$. Since $h(a) = h(b) = 0$ we can apply Rolle's theorem to h on $[a,\ b]$. Thus there exists $c \in\ ]a,\ b[$ such that $h'(c) = 0$.

Using the product rule n times we obtain for $x \in I$ and $x > a$:

$$h'(x) = -f'(x) + \left[f'(x) - f''(x)(b-x) \right] + \left[f''(x)(b-x) - \frac{f^{(3)}(x)(b-x)^2}{2!} \right]$$

$$+ \left[\frac{f^{(3)}(x)(b-x)^2}{2!} - \frac{f^{(4)}(x)(b-x)^3}{3!} \right] + ... + \left[\frac{f^{(n)}(x)(b-x)^{n-1}}{(n-1)!} - \frac{f^{(n+1)}(x)(b-x)^n}{n!} \right]$$

$$+ (n+1)K(b-x)^n$$

$$\therefore \ h'(x) = -\frac{f^{(n+1)}(x)(b-x)^n}{n!} + (n+1)K(b-x)^n$$

Since $h'(c) = 0$, $(n+1)K(b-c)^n = \dfrac{f^{(n+1)}(c)}{n!}(b-c)^n$

$$\therefore \ \ K = \frac{f^{(n+1)}(c)}{(n+1)!}$$

We can repeat the argument with interval $[b,\ a] \subseteq I$, for $x \in I$ and $x < a$.

It follows that $R_n(x : a) = \dfrac{f^{(n+1)}(c)(x-a)^{n+1}}{(n+1)!}$ as required.

Before the invention of sophisticated calculators, calculations involving irrational numbers like e were difficult. Approximations using Taylor polynomials and rational values of x were often used.

Example 40

a Find the 3rd degree Taylor polynomial of $\sin x$ about $\frac{\pi}{4}$.

b Hence estimate $\sin\left(\frac{\pi}{5}\right)$.

c Use the error term to show your approximation is accurate to at least 3 decimal places.

a $f(x) = \sin x$ $\therefore$ $f\left(\frac{\pi}{4}\right) = \sin\left(\frac{\pi}{4}\right) = \frac{1}{\sqrt{2}}$

    $f'(x) = \cos x$ $\therefore$ $f'\left(\frac{\pi}{4}\right) = \cos\left(\frac{\pi}{4}\right) = \frac{1}{\sqrt{2}}$

    $f''(x) = -\sin x$ $\therefore$ $f''\left(\frac{\pi}{4}\right) = -\sin\left(\frac{\pi}{4}\right) = -\frac{1}{\sqrt{2}}$

    $f'''(x) = -\cos x$ $\therefore$ $f'''\left(\frac{\pi}{4}\right) = -\cos\left(\frac{\pi}{4}\right) = -\frac{1}{\sqrt{2}}$

$$\therefore \quad T_3(x) = f\left(\tfrac{\pi}{4}\right) + f'\left(\tfrac{\pi}{4}\right)\left(x - \tfrac{\pi}{4}\right) + \frac{f''\left(\tfrac{\pi}{4}\right)\left(x - \tfrac{\pi}{4}\right)^2}{2!} + \frac{f'''\left(\tfrac{\pi}{4}\right)\left(x - \tfrac{\pi}{4}\right)^3}{3!}$$

$$= \frac{1}{\sqrt{2}} + \frac{1}{\sqrt{2}}\left(x - \tfrac{\pi}{4}\right) - \frac{1}{\sqrt{2}}\frac{\left(x - \tfrac{\pi}{4}\right)^2}{2!} - \frac{1}{\sqrt{2}}\frac{\left(x - \tfrac{\pi}{4}\right)^3}{3!}$$

b $T_3\left(\tfrac{\pi}{5}\right) = \frac{1}{\sqrt{2}} + \frac{1}{\sqrt{2}}\left(\tfrac{\pi}{5} - \tfrac{\pi}{4}\right) - \frac{1}{\sqrt{2}}\dfrac{\left(\tfrac{\pi}{5} - \tfrac{\pi}{4}\right)^2}{2!} - \frac{1}{\sqrt{2}}\dfrac{\left(\tfrac{\pi}{5} - \tfrac{\pi}{4}\right)^3}{3!}$

    ≈ 0.5878

c $\left|R_3\left(\tfrac{\pi}{5} : \tfrac{\pi}{4}\right)\right| = \left|\dfrac{\sin c \left(\tfrac{\pi}{5} - \tfrac{\pi}{4}\right)^4}{4!}\right|$ where $\tfrac{\pi}{5} < c < \tfrac{\pi}{4}$

               $\leqslant \dfrac{\left(-\tfrac{\pi}{20}\right)^4}{4!}$ since $|\sin c| \leqslant 1$

               $< 0.000\,025\,4$

$\therefore$ $\left|T_3\left(\tfrac{\pi}{5}\right) - \sin\left(\tfrac{\pi}{5}\right)\right| < 0.000\,025\,4$

    $\therefore$ $T_3\left(\tfrac{\pi}{5}\right) \approx \sin\left(\tfrac{\pi}{5}\right)$ is accurate to at least 3 decimal places

Example 41

Use a Maclaurin polynomial to estimate $e^{0.4}$ with error less than $0.000\,01$.
You may assume that $e < 2.72$.

    $f(x) = e^x$ $f(0) = e^0 = 1$

    $f'(x) = e^x$ $f'(0) = e^0 = 1$

   $f^{(n)}(x) = e^x$ $f^{(n)}(0) = e^0 = 1$

$\therefore$ $T_n(x) = \displaystyle\sum_{k=0}^{n} \frac{x^k}{k!}$ for all $n \in \mathbb{Z}^+$ and $R_n(x : 0) = \dfrac{f^{(n+1)}(c)x^{n+1}}{(n+1)!}$

                                   $= \dfrac{e^c x^{n+1}}{(n+1)!}$ where $c \in [0, x]$.

We require $R_n(0.4 : 0) < 0.00001$

$$\therefore \quad \frac{e^c(0.4)^{n+1}}{(n+1)!} < 0.00001 \qquad \text{where} \quad 0 < c < 0.4$$

$$\therefore \quad e^0 < e^c < e^{0.4}$$

$$\therefore \quad 1 < e^c < e^{0.4} < e^1 < 2.72$$

$$\therefore \quad \frac{e^c(0.4)^{n+1}}{(n+1)!} < \frac{2.72(0.4)^{n+1}}{(n+1)!}$$

$\therefore$ we need n such that $\dfrac{(2.72)(0.4)^{n+1}}{(n+1)!} < 0.00001$

$$\therefore \quad \frac{(0.4)^{n+1}}{(n+1)!} < 3.676 \times 10^{-6}$$

GRAPHICS
CALCULATOR
INSTRUCTIONS

Using technology, $n \geqslant 6$

$\therefore$ $T_6(0.4) \approx 1.491\,824\,356$ approximates $e^{0.4}$ with an error less than 0.00001.

EXERCISE L.1

1 **a** Find the 3rd degree Maclaurin polynomial $T_3(x)$ of $\sin x$.
   b Hence estimate $\sin\left(\frac{\pi}{5}\right)$ correct to 4 decimal places.
   c Show that $\left|T_3\left(\frac{\pi}{5}\right) - \sin\left(\frac{\pi}{5}\right)\right| < 0.0065$.
   Hence show the approximation is accurate to 1 decimal place.

2 Find an upper bound for the error in using the approximation $\sin x \approx x - \dfrac{x^3}{3!} + \dfrac{x^5}{5!}$ on the interval $-0.3 \leqslant x \leqslant 0.3$.

3 Use the Maclaurin series for $\sin x$ to compute $\sin 3°$ correct to 5 decimal places.

4 Find a Taylor polynomial approximation to $\cos\left(\frac{\pi}{6} + 0.2\right)$ with error < 0.001.

5 Using the power series expansion of e^{-x^2}, evaluate $\displaystyle\int_0^1 e^{-x^2}\, dx$ to 3 decimal places.

6 Using the power series expansion of e^{x^2}, evaluate $\displaystyle\int_0^1 e^{x^2}\, dx$ to 3 decimal places.

7 Estimate the value of e^{-1} to 6 decimal places using the Alternating Series Estimation Theorem.

8 Use a Taylor polynomial to estimate each value with accuracy indicated.
   a e^3 with error < 0.0001 (You may assume $e < 2.72$.)
   b $\sin\left(\frac{\pi}{2} + 0.1\right)$ with error < 0.0001

CONVERGENCE OF THE TAYLOR SERIES

From **Example 41,** the error term for the Maclaurin polynomial approximation of $f(x) = e^x$ is

$$R_n(x:0) = \frac{f^{(n+1)}(c)x^{n+1}}{(n+1)!} = \frac{e^c x^{n+1}}{(n+1)!}, \quad \text{where } c \text{ is between } x \text{ and } 0.$$

By Taylor's formula, $e^x = \sum_{k=0}^{n} \frac{x^k}{k!} + \frac{e^c x^{n+1}}{(n+1)!}$ where c is some value between x and 0.

Consider what happens as $n \to \infty$.

By the Ratio test, $\sum_{k=0}^{\infty} \frac{x^k}{k!}$ converges for all $x \in \mathbb{R}$. (See **Example 38.**)

But before we can conclude that $e^x = \sum_{k=0}^{\infty} \frac{x^k}{k!}$, we need to find $\lim_{n\to\infty} R_n(x:0)$.

Now $\lim_{n\to\infty} |R_n(x:0)| = \lim_{n\to\infty} \frac{e^c |x|^{n+1}}{(n+1)!}$ where e^c is a constant dependent on x.

For any $x \in \mathbb{R}$, $\lim_{n\to\infty} \frac{|x|^{n+1}}{(n+1)!} = 0$ (See **Example 38.**)

$$\therefore \quad \lim_{n\to\infty} |R_n(x:0)| = \lim_{n\to\infty} \frac{e^c |x|^{n+1}}{(n+1)!} = e^c \lim_{n\to\infty} \frac{|x|^{n+1}}{(n+1)!} = 0$$

$$\therefore \quad \lim_{n\to\infty} R_n(x:0) = 0$$

We therefore conclude that $e^x = \sum_{k=0}^{\infty} \frac{x^k}{k!}$ for all $x \in \mathbb{R}$.

TAYLOR'S THEOREM

If $f(x)$ has derivatives of all orders on interval I which contains a, then

1 $f(x) = T_n(x) + R_n(x:a)$ for all $x \in I$, and

2 $f(x) = \sum_{n=0}^{\infty} \frac{f^{(n)}(a)(x-a)^n}{n!}$ if and only if $\lim_{n\to\infty} R_n(x:a) = 0$ where

$R_n(x:a) = \frac{f^{(n+1)}(c)(x-a)^{n+1}}{(n+1)!}$ for some constant c between x and a, where c depends on x.

Proof: **1** Proved above as Taylor's formula.

2 For a general function f and for any $n \in \mathbb{Z}^+$,

$$f(x) = T_n(x) + R_n(x:a) \quad \text{for all } x \in I$$

Now $\lim_{n\to\infty} T_n(x) = \sum_{n=0}^{\infty} \frac{f^{(n)}(a)(x-a)^n}{n!}$ exists if and only if this series converges.

This occurs if and only if $\lim_{n\to\infty} T_n(x) = \lim_{n\to\infty} (f(x) - R_n(x:a))$

$$= f(x) - \lim_{n\to\infty} R_n(x:a) \quad \text{exists.}$$

$$\therefore \quad f(x) = \sum_{n=0}^{\infty} \frac{f^{(n)}(a)(x-a)^n}{n!} \quad \text{if and only if} \quad \lim_{n\to\infty} R_n(x:a) = 0.$$

Taylor's Theorem tells us that the Taylor series of a function f does not necessarily converge, but when it does converge, it equals $f(x)$ if and only if $\lim\limits_{n \to \infty} R_n(x : a) = 0$.

ADDITION OF SERIES

Suppose $\sum\limits_{n=0}^{\infty} a_n x^n$ has radius of convergence R_a and $\sum\limits_{n=0}^{\infty} b_n x^n$ has radius of convergence R_b.

The sum of the two series is $\sum\limits_{n=0}^{\infty} a_n x^n + \sum\limits_{n=0}^{\infty} b_n x^n = \sum\limits_{n=0}^{\infty} (a_n + b_n) x^n$ which has radius of convergence being the minimum of R_a and R_b.

Example 42

a Show that $f(x) = \cos x$ is equal to its Maclaurin series expansion, and find the radius of convergence.

b Hence find Maclaurin series expansions for the following, including their radii of convergence:

   i $\cos(2x)$ ii $\sin x$

a $\begin{aligned} f(x) &= \cos x & \therefore \quad f(0) &= 1 \\ f'(x) &= -\sin x & \therefore \quad f'(0) &= 0 \\ f''(x) &= -\cos x & \therefore \quad f''(0) &= -1 \\ f'''(x) &= \sin x & \therefore \quad f'''(0) &= 0 \\ f^{(4)}(x) &= \cos x & \therefore \quad f^{(4)}(0) &= 1 \end{aligned}$

By Taylor's Theorem,

$f(x) = \cos x$

$$= f(0) + \frac{f'(0)}{1!} x + \frac{f''(0)}{2!} x^2 + \frac{f'''(0)}{3!} x^3 + \ldots + \frac{f^{(n)}(0) x^n}{n!} + R_n(x : 0)$$

$$= 1 - \frac{x^2}{2!} + \frac{x^4}{4!} - \frac{x^6}{6!} + \ldots + (-1)^k \frac{x^{2k}}{(2k)!} + R_{2k+1}(x : 0), \quad k \in \mathbb{Z}^+$$

where $R_{2k+1}(x : 0) = \dfrac{f^{(2k+1)}(c) x^{2k+1}}{(2k+1)!}$ for c a constant between 0 and x

Since $\left| f^{(2k+1)}(c) \right| = |\sin(c)| \leqslant 1$,

$$\lim_{n \to \infty} |R_n(x : 0)| = \lim_{k \to \infty} \left| \frac{f^{(2k+1)}(c) x^{2k+1}}{(2k+1)!} \right|$$

$$\leqslant \lim_{k \to \infty} \frac{|x|^{2k+1}}{(2k+1)!} = 0 \qquad \{\text{see } \textbf{Example 38}\}$$

$\therefore$ by the Squeeze Theorem, $\lim\limits_{n \to \infty} |R_n(x : 0)| = 0$ for all $x \in \mathbb{R}$,

$$\therefore \quad \lim_{n \to \infty} R_n(x : 0) = 0 \quad \text{for all } x \in \mathbb{R}$$

$\therefore \quad f(x) = \cos x = \sum\limits_{n=0}^{\infty} \dfrac{(-1)^n x^{2n}}{(2n)!}$ for all $x \in \mathbb{R}$. The radius of convergence is infinite.

b **i** Since $\cos x = \sum\limits_{n=0}^{\infty} \dfrac{(-1)^n x^{2n}}{(2n)!}$,

$\cos(2x) = \sum\limits_{n=0}^{\infty} \dfrac{(-1)^n (2x)^{2n}}{(2n)!}$ for all $x \in \mathbb{R}$.

The radius of convergence is infinite.

ii Now since the Maclaurin series expansion of $\cos x$ is defined on $\mathbb{R}$, it is both differentiable and integrable on its interval of convergence $\mathbb{R}$.

Since $\cos x = 1 - \dfrac{x^2}{2!} + \dfrac{x^4}{4!} - \dfrac{x^6}{6!} + ...$ for all $x \in \mathbb{R}$

$\dfrac{d}{dx}(\cos x) = -\sin x = -\dfrac{2x}{2!} + \dfrac{4x^3}{4!} - \dfrac{6x^5}{6!} + ...$

$\therefore \quad \sin x = x - \dfrac{x^3}{3!} + \dfrac{x^5}{5!} - ....$ for all $x \in \mathbb{R}$.

Alternatively, $\sin x - \sin(0) = \displaystyle\int_0^x \cos t \, dt$

$\therefore \quad \sin x = \displaystyle\int_0^x \left(\sum\limits_{n=0}^{\infty} \dfrac{(-1)^n t^{2n}}{(2n)!} \right) dt$

$= \sum\limits_{n=0}^{\infty} \left(\displaystyle\int_0^x \dfrac{(-1)^n t^{2n}}{(2n)!} \, dt \right)$

$= \left[\sum\limits_{n=0}^{\infty} \dfrac{(-1)^n t^{2n+1}}{(2n+1)!} \right]_0^x$

$= \sum\limits_{n=0}^{\infty} \dfrac{(-1)^n x^{2n+1}}{(2n+1)!}$ for all $x \in \mathbb{R}$

$= x - \dfrac{x^3}{3!} + \dfrac{x^5}{5!} - \dfrac{x^7}{7!} + ...$ for all $x \in \mathbb{R}$

The radius of convergence is infinite.

EXERCISE L.2

1 **a** Show that $f(x) = \sin x$ is equal to its Maclaurin series expansion, and find the radius of convergence.

   b Hence find the Maclaurin series expansions for the following, including their radii of convergence:

   i $x \sin x$ **ii** $\sin(3x)$ **iii** $\cos x$

2 **a** Show that $f(x) = e^{-x}$ is equal to its Maclaurin series expansion, and find the radius of convergence.

   b Hence find the Maclaurin series expansion for e^{-x^2}, including its radius of convergence.

3 Find the Taylor series expansion about $x = 2$ for $f(x) = \ln x$ and its associated radius of convergence.

4 **a** Find the Maclaurin series expansion for $f(x) = 2^x$ and its associated interval of convergence.

   b *Hence* find a_n such that $\sum\limits_{n=0}^{\infty} a_n = 7$.

Example 43

Let $f(x) = \ln(1 + x)$.

a **i** Find the Maclaurin series for $f(x)$ and its associated interval of convergence I.

ii Show that $f(x) = \ln(1 + x)$ equals its Maclaurin series for $0 < x \leqslant 1$ by showing $\lim\limits_{n \to \infty} R_n(x : 0) = 0$ for $0 < x \leqslant 1$.

b Complete the proof that $\ln(1 + x)$ equals its Maclaurin series for $-1 < x \leqslant 1$ in the following steps:

i Use the geometric series to write down the power series representation for $\dfrac{1}{1 + x}$, $|x| < 1$.

ii Use the fact that $\ln(1 + x) - \ln(1 + 0) = \displaystyle\int_0^x \dfrac{1}{1 + t}\, dt$ to find the Maclaurin series for $\ln(1 + x)$, $|x| < 1$.

c Hence find the exact value of $\displaystyle\sum_{k=1}^{\infty} \dfrac{(-1)^k}{k}$.

a **i** $\qquad f(x) = \ln(1 + x) \qquad\qquad \therefore \quad f(0) = \ln 1 = 0$

$\qquad f'(x) = \dfrac{1}{1 + x} \qquad\qquad\quad \therefore \quad f'(0) = 1$

$\qquad f''(x) = \dfrac{-1}{(1 + x)^2} \qquad\qquad \therefore \quad f''(0) = -1$

$\qquad f'''(x) = \dfrac{-1 \times -2}{(1 + x)^3} \qquad\quad \therefore \quad f'''(0) = (-1)^2\, 2!$

$\qquad\qquad \vdots \qquad\qquad\qquad\qquad\qquad\qquad \vdots$

$\qquad f^{(n)}(x) = \dfrac{(-1)^{n-1}(n - 1)!}{(1 + x)^n} \quad \therefore \quad f^{(n)}(0) = (-1)^{n-1}(n - 1)!$

$\therefore \quad f(x) = T_n(x) + R_n(x : 0)$

$\qquad = 0 + \dfrac{1 \times x}{1!} - \dfrac{1 \times x^2}{2!} + \dfrac{2! x^3}{3!} - \dfrac{3! x^4}{4!} + \dots + \dfrac{(-1)^{n-1}(n - 1)! x^n}{n!} + R_n(x : 0)$

$\qquad = x - \dfrac{x^2}{2} + \dfrac{x^3}{3} - \dfrac{x^4}{4} + \dots + \dfrac{(-1)^{n-1} x^n}{n} + R_n(x : 0)$

where $R_n(x : 0) = \dfrac{f^{(n+1)}(c) x^{n+1}}{(n + 1)!} = \dfrac{(-1)^n\, x^{n+1}}{(1 + c)^{n+1}(n + 1)}$.

Thus the Maclaurin series for $\ln(1 + x)$ is $\displaystyle\sum_{k=1}^{\infty} \dfrac{(-1)^{k+1} x^k}{k} = x - \dfrac{x^2}{2} + \dfrac{x^3}{3} - \dfrac{x^4}{4} + \dots$

By the Ratio test this converges for $|x| < 1$.

We ignore the case $x = -1$, since $f(x)$ is undefined at this point.

If $x = 1$, we have $\displaystyle\sum_{k=1}^{\infty} \dfrac{(-1)^{k+1}}{k}$ which converges by the Alternating Series Test.

Hence the Maclaurin series for $\ln(1 + x)$ has interval of convergence $\,]-1, 1]$.

ii $|R_n(x : 0)| = \left| \dfrac{x^{n+1}}{(1 + c)^{n+1}(n + 1)} \right|$ where c is between 0 and x.

If $0 < c < x \leqslant 1$ then

$\qquad 0 \leqslant |R_n(x : 0)| < \dfrac{x^{n+1}}{n + 1} \leqslant \dfrac{1}{n + 1}$ for $0 < x \leqslant 1$

$\therefore \quad \lim\limits_{n \to \infty} |R_n(x : 0)| = \lim\limits_{n \to \infty} \dfrac{1}{n + 1} = 0.$ {Squeeze Theorem}

b   **i** $$\frac{1}{1-x} = \sum_{k=0}^{\infty} x^k \quad \text{for} \quad |x| < 1$$

$$\therefore \quad \frac{1}{1+x} = \sum_{k=0}^{\infty} (-x)^k$$

$$= \sum_{k=0}^{\infty} (-1)^k x^k$$

$$= 1 - x + x^2 - x^3 + x^4 - \dots \quad \text{for} \quad |-x| < 1, \ \text{which is for} \ |x| < 1$$

ii $\ln(1+x) - \ln(1+0) = \displaystyle\int_0^x \frac{1}{1+t} \, dt$

$$\therefore \quad \ln(1+x) = \int_0^x \sum_{k=0}^{\infty} (-1)^k t^k \, dt \quad \text{for} \ |x| < 1$$

$$= \sum_{k=0}^{\infty} \int_0^x (-1)^k t^k \, dt$$

$$= \sum_{k=0}^{\infty} \left(\frac{(-1)^k x^{k+1}}{k+1} \right) \quad \text{for} \ |x| < 1$$

$$= x - \frac{x^2}{2} + \frac{x^3}{3} - \frac{x^4}{4} + \dots \quad \text{for} \ |x| < 1.$$

c We have seen previously that $\displaystyle\sum_{k=1}^{\infty} \frac{(-1)^k}{k}$ is convergent by the Alternating Series Test.

$$\sum_{k=1}^{\infty} \frac{(-1)^k}{k} = -1 + \tfrac{1}{2} - \tfrac{1}{3} + \tfrac{1}{4} - \tfrac{1}{5} + \dots$$

$$= -\left(1 - \tfrac{1}{2} + \tfrac{1}{3} - \tfrac{1}{4} + \tfrac{1}{5} - \dots \right)$$

$$= -\ln(1+1) \quad \text{since} \ 1 \in I = \,]-1, 1]$$

$$= -\ln 2$$

Example 44

a Use the Maclaurin series expansion for e^x to write down power series expansions for:

   i e^{2x} **ii** e^{4x} **iii** $e^{nx}, \ n \in \mathbb{Z}^+$.

b Use the Maclaurin series expansion for $\cos x$ to find the first two non-zero terms of the Maclaurin series expansion of $\cos(e^x)$.

c Hence show that for x near 0, $\cos(e^x) \approx \cos(1) - \sin(1)x$.

d Find, by direct calculation, the Maclaurin polynomial of degree 2 of $\cos(e^x)$.

---

a $e^x = \displaystyle\sum_{k=0}^{\infty} \frac{x^k}{k!} = 1 + x + \frac{x^2}{2!} + \frac{x^3}{3!} + \dots$

   i $e^{2x} = \displaystyle\sum_{k=0}^{\infty} \frac{(2x)^k}{k!} = 1 + 2x + \frac{4x^2}{2!} + \frac{8x^3}{3!} + \dots$

   ii $e^{4x} = \displaystyle\sum_{k=0}^{\infty} \frac{(4x)^k}{k!} = 1 + 4x + \frac{16x^2}{2!} + \frac{64x^3}{3!} + \dots$

   iii $e^{nx} = \displaystyle\sum_{k=0}^{\infty} \frac{(nx)^k}{k!} = 1 + nx + \frac{n^2 x^2}{2!} + \frac{n^3 x^3}{3!} + \dots$

b $\cos(e^x) = 1 - \dfrac{e^{2x}}{2!} + \dfrac{e^{4x}}{4!} - \dfrac{e^{6x}}{6!} + ...$

$$= 1 - \dfrac{1}{2!}\left(1 + 2x + \dfrac{4x^2}{2!} + ...\right) + \dfrac{1}{4!}\left(1 + 4x + \dfrac{16x^2}{2!} + ...\right) + ...$$

$$+ \dfrac{(-1)^n}{(2n)!}\left(1 + nx + \dfrac{n^2x^2}{2!} + ...\right) + ...$$

$\therefore$ using terms up to the x term,

$$\cos(e^x) \approx 1 + \left(\sum_{n=1}^{\infty} \dfrac{(-1)^n}{(2n)!}\right) + \left(\sum_{n=1}^{\infty} \dfrac{(-1)^n(2n)}{(2n)!}\right)x$$

$$\approx 1 + \sum_{n=1}^{\infty} \dfrac{(-1)^n}{(2n)!} + \sum_{n=1}^{\infty} \dfrac{(-1)^n x}{(2n-1)!}$$

c For x close to 0, higher order terms involving x^2, x^3, ... tend to 0.

$$\therefore \quad \cos(e^x) \approx 1 + \sum_{n=1}^{\infty} \dfrac{(-1)^n}{(2n)!} + \sum_{n=1}^{\infty} \dfrac{(-1)^n x}{(2n-1)!}$$

Now $\cos(1) - 1 = -\dfrac{1}{2!} + \dfrac{1}{4!} - \dfrac{1}{6!} + ... = \displaystyle\sum_{n=1}^{\infty} \dfrac{(-1)^n}{(2n)!}$

and $-\sin(1) = -1 + \dfrac{1}{3!} - \dfrac{1}{5!} + ... = \displaystyle\sum_{n=1}^{\infty} \dfrac{(-1)^n}{(2n-1)!}$

$\therefore \quad \cos(e^x) \approx 1 + (\cos(1) - 1) - \sin(1)x$

$$= \cos(1) - \sin(1)x$$

d Let $f(x) = \cos(e^x)$.

$\therefore \quad f'(x) = -\sin(e^x) \times e^x$

$\therefore \quad f''(x) = -e^x \sin(e^x) - \cos(e^x)e^{2x}$

$\therefore \quad f(0) = \cos(e^0) = \cos(1)$

$\therefore \quad f'(0) = -\sin(1) \times 1 = -\sin(1)$

$\therefore \quad f''(0) = -\sin(1) - \cos(1)$

$\therefore \quad T_2(x) = \cos(1) - \sin(1)x - (\sin(1) + \cos(1))\dfrac{x^2}{2!}$

5 a Use the geometric series to find the Maclaurin series for each given function and find the associated radius of convergence.

    i $f(x) = \dfrac{1}{1 + x^2}$ **ii** $f(x) = \dfrac{1}{1 + x^3}$ **iii** $f(x) = \dfrac{1}{1 - x^3}$

b Hence estimate $\displaystyle\int_0^{\frac{1}{3}} \dfrac{1}{1 + x^3}\, dx$ to 4 decimal places.

6 Obtain the power series representation of $\ln\left(\dfrac{1+x}{1-x}\right)$ and use its first 3 terms to estimate the value of $\ln 2$.

7 a Use the Maclaurin series expansion for e^x to write down the power series expansions for:

    i e^{-x} **ii** e^{-3x} **iii** $e^{-(2k-1)x}$, $k \in \mathbb{Z}^+$.

b Use the Maclaurin series expansion for $\sin x$ to find the first two non-zero terms of the Maclaurin series expansion for $\sin(e^{-x})$.

c Hence find an approximation for $\sin(e^{-x})$ for x near 0.

d Find, by direct calculation, the Maclaurin polynomial of degree 2 of $\sin(e^{-x})$.

8 Let $f(x) = (1+x)^p$, where $p \in \mathbb{R}$.

    a Show that the Maclaurin series for $(1+x)^p$ is $\displaystyle\sum_{n=0}^{\infty} \frac{p(p-1)\,....\,(p-n+1)}{n!}\, x^n$.

    b Find the associated radius of convergence.

    c For $0 \leqslant x < 1$, use the remainder term to show that $(1+x)^p$ equals its Maclaurin series.

THE BINOMIAL SERIES

In the last **Exercise** we considered the **binomial series** for $0 \leqslant x < 1$. In fact, the general result is:

$$(1+x)^p = \sum_{n=0}^{\infty} \frac{p(p-1)\,....\,(p-n+1)}{n!}\, x^n, \quad \text{for all } |x| < 1.$$

The remainder of the proof is done in **Exercise P** question **5**.

For $p = 0$ or $p \in \mathbb{Z}^+$, the coefficient of x^n is zero for $n > p$. In these cases $(1+x)^p = \displaystyle\sum_{n=0}^{p} \binom{p}{n} x^n$, which is the **binomial formula**. This series is finite and therefore convergent for all $x \in \mathbb{R}$.

For other values of p, the series has radius of convergence $R = 1$.

Example 45

    a Use the Maclaurin series expansion of $(1+x)^p$ to write down the Maclaurin series for $(1-x^2)^{-\frac{1}{2}}$.

    b Use the fact that $\arccos x - \arccos(0) = \displaystyle\int_0^x \frac{-1}{\sqrt{1-t^2}}\, dt$ to find a Maclaurin series for $\arccos x$. For which values of x is this valid?

    c   **i** Use the series in **b** to find the first three non-zero terms of $\arccos(x^2)$.

        ii Hence find an approximate value for $\displaystyle\int_0^{0.4} \arccos(x^2)\, dx$.

---

a $(1+x)^p = \displaystyle\sum_{k=0}^{\infty} \frac{p(p-1)\,....\,(p-k+1)}{k!}\, x^k$ for all $|x| < 1$

$\therefore \quad (1-x^2)^{-\frac{1}{2}} = 1 + \displaystyle\sum_{k=1}^{\infty} \frac{\left(-\frac{1}{2}\right)\left(-\frac{3}{2}\right)\,....\,\left(\frac{1}{2}-k\right)}{k!}\, (-x^2)^k$

$\qquad\qquad\qquad\quad = 1 + \displaystyle\sum_{k=1}^{\infty} \frac{\left(-\frac{1}{2}\right)\left(-\frac{3}{2}\right)\,....\,\left(\frac{-2k+1}{2}\right)(-1)^k}{k!}\, x^{2k}$

$\qquad\qquad\qquad\quad = 1 + \displaystyle\sum_{k=1}^{\infty} \frac{(-1)^{2k} \times 1 \times 3 \times 5 \times\,....\,\times (2k-1)}{2^k\, k!}\, x^{2k}$

$\qquad\qquad\qquad\quad = 1 + \displaystyle\sum_{k=1}^{\infty} \frac{1 \times 3 \times 5 \times\,....\,\times (2k-1)}{2^k\, (k!)}\, x^{2k}$

$\qquad\qquad\qquad\quad = 1 + \displaystyle\sum_{k=1}^{\infty} \frac{1 \times 3 \times 5 \times\,....\,\times (2k-1)}{2^k\, k!} \times \frac{2 \times 4 \times 6 \times\,....\,\times 2k}{2 \times 4 \times 6 \times\,....\,\times 2k} \times x^{2k}$

$\qquad\qquad\qquad\quad = 1 + \displaystyle\sum_{k=1}^{\infty} \frac{(2k)!}{2^k\, k!\, 2^k\, k!}\, x^{2k}$

$\therefore$ $(1-x^2)^{-\frac{1}{2}} = 1 + \sum\limits_{k=1}^{\infty} \dfrac{(2k)!}{4^k(k!)^2} x^{2k}$ for all $|x^2| < 1$, which is for all $|x| < 1$.

b $\arccos x - \arccos(0) = \displaystyle\int_0^x \dfrac{-1}{\sqrt{1-t^2}}\, dt$

$\therefore$ $\arccos x - \frac{\pi}{2} = -\displaystyle\int_0^x \left(1 + \sum\limits_{k=1}^{\infty} \dfrac{(2k)!}{4^k(k!)^2} t^{2k} \right) dt$

$= -\left(x + \sum\limits_{k=1}^{\infty} \dfrac{(2k)!}{4^k(k!)^2(2k+1)} x^{2k+1} \right)$

$\therefore$ $\arccos x = \frac{\pi}{2} - x - \sum\limits_{k=1}^{\infty} \dfrac{(2k)!}{4^k(k!)^2(2k+1)} x^{2k+1}$

This is valid provided $|x| < 1$. These values of x all lie in the domain of arccos, so the series is valid for $-1 < x < 1$.

c   **i** $\arccos x = \frac{\pi}{2} - x - \frac{1}{6}x^3$ {using the first 3 terms}

$\arccos(x^2) \approx \frac{\pi}{2} - x^2 - \frac{1}{6}x^6$ for $|x| < 1$

ii $\displaystyle\int_0^{0.4} \arccos\left(x^2\right) dx \approx \int_0^{0.4} \left(\frac{\pi}{2} - x^2 - \frac{x^6}{6} \right) dx$ since $|0.4| < 1$

$= \left[\frac{\pi}{2}x - \frac{x^3}{3} - \frac{x^7}{7} \right]_0^{0.4}$

≈ 0.607

EXERCISE L.3

1   Use the Maclaurin series expansion of $(1+x)^p$ to find the Maclaurin series for each given function and find the associated radius of convergence.

    a $f(x) = \dfrac{1}{1-x^2}$ **b** $f(x) = \dfrac{1}{1+x^3}$ **c** $f(x) = \dfrac{1}{1-x^3}$

2   **a**   Use the Maclaurin series expansion of $(1+x)^p$ to write down the Maclaurin series for $(1+x^2)^{-1}$ and state the associated radius of convergence.

    b   Use the fact that $\arctan x - \arctan(0) = \displaystyle\int_0^x \dfrac{1}{1+t^2}\, dt$ to obtain the Maclaurin series for $\arctan x$. For which values of x is this valid?

    c   **i**   Use the series in **b** to find the first four non-zero terms of $\arctan(x^2)$.

        ii   Hence find an approximate value for $\displaystyle\int_0^1 \arctan(x^2)\, dx$.

3   **a**   Use the $(1+x)^p$ series to write a Maclaurin series for $(1-x^2)^{-\frac{1}{2}}$ and state the radius of convergence R.

    b   Use the fact that $\arcsin x - \arcsin(0) = \displaystyle\int_0^x \dfrac{1}{\sqrt{1-x^2}}\, dx$ to obtain a Maclaurin series expansion for $\arcsin x$ for $|x| < R$.

    c   If $\dfrac{\pi}{6} = \dfrac{1}{2} + \sum\limits_{k=1}^{\infty} a_k$,   find a_k.

PRODUCT OF SERIES

Suppose $\sum\limits_{n=0}^{\infty} a_n x^n$ has radius of convergence R_a and $\sum\limits_{n=0}^{\infty} b_n x^n$ has radius of convergence R_b.

The product of the series is

$$\left(\sum_{n=0}^{\infty} a_n x^n\right)\left(\sum_{n=0}^{\infty} b_n x^n\right) = \sum_{n=0}^{\infty} c_n x^n$$

$$= a_0 b_0 + (a_0 b_1 + a_1 b_0)x + (a_0 b_2 + a_1 b_1 + a_2 b_0)x^2 + \ldots + c_n x^n + \ldots$$

$$\text{where} \quad c_n = a_0 b_n + a_1 b_{n-1} + \ldots + a_n b_0.$$

The radius of convergence is the minimum of R_a and R_b.

Example 46

Let $\sum\limits_{n=0}^{\infty} a_n x^n = \dfrac{x}{\sin x}$ be the power series expansion of $\dfrac{x}{\sin x}$, $x \neq k\pi$, $k \in \mathbb{Z}$.

Use the Maclaurin series expansion of $\sin x$ to find a_0, a_1, a_2 so that $\dfrac{x}{\sin x} \approx a_0 + a_1 x + a_2 x^2$ for x near 0.

Since $\dfrac{x}{\sin x} = \sum\limits_{n=0}^{\infty} a_n x^n$, we find $x = (a_0 + a_1 x + a_2 x^2 + \ldots)\left(x - \dfrac{x^3}{3!} + \dfrac{x^5}{5!} - \ldots\right)$

$$= a_0 x + a_1 x^2 + \left(a_2 - \dfrac{a_0}{3!}\right)x^3 + \ldots$$

Comparing LHS and RHS and equating coefficients, $a_0 = 1$, $a_1 = 0$, $a_2 = \frac{1}{6}$

$$\therefore \quad \dfrac{x}{\sin x} \approx 1 + \tfrac{1}{6}x^2$$

EXERCISE L.4

1 **a** Find the first four terms of the power series representation for $\sqrt{1+x} = (1+x)^{\frac{1}{2}}$, where $|x| < 1$, by letting $\sqrt{1+x} = \sum\limits_{n=0}^{\infty} a_n x^n$ and using $(\sqrt{1+x})^2 = 1 + x$.

   b Check that your answer in **a** agrees with the $(1+x)^p$ series with $p = \frac{1}{2}$.

2 **a** Use known Maclaurin series expansions to find the first four non-zero terms in the Maclaurin series expansion of $e^x \arccos x$.

   b For which values of x does the expansion in **a** equal the full Maclaurin series expansion?

> For the Maclaurin series expansion of $\arccos x$, see **Example 45**.

3 **a** Use known Maclaurin series expansions to find the first three non-zero terms in the Maclaurin series expansion of $\dfrac{x}{\cos x}$.

   b For which values of x does the expansion in **a** equal the full Maclaurin series expansion?

4 Use the Maclaurin series expansions of $\sin x$ and $\cos x$ to determine the first three non-zero terms of the Maclaurin series expansion for $\tan x = \dfrac{\sin x}{\cos x}$.

5 It can be shown that the exponential function equals its Maclaurin series for all $z \in \mathbb{C}$, where $\mathbb{C}$ is the set of all complex numbers.

$$\therefore \quad e^z = \sum_{k=0}^{\infty} \frac{z^k}{k!} \quad \text{for all complex numbers } z.$$

Let $z = i\theta$ where $\theta \in \mathbb{R}$.

  a Use the above result to write down the simplified expanded series for $e^{i\theta}$.

  b Hence, using the known Maclaurin series for $\cos\theta$ and $\sin\theta$, $\theta \in \mathbb{R}$, prove **Euler's formula**
$$e^{i\theta} = \cos\theta + i\sin\theta.$$

6   **a** Prove that $1 + x \leqslant e^x$ for all $x \geqslant 0$.

  b Hence show that if $u_k \geqslant 0$ for all k, then
$$\prod_{k=1}^{n}(1 + u_k) = (1 + u_1)(1 + u_2)\dots(1 + u_n) \leqslant e^{u_1 + u_2 + \dots + u_n}.$$

  c If $\displaystyle\sum_{n=1}^{\infty} u_k$ converges, deduce the behaviour of

$$\prod_{k=1}^{n}(1 + u_k) \quad \text{as } n \to \infty.$$

$$\prod_{k=1}^{n} u_k = u_1 \times u_2 \times \dots \times u_n$$

7 In this question, use the following steps for Euler's proof of $\displaystyle\sum_{n=1}^{\infty} \frac{1}{n^2} = \frac{\pi^2}{6}$.

You may assume that $\sin x = x - \dfrac{x^3}{3!} + \dfrac{x^5}{5!} - \dfrac{x^7}{7!} + \dots$ for all $x \in \mathbb{R}$.

  a Find *all* the zeros of $\sin x$ and of $\dfrac{\sin x}{x}$ for $x \in \mathbb{R}$.

  b Find the power series expansion for $\dfrac{\sin x}{x}$ and its interval of convergence.

  c Find all the zeros of $\left(1 - \dfrac{x}{\pi}\right)\left(1 + \dfrac{x}{\pi}\right)\left(1 - \dfrac{x}{2\pi}\right)\left(1 + \dfrac{x}{2\pi}\right)\dots$

  d Show that:
$$\left(1 - \frac{x}{\pi}\right)\left(1 + \frac{x}{\pi}\right)\left(1 - \frac{x}{2\pi}\right)\left(1 + \frac{x}{2\pi}\right)\dots = \left(1 - \frac{x^2}{\pi^2}\right)\left(1 - \frac{x^2}{4\pi^2}\right)\left(1 - \frac{x^2}{9\pi^2}\right)\dots$$

and comment on Euler's claim that
$$1 - \frac{x^2}{3!} + \frac{x^4}{5!} - \frac{x^6}{7!} + \dots = \left(1 - \frac{x^2}{\pi^2}\right)\left(1 - \frac{x^2}{4\pi^2}\right)\left(1 - \frac{x^2}{9\pi^2}\right)\dots$$

  e By equating the coefficients of x^2 in this last equation, prove that:
$$\sum_{n=1}^{\infty} \frac{1}{n^2} = \frac{1}{1^2} + \frac{1}{2^2} + \frac{1}{3^2} + \frac{1}{4^2} + \dots = \frac{\pi^2}{6}.$$

  f As $\displaystyle\sum_{n=1}^{\infty} \frac{1}{n^2}$ is absolutely convergent, we can write $\displaystyle\sum_{n=1}^{\infty} \frac{1}{n^2} = \underbrace{\sum_{r=1}^{\infty} \frac{1}{(2r)^2}}_{\text{even } n} + \underbrace{\sum_{r=1}^{\infty} \frac{1}{(2r-1)^2}}_{\text{odd } n}.$

Use this last equation to find the exact values of $\displaystyle\sum_{n=1}^{\infty} \frac{1}{(2n)^2}$ and $\displaystyle\sum_{n=1}^{\infty} \frac{1}{(2n-1)^2}$.

HISTORICAL NOTE

Euler was able to derive a method to sum **all** series of the form $\displaystyle\sum_{n=1}^{\infty} \frac{1}{n^{2k}}$, $k \in \mathbb{Z}^+$.

However, the exact value of $\displaystyle\sum_{n=1}^{\infty} \frac{1}{n^{2k+1}}$, for **any** $k \in \mathbb{Z}^+$ is still an open problem.

DIFFERENTIAL EQUATIONS

A **differential equation** is an equation involving the derivative(s) of an unknown function.

Suppose y is a function of x, so $y = y(x)$. Examples of differential equations for this function are:

$$\frac{dy}{dx} = \frac{x^2}{y} \qquad\qquad \frac{dy}{dx} = -0.075y^3 \qquad\qquad \frac{d^2y}{dx^2} - 3\frac{dy}{dx} + 4y = 0$$

Such equations not only arise in pure mathematics, but are also used to model and solve problems in applied mathematics, physics, engineering, and the other sciences. For example:

A falling object	**A parachutist**	**Object on a spring**

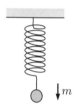

$$\frac{d^2y}{dx^2} = 9.8 \qquad\qquad m\frac{dv}{dt} = mg - av^2 \qquad\qquad m\frac{d^2y}{dt^2} = -ky$$

Current in an RL Circuit	**Water from a tank**	**Dog pursuing cat**

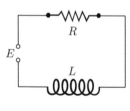

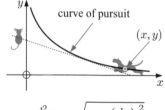

$$L\frac{dI}{dt} + RI = E \qquad\qquad \frac{dH}{dt} = -a\sqrt{H} \qquad\qquad x\frac{d^2y}{dx^2} = \sqrt{1 + \left(\frac{dy}{dx}\right)^2}$$

FIRST ORDER DIFFERENTIAL EQUATIONS

In this course we will only deal with differential equations of the form

$$f(x, y)\frac{dy}{dx} + g(x, y) = 0 \quad \text{where } y = y(x).$$

These are known as **first order** differential equations since there is only one derivative in the equation, and it is a first derivative.

SOLUTIONS OF DIFFERENTIAL EQUATIONS

A function $y(x)$ is said to be a **solution** of a differential equation if it satisfies the differential equation for all values of x in the domain of y.

For example, a very simple differential equation is $\dfrac{dy}{dx} = x$.

In this case we can use direct integration to find $y = \displaystyle\int x\,dx = \frac{1}{2}x^2 + c$.

In solving the differential equation we obtain a constant of integration. We say that $y = \frac{1}{2}x^2 + c$ is a **general solution** to the differential equation. It describes a family of curves which all satisfy the differential equation.

If we are given **initial conditions** for the problem, such as a value of y or $\frac{dy}{dx}$ for a specific value of x, then we can evaluate c. This gives us a **particular solution** to the problem, which is one particular curve from the family of curves described by the general solution.

Example 47

Consider the differential equation $\dfrac{dy}{dx} - 3y = 3$.

a Show that $y = ce^{3x} - 1$ is a solution to the differential equation for any constant c.

b Sketch the solution curves for $c = \pm 1, \pm 2, \pm 3$.

c Find the particular solution which passes through $(0, 2)$.

d Find the equation of the tangent to the particular solution at $(0, 2)$.

---

a If $y = ce^{3x} - 1$ then $\dfrac{dy}{dx} = 3ce^{3x}$.

$\therefore \quad \dfrac{dy}{dx} - 3y = 3ce^{3x} - 3(ce^{3x} - 1)$
$$= 3ce^{3x} - 3ce^{3x} + 3$$
$$= 3$$

$\therefore$ the differential equation is satisfied for all $x \in \mathbb{R}$.

b The solution curves for $c = \pm 1, \pm 2, \pm 3$ are shown alongside:

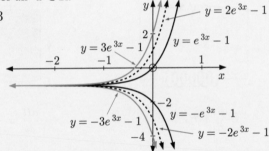

c $y = ce^{3x} - 1$ is a general solution to the differential equation.

The particular solution passes through $(0, 2)$, so $2 = ce^{3 \times 0} - 1$

$$\therefore \quad c = 3$$

$$\therefore \quad \text{the particular solution is} \quad y = 3e^{3x} - 1$$

d $\dfrac{dy}{dx} = 3 + 3y$

$\therefore$ at the point $(0, 2)$, $\dfrac{dy}{dx} = 3 + 3 \times 2 = 9$

$\therefore$ the gradient of the tangent to the particular solution $y = 3e^{3x} - 1$ at $(0, 2)$, is 9.

$\therefore$ the equation of the tangent is

$$\dfrac{y - 2}{x - 0} = 9$$

$$\therefore \quad y = 9x + 2$$

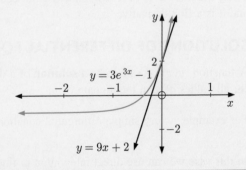

SLOPE FIELDS

Given any first order differential equation of the form $f(x, y)\dfrac{dy}{dx} + g(x, y) = 0$ where $y = y(x)$,

we can write $\dfrac{dy}{dx} = -\dfrac{g(x, y)}{f(x, y)} = h(x, y)$.

We may therefore deduce the gradient of the solution curves to the differential equation at any point (x, y) in the plane where $h(x, y)$ is defined, and hence the equations of the tangents to the solution curves.

> The set of tangents at all points (x, y) is called the **slope field** of the differential equation.

For example, the table alongside shows the values of $\dfrac{dy}{dx} = x(y - 1)$ for the integer grid points $x, y \in [-2, 2]$.

		x				
		-2	-1	0	1	2
	-2	6	3	0	-3	-6
	-1	4	2	0	-2	-4
y	0	2	1	0	-1	-2
	1	0	0	0	0	0
	2	-2	-1	0	1	2

By representing the gradients at many different grid points as line segments, we obtain a **slope field** of the tangents to the solution curves as shown.

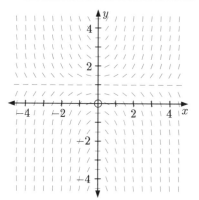

Now the tangent to a curve approximates that curve at and near the points of tangency. Therefore, by following the direction given by the slope field at a given point, we can approximate solution curves of the differential equation.

The horizontal line in the figure is the solution curve corresponding to the initial condition that $y = 1$ when $x = 0$.

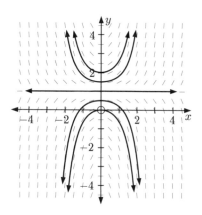

SLOPE
FIELDS

Although it is quite straightforward to obtain a few slope field points by hand, a larger or more refined field is best obtained using technology. You can click on the icon online or else download software for your graphics calculator.

An **isocline** is the set of all points on a slope field at which the tangents to the solution curves have the same gradient.

For a first order differential equation written in the form $\dfrac{dy}{dx} = h(x, y)$, an isocline is a curve given by $h(x, y) = k$, where k is a particular constant.

> Isoclines are *not* solutions to the differential equation. In general, they are not straight lines.

There may also be an isocline corresponding to points where the gradients of the tangents to the solution curve are undefined.

For example, suppose $\dfrac{dy}{dx} = \dfrac{1 - x^2 - y^2}{y - x + 2}$.

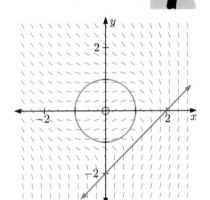

- $\dfrac{dy}{dx}$ is discontinuous when $y - x + 2 = 0$, which is when $y = x - 2$. This isocline is the red line on the slope field.

- $\dfrac{dy}{dx}$ is zero when $1 - x^2 - y^2 = 0$,

  which is when $x^2 + y^2 = 1$.
  This isocline is the green circle on the slope field.

Example 48

Consider the differential equation $\dfrac{dy}{dx} = xy$ where $x, y \geqslant 0$.

a Verify that $y = ce^{\frac{x^2}{2}}$ is a general solution for any constant $c \in \mathbb{R}$, $c \geqslant 0$.

b Construct the slope field using integer grid points for $x, y \in [0, 4]$.

c Sketch the particular solution curve through $P(2, 1)$.

d Verify algebraically that the curve you have sketched is $y = \dfrac{1}{e^2} e^{\frac{x^2}{2}}$.

e Draw the isoclines corresponding to $k = 1, 3$, and 6.

---

a If $y = ce^{\frac{x^2}{2}}$ then $\dfrac{dy}{dx} = 2 \times \dfrac{x}{2} \times ce^{\frac{x^2}{2}}$

$$= xce^{\frac{x^2}{2}}$$

$$= x \left(ce^{\frac{x^2}{2}} \right)$$

$$= xy$$

$e^{\frac{x^2}{2}} > 0$ for all x

$\therefore$ since $y > 0$, $c \geqslant 0$, $y = ce^{\frac{x^2}{2}}$ is a solution for all $c \in \mathbb{R}$, $c \geqslant 0$.

b, c

		0	1	2	3	4
				x		
	0	0	0	0	0	0
	1	0	1	2	3	4
y	2	0	2	4	6	8
	3	0	3	6	9	12
	4	0	4	8	12	16

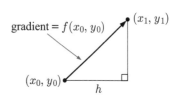

d The general solution is $y = ce^{\frac{x^2}{2}}$.

The particular solution passes through $(2, 1)$

$$\therefore \quad 1 = ce^{\frac{2^2}{2}}$$
$$\therefore \quad 1 = ce^2$$
$$\therefore \quad c = \frac{1}{e^2}$$

Hence P$(2, 1)$ lies on the particular solution curve $y = \frac{1}{e^2}e^{\frac{x^2}{2}}$.

e The isoclines are shown in red.

EULER'S METHOD OF NUMERICAL INTEGRATION

Euler's Method uses the same principle as slope fields to find a numerical approximation to the solution of the differential equation $\dfrac{dy}{dx} = f(x, y)$.

Since the gradient $\dfrac{dy}{dx}$ indicates the direction in which the solution curve goes at any point, we reconstruct the graph of the solution as follows:

We start at a point (x_0, y_0) and move a small distance in the direction of the slope field to find a new point (x_1, y_1). We then move a small distance in the direction of the slope field at this new point, and so on.

gradient $= f(x_0, y_0)$ (x_1, y_1) (x_0, y_0) h

If we step h units to the right each time, then
$$x_1 = x_0 + h \quad \text{and} \quad y_1 = y_0 + h\,f(x_0, y_0).$$

More generally,
$$x_{n+1} = x_n + h \quad \text{and} \quad y_{n+1} = y_n + h\,f(x_n, y_n).$$

Clearly, Euler's Method only gives an approximate solution to an initial value problem. However, by decreasing the **step size** h and hence increasing the number of course corrections, we can usually improve the accuracy of the approximation.

Euler's Method will be less accurate when the gradient $f(x, y)$ is large.

Example 49

Suppose $\dfrac{dy}{dx} = x + y$ where $y(0) = 1$.   Use Euler's Method with a step size of 0.2 to find an approximate value for $y(1)$.

If we are given a differential equation and an initial point, we call it an **initial value problem** or IVP.

Now $x_{n+1} = x_n + h$ and $y_{n+1} = y_n + h\,f(x_n, y_n)$

$\therefore$ given $f(x, y) = \dfrac{dy}{dx} = x + y$ and step size $h = 0.2$,

$\qquad x_{n+1} = x_n + 0.2$ and $y_{n+1} = y_n + 0.2(x_n + y_n)$

Using the initial conditions,

$x_0 = 0$ $\qquad\qquad\qquad y_0 = 1$

$x_1 = 0 + 0.2 = 0.2$ $\qquad y_1 = 1 + 0.2(0 + 1) = 1.2$

$x_2 = 0.2 + 0.2 = 0.4$ $\qquad y_2 = 1.2 + 0.2(0.2 + 1.2) = 1.48$

$x_3 = 0.4 + 0.2 = 0.6$ $\qquad y_3 = 1.48 + 0.2(0.4 + 1.48) = 1.856$

$x_4 = 0.6 + 0.2 = 0.8$ $\qquad y_4 = 1.856 + 0.2(0.6 + 1.856) = 2.3472$

$x_5 = 0.8 + 0.2 = 1$ $\qquad y_5 = 2.3472 + 0.2(0.8 + 2.3472) = 2.9766$

So, $y(1) \approx 2.98$.

EXERCISE M

1   Consider the differential equation $\dfrac{dy}{dx} = 2x - y$.

    a   Show that $y = 2x - 2 + ce^{-x}$ is a solution to the differential equation for any constant c.

    b   Sketch the solution curves for $c = 0, \pm 1, \pm 2$.

    c   Find the particular solution which passes through $(0, 1)$.

    d   Find the equation of the tangent to the particular solution at $(0, 1)$.

2   **a**   Show that $y = \sqrt{x^2 + c}$ is a general solution to the differential equation $\dfrac{dy}{dx} = \dfrac{x}{y}$, $y > 0$,

       for any $c \in \mathbb{R}$.

    b   Hence solve the IVP $\dfrac{dy}{dx} = \dfrac{x}{y}$, $y(3) = 4$.

3   Slope fields for two differential equations are plotted below for $x, y \in [-2, 2]$.   Use the slope fields to graph the solution curves satisfying $y(1) = 1$.

    a

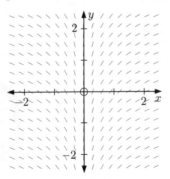

    b

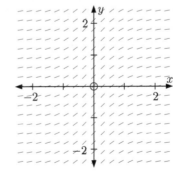

4 Consider the differential equation $\dfrac{dy}{dx} = 10y \tan x$ where x is measured in degrees. Draw the slope field using integer grid points where $x, y \in [-2, 2]$.

5 Consider the differential equation $\dfrac{dy}{dx} = x^2 + y - 1$.

Sketch isoclines for $k = 0, 2, 4$ on a grid for $x, y \in [-5, 5]$. Hence construct a slope field, and sketch the solution curve satisfying $y(0) = 1$.

6 The slope field for the differential equation
$$\frac{dy}{dx} = \frac{-1 + x^2 + 4y^2}{y - 5x + 10} \quad \text{is shown alongside.}$$

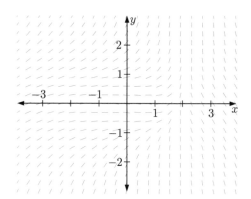

  a Sketch the particular solution passing through the origin.

  b Sketch the isocline corresponding to:

   i $\dfrac{dy}{dx}$ being undefined   **ii** $\dfrac{dy}{dx} = 0$.

7 Use Euler's Method with step size 0.2 to estimate $y(1)$ for the initial value problem
$\dfrac{dy}{dx} = 1 + 2x - 3y, \quad y(0) = 1$.

8 Use Euler's Method with step size 0.1 to estimate $y(0.5)$ for the initial value problem
$\dfrac{dy}{dx} = \sin(x + y), \quad y(0) = 0.5$. Assume x and y are in radians.

N   SEPARABLE DIFFERENTIAL EQUATIONS

Differential equations which can be written in the form $\dfrac{dy}{dx} = \dfrac{f(x)}{g(y)}$, where $y = y(x)$, are known as **separable differential equations**.

Notice that if $\dfrac{dy}{dx} = \dfrac{f(x)}{g(y)}$ then $g(y)\dfrac{dy}{dx} = f(x)$.

If we integrate both sides of this equation with respect to x we obtain

$$\int g(y)\frac{dy}{dx}\,dx = \int f(x)\,dx$$

$\therefore$ by the Chain Rule, $\displaystyle\int g(y)\,dy = \int f(x)\,dx.$

The problem of solving the differential equation is hence reduced to the problem of finding two separate integrals.

Example 50

Solve the initial value problem $2x\dfrac{dy}{dx} - 1 = y^2$, $y(1) = 1.$

$2x\dfrac{dy}{dx} - 1 = y^2$

$\therefore$ $2x\dfrac{dy}{dx} = y^2 + 1$

$\therefore$ $\dfrac{1}{y^2+1}\dfrac{dy}{dx} = \dfrac{1}{2x}$

Integrating both sides with respect to x gives $\displaystyle\int \frac{1}{y^2+1}\frac{dy}{dx}\,dx = \int \frac{1}{2x}\,dx$

$\therefore$ $\displaystyle\int \frac{1}{y^2+1}\,dy = \int \frac{1}{2x}\,dx$

$\therefore$ $\arctan y = \tfrac{1}{2}\ln|x| + c$

$\therefore$ $y = \tan\left(\tfrac{1}{2}\ln|x| + c\right)$

But $y(1) = 1$,   so $1 = \tan\left(\tfrac{1}{2}\ln 1 + c\right)$

$\therefore$ $1 = \tan c$

$\therefore$ $c = \tfrac{\pi}{4}$

$\therefore$ the particular solution of the differential equation is $y = \tan\left(\tfrac{1}{2}\ln|x| + \tfrac{\pi}{4}\right).$

Example 51

a Show that $\dfrac{2}{x^2 - 1} = \dfrac{1}{x-1} - \dfrac{1}{x+1}.$

b Find the general solution of the differential equation $\dfrac{dy}{dx} = \dfrac{x^2 y + y}{x^2 - 1}.$

---

a $\dfrac{1}{x-1} - \dfrac{1}{x+1} = \dfrac{x+1-(x-1)}{(x-1)(x+1)} = \dfrac{2}{x^2-1}$ as required.

b $\dfrac{dy}{dx} = \dfrac{x^2y + y}{x^2 - 1}$

$\qquad = \dfrac{y(x^2 + 1)}{x^2 - 1}$

$\therefore \quad \dfrac{1}{y}\dfrac{dy}{dx} = \dfrac{x^2 + 1}{x^2 - 1}$

$\qquad\qquad = \dfrac{x^2 - 1 + 2}{x^2 - 1}$

$\qquad\qquad = 1 + \dfrac{2}{x^2 - 1}$

$\qquad\qquad = 1 + \dfrac{1}{x - 1} - \dfrac{1}{x + 1}$ {using **a**}

Integrating both sides with respect to x gives

$$\int \dfrac{1}{y}\dfrac{dy}{dx}\,dx = \int \left(1 + \dfrac{1}{x - 1} - \dfrac{1}{x + 1}\right)dx$$

$$\therefore \quad \int \dfrac{1}{y}\,dy = x + \ln|x - 1| - \ln|x + 1| + c$$

$$\ln|y| = x + \ln\left(A\left|\dfrac{x - 1}{x + 1}\right|\right) \quad \text{where} \quad \ln A = c$$

$$\therefore \quad y = Ae^x\left(\dfrac{x - 1}{x + 1}\right) \quad \text{is the general solution of the differential equation.}$$

Example 52

When an object travels through a resistive medium, the rate at which it loses speed at any given instant is given by kv m s^{-2}, where v is the speed of the body at that instant and k is a positive constant.

Suppose the initial speed is u m s^{-1}. By formulating and solving an appropriate differential equation, show that the time taken for the body to decrease its speed to $\frac{1}{2}u$ m s^{-1} is $\frac{1}{k}\ln 2$ seconds.

The rate of change of speed is given by $\dfrac{dv}{dt}$.

Our differential equation must reflect that the body *loses* speed, so $\dfrac{dv}{dt} = -kv$.

Separating the variables, we find $\dfrac{1}{v}\dfrac{dv}{dt} = -k$.

Integrating both sides with respect to t gives $\qquad \displaystyle\int \dfrac{1}{v}\,dv = -k\int dt$

$\qquad\qquad\qquad \therefore \quad \ln|v| = -kt + c$

$\qquad\qquad\qquad\qquad \therefore \quad v = Ae^{-kt} \quad \text{where} \quad A = e^c$

The initial speed (at $t = 0$) is u, so $u = Ae^{-k \times 0} = A$.

$\therefore \quad v = ue^{-kt}$ is the particular solution of the differential equation.

When $v = \frac{1}{2}u$ we have $\quad \frac{1}{2}u = ue^{-kt}$

$\qquad\qquad\qquad \therefore \quad \frac{1}{2} = e^{-kt}$

$\qquad \therefore \quad -\ln 2 = -kt$

$\qquad\qquad \therefore \quad t = \dfrac{1}{k}\ln 2 \quad \text{as required.}$

Example 53

Consider a curve in the first quadrant. The tangent at any point P cuts the x-axis at Q.

Given that $OP = PQ$, where O is the origin, and that the point $(1, 4)$ lies on the curve, find the equation of the curve.

Since $OP = PQ$, triangle OPQ is isosceles. Hence [PA] is the perpendicular bisector of [OQ].

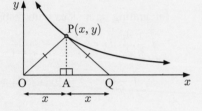

The coordinates of A are $(x, 0)$, so the coordinates of Q are $(2x, 0)$.

Since (PQ) is the tangent to the curve at P, the gradient of the curve at P is the same as the gradient of [PQ].

Hence $\dfrac{dy}{dx} = -\dfrac{y}{x}$

$\therefore \quad \dfrac{1}{y}\dfrac{dy}{dx} = -\dfrac{1}{x}$

Integrating both sides with respect to x gives $\displaystyle \int \dfrac{1}{y}\, dy = -\int \dfrac{1}{x}\, dx$

$\therefore \quad \ln|y| = -\ln|x| + c$

$\therefore \quad \ln|x| + \ln|y| = c$

$\therefore \quad \ln|xy| = c$

$\therefore \quad xy = e^c = k \quad$ where k is a constant.

Since the curve passes through $(1, 4)$, $1 \times 4 = k$

$\therefore \quad$ the equation of the curve is $xy = 4$ or $y = \dfrac{4}{x}$, where $x > 0$.

HOMOGENEOUS DIFFERENTIAL EQUATIONS

Differential equations of the form $\dfrac{dy}{dx} = f\left(\dfrac{y}{x}\right)$, where $y = y(x)$, are known as **homogeneous differential equations**.

They can be solved using the substitution $y = vx$ where v is a function of x. The substitution will always reduce the differential equation to a separable differentiable equation as follows.

If $y = vx$ where v is a function of x, then

$$\dfrac{dy}{dx} = \dfrac{dv}{dx}x + v \quad \{\text{product rule}\}$$

$$\therefore \quad \dfrac{dv}{dx}x + v = f\left(\dfrac{vx}{x}\right) = f(v)$$

$$\therefore \quad \dfrac{dv}{dx} = \dfrac{f(v) - v}{x}$$

$$\therefore \quad \dfrac{1}{f(v) - v}\dfrac{dv}{dx} = \dfrac{1}{x} \quad \text{which is a separable differential equation.}$$

Example 54

a Use the substitution $y = vx$, where v is a function of x, to solve $\dfrac{dy}{dx} = \dfrac{x + 2y}{x}$.

b Find the particular solution if $y = \frac{3}{2}$ when $x = 3$.

a If $y = vx$, then using the product rule we obtain $\dfrac{dy}{dx} = v + x\,\dfrac{dv}{dx}$.

Comparing with the differential equation, we find $\quad v + x\,\dfrac{dv}{dx} = \dfrac{x + 2vx}{x}$

$$\therefore \quad v + x\,\frac{dv}{dx} = 1 + 2v$$

$$\therefore \quad x\,\frac{dv}{dx} = 1 + v$$

$$\therefore \quad \frac{1}{1+v}\frac{dv}{dx} = \frac{1}{x}$$

Integrating with respect to x gives $\quad \displaystyle\int \frac{1}{v+1}\,dv = \int \frac{1}{x}\,dx$

$$\therefore \quad \ln|v + 1| = \ln|x| + c$$
$$\therefore \quad \ln|v + 1| = \ln|Ax| \quad \text{where } \ln|A| = c$$
$$\therefore \quad v + 1 = Ax$$

But $v = \frac{y}{x}$, so $\quad \frac{y}{x} + 1 = Ax$

$$\therefore \quad y = Ax^2 - x, \quad \text{where } A \text{ is a constant.}$$

b Substituting $y = \frac{3}{2}$ and $x = 3$ into the general solution, we find $\quad \frac{3}{2} = A \times 3^2 - 3$

$$\therefore \quad 9A = \frac{9}{2}$$
$$\therefore \quad A = \frac{1}{2}$$

$\therefore \quad$ the particular solution is $y = \frac{1}{2}x^2 - x$.

EXERCISE N

1 Solve the following initial value problems:

a $(2 - x)\dfrac{dy}{dx} = 1, \quad y(4) = 3$

b $\dfrac{dy}{dx} - 3x \sec y = 0, \quad y(1) = 0$

c $e^y(2x^2 + 4x + 1)\dfrac{dy}{dx} = (x + 1)(e^y + 3), \quad y(0) = 2$

d $x\dfrac{dy}{dx} = \cos^2 y, \quad y(e) = \frac{\pi}{4}$

2 a Show that $\dfrac{3 - x}{x^2 - 1} = \dfrac{1}{x - 1} - \dfrac{2}{x + 1}$.

b Solve $\dfrac{dy}{dx} = \dfrac{3y - xy}{x^2 - 1}, \quad y(0) = 1$.

3 According to Newton's law of cooling, the rate at which a body loses temperature at time t is proportional to the amount by which the temperature $T(t)$ of the body at that instant exceeds the temperature R of its surroundings.

a Express this information as a differential equation in terms of t, T, and R.

b A container of hot liquid is placed in a room with constant temperature $18°C$. The liquid cools from $82°C$ to $50°C$ in 6 minutes. Show that it takes 12 minutes for the liquid to cool from $26°C$ to $20°C$.

4 The tangent at any point P on a curve cuts the x-axis at the point Q.

Given that $O\widehat{P}Q = 90°$, where O is the origin, and that the point $(1, 2)$ lies on the curve, find the equation of the curve.

5 The tangent at any point P on a curve cuts the x-axis at A and the y-axis at B.

Given that $AP : PB = 2 : 1$ and that the curve passes through $(1, 1)$, find the equation of the curve.

6 A radioactive substance decays at a rate proportional to the mass $m(t)$ remaining at the time. Suppose the initial mass is m_0.

    a Construct and solve the appropriate initial value problem and hence obtain a formula for $m(t)$.

    b If the mass is reduced to $\frac{4}{5}$ of its original value in 30 days, calculate the time required for the mass to decay to half its original value.

7 Solve the following homogeneous differential equations using the substitution $y = vx$, where v is a function of x.

    a $\dfrac{dy}{dx} = \dfrac{x - y}{x}$
        b $\dfrac{dy}{dx} = \dfrac{x + y}{x - y}$
        c $\dfrac{dy}{dx} = \dfrac{y^2 - x^2}{2xy}$

8   **a** Show that the substitution $y = vx$ (where v is a function of x) will reduce all inhomogeneous

      differential equations of the form $\dfrac{dy}{dx} = \dfrac{y}{x} + f\left(\dfrac{y}{x}\right) g(x)$ to separable form.

    b Solve $x\dfrac{dy}{dx} = y + e^{\frac{y}{x}}$ using this method.

O THE INTEGRATING FACTOR METHOD

Suppose a first order linear differential equation is of the form $\dfrac{dy}{dx} + P(x)y = Q(x)$, where $y = y(x)$.

Generally, but not always, this type of equation is not separable.

However, suppose there is a function $I(x)$, called an **integrating factor**, such that

$$\frac{d}{dx}\left(I(x)y\right) = I(x)\frac{dy}{dx} + I(x)\,P(x)y \quad \text{.... } (*)$$
$$= I(x)\,Q(x)$$

Then integrating both sides with respect to x would give

$$I(x)y = \int I(x)\,Q(x)\,dx$$

$$\therefore \quad y = \frac{1}{I(x)}\int I(x)\,Q(x)\,dx \quad \text{and we could hence find a solution for } y.$$

Now if such an integrating factor exists, then from $(*)$,

$$I(x)\frac{dy}{dx} + I'(x)y = I(x)\frac{dy}{dx} + I(x)\,P(x)y$$

$$\therefore \quad I'(x) = I(x)\,P(x)$$

$$\therefore \quad \frac{I'(x)}{I(x)} = P(x)$$

Integrating both sides with respect to x,

$$\int \frac{I'(x)}{I(x)}\,dx = \int P(x)\,dx$$

$$\ln|I| + c = \int P(x)\,dx$$

$$\therefore \quad I(x) = Ae^{\int P(x)\,dx} \quad \text{where } A = e^{-c} \text{ and is conventionally set as 1.}$$

Thus the **integrating factor** is $\qquad \boxed{I(x) = e^{\int P(x)\,dx}}.$

THE INTEGRATION FACTOR METHOD

Suppose $\dfrac{dy}{dx} + P(x)\,y = Q(x)$ where $y = y(x)$.

1 Calculate the **integrating factor** $I(x) = e^{\int P(x)\,dx}$. You do not need a constant of integration.

2 Multiply the differential equation through by $I(x)$.

3 Simplify the LHS and hence obtain $I(x)\,y = \displaystyle\int I(x)\,Q(x)\,dx + c$, where c is a constant.

4 Integrate to obtain the general solution.

Example 55

Solve the differential equation $\dfrac{dy}{dx} + 3x^2 y = 6x^2$.

The integrating factor is $I(x) = e^{\int 3x^2\, dx} = e^{x^3}$

Multiplying the differential equation through by e^{x^3} gives

$$e^{x^3} \frac{dy}{dx} + 3x^2 e^{x^3} y = 6x^2 e^{x^3}$$

$$\therefore \quad \frac{d}{dx}\left(y e^{x^3} \right) = 6x^2 e^{x^3}$$

$$\therefore \quad y e^{x^3} = \int 6x^2 e^{x^3}\, dx$$

$$\therefore \quad y e^{x^3} = 2 e^{x^3} + c$$

$$\therefore \quad y = 2 + c e^{-x^3}$$

Example 56

Solve the initial value problem $\cos x \dfrac{dy}{dx} = y \sin x + \sin(2x), \quad y(0) = 1.$

We can rewrite the differential equation as $\dfrac{dy}{dx} - \dfrac{\sin x}{\cos x} y = \dfrac{\sin(2x)}{\cos x}$

$$\therefore \quad \frac{dy}{dx} + (-\tan x) y = 2 \sin x$$

The differential equation is not separable, but is of a form such that we can use an integrating factor.

The integrating factor is $I(x) = e^{\int -\tan x\, dx}$

$$= e^{\ln(\cos x)}$$

$$= \cos x.$$

Multiplying the equation through by the integrating factor gives

$$\cos x \frac{dy}{dx} + (-\cos x \tan x) y = \sin(2x)$$

$$\therefore \quad \frac{d}{dx}(y \cos x) = \sin(2x)$$

$$\therefore \quad y \cos x = \int \sin(2x)\, dx$$

$$= -\tfrac{1}{2} \cos(2x) + c$$

But when $x = 0, \quad y = 1$

$$\therefore \quad 1 = -\tfrac{1}{2} \cos(0) + c$$

$$\therefore \quad c = \tfrac{3}{2}$$

$\therefore$ the solution of the initial value problem is $y \cos x = \tfrac{3}{2} - \tfrac{1}{2} \cos(2x)$

$$\therefore \quad y = \frac{3 - \cos(2x)}{2 \cos x}$$

EXERCISE O

1 Solve the following using the integrating factor method.

    a $\dfrac{dy}{dx} + 4y = 12$ **b** $\dfrac{dy}{dx} - 3y = e^x, \quad y(0) = 2$

    c $\dfrac{dy}{dx} + y = x + e^x, \quad y(1) = 1$ **d** $x\dfrac{dy}{dx} + y = x\cos x$

2 Solve the differential equation $(x+1)y + x\dfrac{dy}{dx} = x - x^2$.

ACTIVITY   LAPLACE TRANSFORMS

Laplace transforms provide a useful link between improper integrals and differential equations.

The Laplace transform of a function $f(x)$ is defined as $F(s) = \mathcal{L}\{f(x)\} = \displaystyle\int_0^\infty e^{-sx} f(x)\,dx$.

What to do:

1 Show that:

    a $\mathcal{L}\{e^{ax}\} = \dfrac{1}{s-a}, \quad s > a$ **b** $\mathcal{L}\{x\} = \dfrac{1}{s^2}, \quad s > 0$

    c $\mathcal{L}\{\sin(ax)\} = \dfrac{a}{s^2 + a^2}, \quad s > 0$

2 Show that:

    a $\mathcal{L}\{f'(x)\} = s\mathcal{L}\{f(x)\} - f(0)$ **b** $\mathcal{L}\{f''(x)\} = s^2\mathcal{L}\{f(x)\} - sf(0) - f'(0)$

3 Consider the differential equation $f''(x) + f(x) = x, \quad f(0) = 0, \quad f'(0) = 2$.

Assuming that $\mathcal{L}\{g(x) + h(x)\} = \mathcal{L}\{g(x)\} + \mathcal{L}\{h(x)\}$,   show that $\mathcal{L}\{f(x)\} = \dfrac{1}{s^2} + \dfrac{1}{s^2 + 1}$.

Hence find a possible solution function $f(x)$ and check your answer.

P | TAYLOR OR MACLAURIN SERIES DEVELOPED FROM A DIFFERENTIAL EQUATION

Consider a first order differential equation with initial condition:

$$\frac{dy}{dx} = h(x, y) \quad \text{where} \quad y(x_0) = y_0 \quad \text{for some constants} \quad x_0, y_0 \in \mathbb{R}.$$

Depending on the form of $h(x, y)$, it may or may not be possible to obtain an explicit particular solution $y(x)$.

However, provided the necessary derivatives exist, we can determine the nth degree Taylor polynomial approximation to the particular solution $y(x)$ about x_0 as follows:

$$y(x_0) = y_0$$
$$y'(x) = h(x, y) \qquad \therefore \quad y'(x_0) = h(x_0, y_0)$$
$$y''(x) = \frac{d}{dx}(h(x, y)) \qquad \therefore \quad \text{we can obtain } y''(x_0) \text{ using } x_0, y_0, \text{ and } y'(x_0) \text{ found above.}$$
$$y'''(x) = \frac{d}{dx}(y''(x)) \; ....$$

Once $y(x_0), y'(x_0), y''(x_0), ..., y^{(n)}(x_0)$ have been determined, the nth degree Taylor polynomial approximation to $y(x)$ about x_0 can then be written as:

$$T_n(x) = y(x_0) + y'(x_0)(x - x_0) + \frac{y''(x_0)(x - x_0)^2}{2!} + ... + \frac{y^{(n)}(x_0)(x - x_0)^n}{n!}.$$

Example 57

Consider the initial value problem $\dfrac{dy}{dx} = x - 4xy, \quad y(0) = 1.$

a Without solving the system, find the first three non-zero terms of the Maclaurin polynomial expansion for y.

b Solve the system exactly to find the particular solution.

a $\qquad \dfrac{dy}{dx} = x - 4xy = x(1 - 4y)$

$\therefore \quad \dfrac{d^2 y}{dx^2} = \dfrac{d}{dx}(x(1 - 4y))$

$\qquad\qquad = 1 - 4y + x\left(-4\dfrac{dy}{dx}\right)$

$\therefore \quad \dfrac{d^3 y}{dx^3} = -4\dfrac{dy}{dx} + 1 \times \left(-4\dfrac{dy}{dx}\right) + x\left(-4\dfrac{d^2 y}{dx^2}\right)$

$\qquad\qquad = -8\dfrac{dy}{dx} - 4x\dfrac{d^2 y}{dx^2}$

$\therefore \quad \dfrac{d^4 y}{dx^4} = -8\dfrac{d^2 y}{dx^2} - 4\dfrac{d^2 y}{dx^2} + x\left(-4\dfrac{d^3 y}{dx^3}\right)$

$\qquad\qquad = -12\dfrac{d^2 y}{dx^2} - 4x\dfrac{d^3 y}{dx^3}$

Now $y(0) = 1$,   so at $(0, 1)$: $\dfrac{dy}{dx} = 0$

$$\dfrac{d^2y}{dx^2} = 1 - 4 + 0 = -3$$

$$\dfrac{d^3y}{dx^3} = 0$$

$$\dfrac{d^4y}{dx^4} = 36$$

$\therefore$ y has Maclaurin polynomial $1 - \dfrac{3x^2}{2!} + \dfrac{36x^4}{4!}$ .... which is $1 - \frac{3}{2}x^2 + \frac{3}{2}x^4$ ....

b $\dfrac{dy}{dx} = x\,(1 - 4y)$

$$\dfrac{1}{1 - 4y}\dfrac{dy}{dx} = x$$

$\therefore$ $\displaystyle\int \dfrac{1}{1 - 4y}\,dy = \int x\,dx$

$-\frac{1}{4}\ln|1 - 4y| = \dfrac{x^2}{2} + c$

$\ln|1 - 4y| = -2x^2 + c$

$1 - 4y = Ae^{-2x^2}$

$y = \frac{1}{4} - Be^{-2x^2}$

But $y(0) = 1$

$\therefore$ $\frac{1}{4} - B = 1$

$\therefore$ $B = -\frac{3}{4}$

$\therefore$ $y = \frac{1}{4}\left(1 + \dfrac{3}{e^{2x^2}}\right)$

EXERCISE P

1 Consider the differential equation $\dfrac{dy}{dx} = \dfrac{e^{-y}}{3} - 1$,   where $y(0) = 0$.

  a Find the first three non-zero terms in the Maclaurin polynomial expansion of y.

  b Verify that $y = \ln\left(\dfrac{1 + 2e^{-x}}{3}\right)$ is a particular solution.

2 Consider the differential equation $\dfrac{dy}{dx} = 2x + \dfrac{y}{x}$,   where $\dfrac{dy}{dx} = 1$ when $x = 1$.

  a Find the first three non-zero terms in the Maclaurin polynomial expansion of y about $x = 1$.

  b Solve the system exactly to find the particular solution.

3 Consider the initial value problem $\dfrac{dy}{dx} = \dfrac{3x - 2y}{x}$, $y(1) = 0$.

  a Without solving the system, find the first three non-zero terms of the Taylor polynomial expansion for y about $x = 1$.

  b Solve the system exactly to find the particular solution.

4 Consider the initial value problem $\cos x\,\dfrac{dy}{dx} + y\sin x = 1$, $y(0) = 2$.

  a Find the first three non-zero terms in the Maclaurin polynomial expansion of y.

  b Solve the system exactly to find the particular solution.

Example 58

Given that $\sum_{k=0}^{\infty} \dfrac{x^k}{k!}$ is convergent for all $x \in \mathbb{R}$, show that $e^x = \sum_{k=0}^{\infty} \dfrac{x^k}{k!}$ using the following steps.

a Show that if $y(x) = \sum_{k=0}^{\infty} \dfrac{x^k}{k!}$, then $\dfrac{dy}{dx} = y$.

b Solve the differential equation $\dfrac{dy}{dx} = y$ to obtain the general solution.

c Hence prove $e^x = \sum_{k=0}^{\infty} \dfrac{x^k}{k!}$.

a Let $y(x) = \sum_{k=0}^{\infty} \dfrac{x^k}{k!} = 1 + x + \dfrac{x^2}{2!} + \dfrac{x^3}{3!} + ...$

$\therefore \dfrac{dy}{dx} = 1 + \dfrac{2x}{2!} + \dfrac{3x^2}{3!} + \dfrac{4x^3}{4!} + ...$

$= 1 + x + \dfrac{x^2}{2!} + \dfrac{x^3}{3!} + ...$

$= \sum_{k=0}^{\infty} \dfrac{x^k}{k!}$

$= y$

b Consider $\dfrac{dy}{dx} = y$

$\therefore \dfrac{1}{y}\dfrac{dy}{dx} = 1$

$\therefore \int \dfrac{1}{y}\,dy = \int 1\,dx$

$\therefore \ln|y| = x + c$, where c is a constant

$\therefore y = Ae^x$, where $A = \pm e^c$ is a constant.

c Since $y(x) = \sum_{k=0}^{\infty} \dfrac{x^k}{k!}$ is a solution to the differential equation for all $x \in \mathbb{R}$,

$y(x) = \sum_{k=0}^{\infty} \dfrac{x^k}{k!} = Ae^x$ for some constant A.

Now $y(0) = 1$, so $A = 1$

Hence $e^x = \sum_{k=0}^{\infty} \dfrac{x^k}{k!}$ for all $x \in \mathbb{R}$.

5 Let $y(x) = \sum_{n=0}^{\infty} \dfrac{p(p-1)....(p-n+1)x^n}{n!}$ for $|x| < 1$. From **Exercise L.2** question **8**, y is a well defined function on $|x| < 1$ since the binomial series was shown to be convergent on the interval $-1 < x < 1$.

a Show that for $-1 < x < 1$, y satisfies the differential equation $(1+x)\dfrac{dy}{dx} = py$.

b Find the general solution to the differential equation in **a**.

c Hence show that $y(x) = (1+x)^p$ for all $x \in \,]-1, 1[$.

REVIEW SET A

1 Prove that $\lim\limits_{x\to\infty}\dfrac{\ln x}{x}=0$.

2 Find $\lim\limits_{x\to0}\dfrac{e^x\sin x}{x}$.

3 Find the limit, if it exists, of the sequence $\{u_n\}$ as n tends to infinity, if u_n equals:

a $\dfrac{8-2n-2n^2}{4+6n+7n^2}$

b $3+\dfrac{1}{n}+n\left[1+(-1)^n\right]$

c $\dfrac{2n+13}{\sqrt{6n^2+5n-7}}$

d $\arctan n$

4 Prove that the series $\dfrac{1}{1^3+1}+\dfrac{2}{2^3+1}+\dfrac{3}{3^3+1}+\dfrac{4}{4^3+1}+\dfrac{5}{5^3+1}+....$ converges.

5 **a** For what values of x does $\sum\limits_{n=1}^{\infty}\left(\dfrac{3x}{x-2}\right)^n$ converge?

b Find $\sum\limits_{n=0}^{\infty}\left(\dfrac{3x}{x-2}\right)^n$ in terms of x.

c Show that $\sum\limits_{n=0}^{\infty}\dfrac{n(3x)^{n-1}}{(x-2)^{n+1}}=\dfrac{1}{4(x+1)^2}$ for the x values found in **a**.

6 Find the set of real numbers for which the series $x+\dfrac{x^2}{1-x}+\dfrac{x^3}{(1-x)^2}+....$ converges.

7 Using an appropriate Maclaurin series, evaluate $\displaystyle\int_0^1\sin(x^2)\,dx$ to three decimal places.

8 Let X be a random variable such that $P(X=x)=\dfrac{e^{-\lambda}\lambda^x}{x!}$ for $x=0,1,2,....$

Prove that $\sum\limits_{x=0}^{\infty}P(X=x)=1$.

9 **a** Draw the slope field using integer grid points for $x,y\in[-3,3]$ for the differential equation $\dfrac{dy}{dx}=\dfrac{x}{y}$.

b Draw on your slope field the isoclines $\dfrac{dy}{dx}=k$ for $k=0,\pm1,\pm4$.

10 Solve the differential equation $\dfrac{dy}{dx}=\dfrac{xy}{x-1}$ given that $y=2$ when $x=2$.

11 By finding a suitable integrating factor, solve $\dfrac{dy}{dx}-\dfrac{y}{x}=\sqrt{x}$, $y(4)=0$.

12 On the slope field for $\dfrac{dy}{dx} = 2x - y^2$ shown, sketch the solution curves through

  a $(0, 0)$ **b** $(2, 3)$.

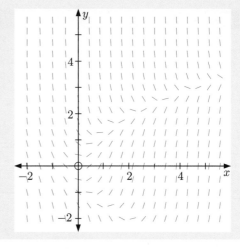

REVIEW SET B

1 Find the limit, if it exists, of the sequence $\{u_n\}$ as n tends to infinity, if u_n equals:

  a $\dfrac{(-1)^n (2n - 1)}{n}$

  b $\dfrac{0.9^n}{1 + 0.1^n}$

  c $\sqrt{n + 5} - \sqrt{n - 1}$

  d $\dfrac{n^2}{3n + 1} - \dfrac{2n^3}{6n^2 + 1}$

2 Prove that the series $x + \dfrac{x^2}{2} + \dfrac{x^3}{3} + \dfrac{x^4}{4} + ...$ is convergent for $-1 < x < 1$ and divergent for $|x| > 1$. Determine the convergence or divergence of the series for $x = \pm 1$.

3 Determine whether or not the series $\displaystyle\sum_{k=1}^{\infty} \sin\left(\dfrac{(k - 1)\pi}{2k}\right)$ is convergent.

4 Use the Comparison Test to prove that the series $\displaystyle\sum_{r=1}^{\infty} \dfrac{1 + r}{1 + r^2}$ diverges.

5 **a** Show that the series $S_n = \displaystyle\sum_{k=3}^{n} \dfrac{(-1)^{k+1}}{\ln(k - 1)}$ converges as $n \to \infty$.

  b Find the maximum possible error in using S_{10} to estimate $\displaystyle\sum_{k=3}^{\infty} \dfrac{(-1)^{k+1}}{\ln(k - 1)}$.

6 Find the Taylor series expansion of $(x - 1)e^{x-1}$ about $x = 1$ up to the term $(x - 1)^3$.

7 Find constants a and b such that $y = ax + b$ is a solution of the differential equation $\dfrac{dy}{dx} = 4x - 2y$.

8 Find the general solution of the differential equation $\dfrac{dy}{dx} = 2xy^2 - y^2$.

9 Find the equation of the curve through $(2, 1)$ given that for any point (x, y) on the curve, the y-intercept of the tangent to the curve is $3x^2y^3$.

10 Match the slope fields **A**, **B**, and **C** to the differential equations:

   a $\dfrac{dy}{dx} = y + 1$ **b** $\dfrac{dy}{dx} = x - y$ **c** $\dfrac{dy}{dx} = x - y^2$

   A   **B**   **C**

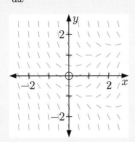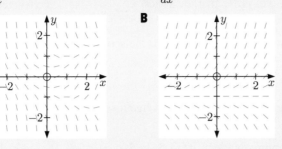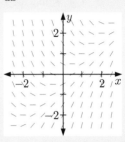

11 The population P of an island is currently 154. The population growth in the foreseeable future is given by $\dfrac{dP}{dt} = 0.2P\left(1 - \dfrac{P}{400}\right)$, $t > 0$.

   a Write $\dfrac{1}{P} + \dfrac{1}{400 - P}$ as a single fraction.

   b Find P as a function of time t years.

   c Estimate the population in 20 years' time.

   d Is there a limiting population size? If so, what is it?

12 Let $f(x) = \displaystyle\sum_{i=1}^{\infty} \dfrac{x^2}{(1 + x^2)^i}$.

   a Find $f(0)$.

   b For $x \neq 0$, show that $\dfrac{(1 + x^2)}{x^2} f(x) = \displaystyle\sum_{i=0}^{\infty} r^i$ where $r = \dfrac{1}{1 + x^2}$.

   c For which values of $x \in \mathbb{R}$ is $f(x)$ convergent? Hence state the domain of f.

   d For each x for which $f(x)$ is convergent, find the value of $f(x)$.

   e Sketch $y = f(x)$.

REVIEW SET C

1 Find the limit, if it exists, of the sequence $\{u_n\}$ as n tends to infinity, if u_n equals:

   a $n - \sqrt{n^2 + n}$ **b** $(3^n + 2^n)^{\frac{1}{n}}$ **c** $\dfrac{e^n}{n!}$ **d** $(-1)^n\, n\, e^{-n}$

2 Explain why the series $\displaystyle\sum_{r=1}^{\infty} 3^{\frac{1}{r}}$ is not convergent.

3 Determine whether $\displaystyle\sum_{n=2}^{\infty} \dfrac{1}{\ln(n^2)}$ is convergent or divergent.

4 Suppose $\displaystyle\sum_{n=1}^{\infty} a_n$ is convergent, where $a_n > 0$ for all $n \in \mathbb{Z}^+$.

   a Prove that $\displaystyle\sum_{n=1}^{\infty} a_n^2$ and $\displaystyle\sum_{n=1}^{\infty} \left(a_n - \dfrac{1}{n}\right)^2$ are also convergent.

   b Would these results follow if $a_n \in \mathbb{R}$?

5   **a** Show that $\dfrac{1}{x(x+1)} = \dfrac{1}{x} - \dfrac{1}{x+1}$.

   b Use **a** and the Integral Test to prove that the series $\displaystyle\sum_{n=1}^{\infty} \dfrac{1}{n(n+1)}$ converges.

   c Let $S_n = \displaystyle\sum_{i=1}^{n} \dfrac{1}{i(i+1)}$ be the nth partial sum for the series in **b**.

   i Use **a** to show that $S_n = 1 - \dfrac{1}{n+1}$.

   ii Hence find the value of the sum of the convergent series $\displaystyle\sum_{n=1}^{\infty} \dfrac{1}{n(n+1)}$.

6   Let R_n be the error term in approximating $f(x) = \ln(1+x)$ for $0 \leqslant x < 1$ using the first $n+1$ terms of its Maclaurin series. Prove that $|R_n| \leqslant \dfrac{1}{n+1}$ for $0 \leqslant x < 1$.

7   Find a simplified expression for $1 - x + x^2 - x^3 + ...$ where $-1 < x < 1$.
   Hence find a power series expansion for $f(x) = \ln(1+x)$ for $-1 < x < 1$.

8   A curve passes through the point $(1,\ 2)$ and satisfies the differential equation
   $$\dfrac{dy}{dx} = x - 2y.$$
   Use Euler's Method with step size 0.1 to estimate the value of y when $x = 1.6$.

9   A water tank of height 1 m has a square base 2 m × 2 m. When a tap at its base is opened, the water flows out at a rate proportional to the square root of the depth of the water at any given time. Suppose the depth of the water is h m, and V is the volume of water remaining in the tank after t minutes.

   a Write down a differential equation involving $\dfrac{dV}{dt}$ and h.

   b Explain why $V = 4h$ m^3 at time t. Hence write down a differential equation involving $\dfrac{dh}{dt}$ and h.

   c Initially the tank is full. When the tap is opened, the water level drops by 19 cm in 2 minutes. Find the time it takes for the tank to empty.

10 Use the substitution $y = vx$ where v is a function of x, to solve the differential equation
   $\dfrac{dy}{dx} = \dfrac{x}{y} + \dfrac{y}{x}$.

11 Use an integrating factor to solve $\dfrac{dy}{dx} = \cos x - y \cot x, \quad y\left(\dfrac{\pi}{2}\right) = 0$.

REVIEW SET D

1   Find the limit, if it exists, of the sequence $\{u_n\}$ as n tends to infinity, if u_n equals:

   a $\dfrac{3 \times 5 \times 7 \times .... \times (2n+1)}{2 \times 5 \times 8 \times .... \times (3n-1)}$

   b $n(2 \cos\left(\dfrac{1}{n}\right) - \sin\left(\dfrac{1}{n}\right) - 2)$

2   Prove that the series $\displaystyle\sum_{n=2}^{\infty} \dfrac{1}{n(\ln n)^2}$ is convergent.

3 Determine the interval and radius of convergence of the series $\sum\limits_{n=1}^{\infty} \dfrac{(x-3)^n}{n^{\frac{3}{2}}}$.

4 Determine whether the series $\sum\limits_{n=0}^{\infty} \left(\dfrac{n}{n+5}\right)^n$ converges or diverges.

5 Estimate $e^{0.3}$ correct to three decimal places using the Maclaurin approximation:

$$f(x) = f(0) + f'(0)\,x + \frac{f''(0)\,x^2}{2!} + \dots + \frac{f^{(n)}(0)\,x^n}{n!} + \frac{f^{(n+1)}(c)\,x^{n+1}}{(n+1)!}$$

6 Use the substitution $y = vx$ where v is a function of x, to solve the initial value problem $xy\dfrac{dy}{dx} = 1 + x + y^2$, $y(1) = 0$.

7 **a** Prove that $e - \sum\limits_{k=0}^{n} \dfrac{1}{k!} = \dfrac{e^c}{(n+1)!}$ where $0 < c < 1$.

   b Using the fact that $e < 3$, show that for $n \geqslant 3$:

   i $\dfrac{1}{(n+1)!} < e - \sum\limits_{k=0}^{n} \dfrac{1}{k!} < \dfrac{3}{(n+1)!}$ and hence

   ii $\dfrac{1}{n+1} < n!e - \sum\limits_{k=0}^{n} \dfrac{n!}{k!} < \dfrac{3}{n+1} \leqslant \dfrac{3}{4}$

   c Hence, prove by contradiction that e is an irrational number.

8 By finding a suitable integrating factor, solve $\dfrac{dy}{dx} + \dfrac{3y}{x} = 8x^4$, $y(1) = 0$.

9

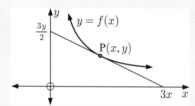

The tangent to a curve at the general point $P(x, y)$ has x-intercept $3x$ and y-intercept $\dfrac{3y}{2}$.

Given that $x > 0$, find the equation of the curve which passes through the point $(1, 5)$.

10 The inside surface of $y = f(x)$ is a mirror.
Light is emitted from $O(0, 0)$.
All rays that strike the surface of the mirror are reflected so that they emerge parallel to the axis of symmetry (the x-axis).

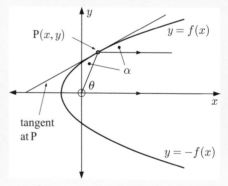

   a Explain why $\theta = 2\alpha$.

   b Explain why the gradient of the tangent at a general point $P(x, y)$ on the mirror is given by $\dfrac{dy}{dx} = \tan\alpha$.

   c Use the identity $\tan(2\alpha) = \dfrac{2\tan\alpha}{1 - \tan^2\alpha}$ to deduce that $\tan\alpha = \dfrac{\sqrt{x^2 + y^2} - x}{y}$.

   d Find the general solution to the differential equation $\dfrac{dy}{dx} = \dfrac{\sqrt{x^2 + y^2} - x}{y}$ by making the substitution $r^2 = x^2 + y^2$.

   e What is the nature of $y = f(x)$?

11 Consider the differential equation $\dfrac{dy}{dx} = y \ln x$, $x > 0$, where $y(1) = 1$.

    a Find the first three non-zero terms in the Taylor polynomial expansion of y about $x = 1$.

    b Hence estimate the solution to the initial value problem $\dfrac{dy}{dx} = y \ln x$, $y(1) = 1$.

    c Solve the initial value problem in **b** exactly.

THEORY OF KNOWLEDGE   TORRICELLI'S TRUMPET

Consider $f(x) = \dfrac{1}{x}$. An infinite area sweeps out a finite volume. Can this be reconciled with our intuition? What does this tell us about mathematical knowledge?

Calculus provides us with a set of procedures for manipulating symbols, such as differentiation and integration. Justifying how, and importantly *when*, such manipulations lead to correct answers is the subject of *analysis* which underpins calculus. These justifications need to make use of arguments involving infinite processes such as infinitely small quantities and limits over an infinitely large range.

These are very subtle concepts which mathematicians and philosophers have discussed and debated for many thousands of years, such as in Archimedes' work in finding areas and volumes. Much of the debate has focused on paradoxes.

A **paradox** is an argument that appears to produce an inconsistency, such as resulting in $1 = 0$. Often the paradox enables a definition, technique, or logical argument to be refined.

However there are still some things which appear to be paradoxical and Torricelli's trumpet, also sometimes called Gabriel's Horn, is one of these.

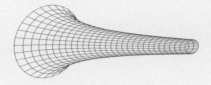   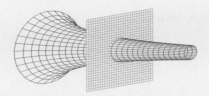

To create this shape we take the graph of $y = \dfrac{1}{x}$ for $x \geqslant 1$ and rotate it around the x-axis to create a *solid of revolution*. The two questions we wish to ask are:

- What is the volume of this shape?
- What is the surface area of this shape?

To answer these questions we shall use the modern techniques of calculus. Torricelli's original arguments, made in the early 1600s, predate the systematic development of calculus by Newton and Leibnitz later that century. His argument relied on *Cavalieri's Principle*:

> Take two solids included between parallel planes, and cut the solids with another parallel plane. If the areas are always in the same ratio, then the volumes are also in the same ratio.

Think of a solid, such as a cone, made up of a stack of cards. You can displace the cards without altering the volume. If you can change the shape of the cards without altering the areas then you also don't change the volume. Cavalieri's Principle is another extension to the case when the respective areas are in constant ratio.

1   What place does an "intuitive" rule such as Cavalieri's Principle have in mathematics?

2   How can Cavalieri's Principle be used to find the volume of a sphere from the known volume of a circular cone? Can this be regarded as a valid proof of the formula?

In order to consider the volume and surface area we will look at a *finite* part of the trumpet from $x = 1$ to $x = N$ and then let $N \to \infty$.

VOLUME

We imagine a plane perpendicular to the x-axis, cutting the axis at x.

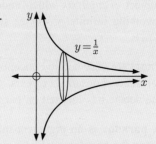

The trumpet and the plane intersect at a circle of radius $\dfrac{1}{x}$.

The area of the circle is simply $\pi \dfrac{1}{x^2}$.

To calculate the volume we sum the infinitesimal areas of these

discs as $\pi \displaystyle\int_1^N \dfrac{1}{x^2}\, dx = \pi \left[-\dfrac{1}{x} \right]_1^N = \pi \left(1 - \dfrac{1}{N} \right)$.

As $N \to \infty$ we see that the volume converges to π. It is somewhat surprising that an infinite shape can have a finite volume. However, this is similar to the idea that an infinite series of positive terms can sum to a finite *length*.

SURFACE AREA

To calculate the surface area we use the formula $S = 2\pi \displaystyle\int_1^N y \sqrt{1 + \left(\dfrac{dy}{dx} \right)^2}\, dx$.

Since $y = \dfrac{1}{x}$ we have $\dfrac{dy}{dx} = -\dfrac{1}{x^2}$ and so the integral becomes $S = 2\pi \displaystyle\int_1^N \dfrac{1}{x} \sqrt{1 + \dfrac{1}{x^4}}\, dx$.

Noting that $\dfrac{1}{x}\sqrt{1 + \dfrac{1}{x^4}} > \dfrac{1}{x}$,   we find that

$$S = 2\pi \int_1^N \dfrac{1}{x} \sqrt{1 + \dfrac{1}{x^4}}\, dx > 2\pi \int_1^N \dfrac{1}{x}\, dx = 2\pi \ln(N).$$

As $N \to \infty$, $\ln(N)$ diverges, and so the surface area S also diverges.

Hence we have a finite volume with an infinite surface area. This is a strange and controversial result. Thomas Hobbes, the English Philosopher, said "*to understand this for sense, it is not required that a man should be a geometrician or logician, but that he should be mad*".

3   Imagine filling the trumpet with a liquid. While the trumpet holds a finite volume, what happens when a thin layer coats the surface?

4   What do we do when a physical problem yields a mathematical result with no physical meaning?

APPENDIX A: METHODS OF PROOF

Greek mathematicians more than 2000 years ago realised that progress in mathematical thinking could be brought about by conscious formulation of the methods of **abstraction** and **proof**.

By considering a few examples, one might notice a certain common quality or pattern from which one could predict a rule or formula for the general case. In mathematics this prediction is known as a **conjecture**. Mathematicians love to find patterns, and try to understand why they occur.

Experiments and further examples might help to convince you that the conjecture is true. However, problems will often contain extra information which can sometimes obscure the essential detail, particularly in applied mathematics. Stripping this away is the process of **abstraction**.

For example, by considering the given table of values one may conjecture:

"If a and b are real numbers then $a < b$ implies that $a^2 < b^2$."

However, on observing that $-2 < 1$ but $(-2)^2 \not< 1^2$ we have a **counter-example**.

In the light of this we reformulate and refine our conjecture:

a	b	a^2	b^2
1	2	1	4
3	5	9	25
4	5	16	25
5	7	25	49
6	9	36	81

"If a and b are *positive* real numbers then $a < b$ implies $a^2 < b^2$."

The difficulty is that this process might continue with reformulations, counter-examples, and revised conjectures indefinitely. At what point are we certain that the conjecture is true? A **proof** is a flawless logical argument which leaves no doubt that the conjecture is indeed a truth. If we have a proof then the conjecture can be called a **theorem**.

Mathematics has evolved to accept certain types of arguments as valid proofs. They include a mixture of both logic and calculation. Generally mathematicians like elegant, efficient proofs. It is common not to write every minute detail. However, when you write a proof you should be prepared to expand and justify every step if asked to do so.

We have already examined in the HL Core text, proof by **the principle of mathematical induction**. Now we consider other methods.

DIRECT PROOF

In a **direct proof** we start with a known truth and by a succession of correct deductions finish with the required result.

Example 1:   Prove that if $a, b \in \mathbb{R}$ then $a < b \implies a < \dfrac{a+b}{2}$

Proof: $a < b \implies \dfrac{a}{2} < \dfrac{b}{2}$ {as we are dividing by 2 which is > 0}

$\implies \dfrac{a}{2} + \dfrac{a}{2} < \dfrac{a}{2} + \dfrac{b}{2}$ {adding $\dfrac{a}{2}$ to both sides}

$\implies a < \dfrac{a+b}{2}$

Sometimes it is not possible to give a direct proof of the full result and so the different possible cases (called **exhaustive cases**) need to be considered and proved separately.

Example 2:   Prove the **geometric progression**:   For $n \in \mathbb{Z}$, $n \geqslant 0$,

$$1 + r^1 + r^2 + ... + r^n = \begin{cases} \dfrac{r^{n+1} - 1}{r - 1}, & r \neq 1 \\ n + 1, & r = 1 \end{cases}$$

Proof: **Case $r = 1$:** $1 + r^1 + r^2 + ... + r^n$

$= 1 + 1 + 1 + ... + 1$ $\{n + 1 \text{ times}\}$

$= n + 1$

Case $r \neq 1$:   Let $S_n = 1 + r^1 + r^2 + ... + r^n$.

Then $rS_n = r^1 + r^2 + r^3 + ... + r^{n+1}$

$\therefore \ rS_n - S_n = r^{n+1} - 1$ $\{\text{after cancellation of terms}\}$

$\therefore \ (r - 1)S_n = r^{n+1} - 1$

$\therefore \ S_n = \dfrac{r^{n+1} - 1}{r - 1}$ $\{\text{dividing by } r - 1 \text{ since } r \neq 1\}$

Example 3:   Alice looks at Bob and Bob looks at Clare. Alice is married, but Clare is not. Prove that a married person looks at an unmarried person.

Proof: We do not know whether Bob is married or not, so we consider the different (exhaustive) cases:

Case: Bob is married.   If Bob is married, then a married person (Bob) looks at an unmarried person (Clare).

Case: Bob is unmarried.   If Bob is unmarried, then a married person (Alice) looks at an unmarried person (Bob).

Since we have considered all possible cases, the full result is proved.

EXERCISE

1   Let $I = \sqrt{2}$, which is irrational. Consider I^I and I^{I^I}, and hence prove that an irrational number to the power of an irrational number can be rational.

PROOF BY CONTRADICTION (AN INDIRECT PROOF)

In **proof by contradiction** we deliberately assume the opposite to what we are trying to prove. By a series of correct steps we show that this is impossible, our assumption is false, and hence its opposite is true.

Example 4:   Consider **Example 1** again but this time use proof by contradiction:

Prove that if $a, b \in \mathbb{R}$ then $a < b \implies a < \dfrac{a+b}{2}$.

Proof (by contradiction):

For $a < b$, suppose that $a \geqslant \dfrac{a+b}{2}$.

$$\implies \quad 2a \geqslant 2\left(\frac{a+b}{2}\right) \qquad \{\text{multiplying both sides by 2}\}$$

$$\implies \quad 2a \geqslant a + b$$

$$\implies \quad a \geqslant b \qquad \{\text{subtracting } a \text{ from both sides}\}$$

which is false.

Since the steps of the argument are correct, the supposition must be false and the alternative, $a < \dfrac{a+b}{2}$ must be true.

Example 5:   Prove that the solution of $3^x = 8$ is irrational.

Proof (by contradiction):

Suppose the solution of $3^x = 8$ is rational, or in other words, that x is rational. Notice that $x > 0$.

$$\implies \qquad x = \frac{p}{q} \quad \text{where } p, q \in \mathbb{Z}, \ q \neq 0 \quad \{\text{and since } x > 0, \text{ integers } p, q > 0\}$$

$$\implies \qquad 3^{\frac{p}{q}} = 8$$

$$\implies \qquad \left(3^{\frac{p}{q}}\right)^q = 8^q$$

$$\implies \qquad 3^p = 8^q$$

which is impossible since for the given possible values of p and q, 3^p is always odd and 8^q is always even. Thus, the assumption is false and its opposite must be true. Hence x is irrational.

Example 6:   Prove that no positive integers x and y exist such that $x^2 - y^2 = 1$.

Proof (by contradiction):

Suppose $x, y \in \mathbb{Z}^+$ exist such that $x^2 - y^2 = 1$.

$\implies$ $(x+y)(x-y) = 1$

$\implies$ $\underbrace{x + y = 1 \text{ and } x - y = 1}_{\text{case 1}}$ **or** $\underbrace{x + y = -1 \text{ and } x - y = -1}_{\text{case 2}}$

$\implies$ $x = 1, \ y = 0$ (from case 1) **or** $x = -1, \ y = 0$ (from case 2)

Both cases provide a contradiction to $x, y > 0$.
Thus, the supposition is false and its opposite is true.
There do *not* exist positive integers x and y such that $x^2 - y^2 = 1$.

Indirect proof often seems cleverly contrived, especially if no direct proof is forthcoming. It is perhaps more natural to seek a direct proof for the first attempt to prove a conjecture.

ERRORS IN PROOF

One must be careful not to make errors in algebra or reasoning. Examine carefully the following examples.

Example 7:   Consider **Example 5** again: Prove that the solution of $3^x = 8$ is irrational.

Invalid argument:
$$3^x = 8$$
$$\Rightarrow \quad \log 3^x = \log 8$$
$$\Rightarrow \quad x \log 3 = \log 8$$
$$\Rightarrow \quad x = \frac{\log 8}{\log 3} \quad \text{where both } \log 8 \text{ and } \log 3 \text{ are irrational.}$$
$$\Rightarrow \quad x \text{ is irrational.}$$

The last step is not valid. The argument that an irrational divided by an irrational is always irrational is not correct. For example, $\frac{\sqrt{2}}{\sqrt{2}} = 1$, and 1 is rational.

Dividing by zero is *not* a valid operation. $\frac{a}{0}$ is not defined for any $a \in \mathbb{R}$, in particular $\frac{0}{0} \neq 1$.

Example 8:   Invalid "proof" that $5 = 2$

$$0 = 0$$
$$\Rightarrow \quad 0 \times 5 = 0 \times 2$$
$$\Rightarrow \quad \frac{0 \times 5}{0} = \frac{0 \times 2}{0} \quad \{\text{dividing through by } 0\}$$
$$\Rightarrow \quad 5 = 2, \quad \text{which is clearly false.}$$

This invalid step is not always obvious, as illustrated in the following example.

Example 9:   Invalid "proof" that $0 = 1$:

$$\text{Suppose} \quad a = 1$$
$$\Rightarrow \quad a^2 = a$$
$$\Rightarrow \quad a^2 - 1 = a - 1$$
$$\Rightarrow \quad (a+1)(a-1) = a - 1$$
$$\Rightarrow \quad a + 1 = 1 \quad \text{.... } (*)$$
$$\Rightarrow \quad a = 0$$
$$\text{So,} \quad 0 = 1$$

The invalid step in the argument is $(*)$ where we divide both sides by $a - 1$. Since $a = 1$, $a - 1 = 0$, and so we are dividing both sides by zero.

Another trap to be avoided is to begin by assuming the result we wish to prove is true. This readily leads to invalid circular arguments.

Example 10:   Prove without decimalisation that $\sqrt{3} - 1 > \frac{1}{\sqrt{2}}$.

Invalid argument:

$$\sqrt{3} - 1 > \frac{1}{\sqrt{2}}$$

$$\Rightarrow \quad (\sqrt{3} - 1)^2 > \left(\frac{1}{\sqrt{2}}\right)^2 \quad \{\text{both sides are } > 0, \text{ so we can square them}\}$$

$$\Rightarrow \quad 4 - 2\sqrt{3} > \tfrac{1}{2}$$

$$\Rightarrow \quad \tfrac{7}{2} > 2\sqrt{3}$$

$$\Rightarrow \quad 7 > 4\sqrt{3}$$

$$\Rightarrow \quad 7^2 > 48 \qquad \{\text{squaring again}\}$$

$$\Rightarrow \quad 49 > 48 \qquad \text{which is true.}$$

Hence $\sqrt{3} - 1 > \frac{1}{\sqrt{2}}$ is true.

Although $\sqrt{3} - 1 > \frac{1}{\sqrt{2}}$ is in fact true, the above argument is invalid because we began by assuming the result.

A valid method of proof for $\sqrt{3} - 1 > \frac{1}{\sqrt{2}}$ can be found by either:

- reversing the steps of the above argument, or by
- using proof by contradiction (supposing $\sqrt{3} - 1 \leqslant \frac{1}{\sqrt{2}}$).

It is important to distinguish **errors in proof** from a **false conjecture**.

Consider the table alongside, which shows values of $n^2 - n + 41$ for various values of $n \in \mathbb{N}$.

From the many examples given, one might conjecture:

"For all natural numbers n, $n^2 - n + 41$ is prime."

This conjecture is in fact false.

For example, for $n = 41$, $n^2 - n + 41 = 41^2$ is clearly not prime.

n	$n^2 - n + 41$
1	41
2	43
3	47
4	53
5	61
6	71
7	83
8	97
9	113
10	131
11	151
12	173
13	197
. . .	. . .
30	911
. . .	. . .
99	9743
. . .	. . .

It takes only one counter-example to prove a conjecture is false.

IMPLICATIONS AND THEIR CONVERSE

If .... then ....

Many statements in mathematics take the form of an **implication** "If A then B", where A and B are themselves statements. The statement A is known as the **hypothesis**. The statement B is known as the **conclusion**.

Implications can be written in many forms in addition to "If A then B". For example, the following all have the same meaning:

$$A \left\{ \begin{array}{c} \text{implies} \\ \text{so} \\ \text{hence} \\ \text{thus} \\ \text{therefore} \end{array} \right\} B.$$

Given a statement of the form "If A then B", we can write a **converse** statement "If B then A".

If we know the truth, or otherwise, of a given statement, we can say nothing about the truth of the converse. It could be true or false.

A statement and its converse are said to be (logically) *independent*.

For example, suppose x is an integer.

- The statement "If x is odd, then $2x$ is even" is *true*, but its converse "If $2x$ is even, then x is odd" is *false*.
- The statement "If $2x$ is even, then x is odd" is *false*, but its converse "If x is odd, then $2x$ is even" is *true*.
- The statement "If $x > 1$, then $\ln x > 0$" is *true*, and its converse "If $\ln x > 0$, then $x > 1$" is also *true*.
- The statement "If $x = 5$, then $x^2 = 16$" is *false*, and its converse "If $x^2 = 16$, then $x = 5$" is also *false*.

EXERCISE

Prove or disprove:

1 If x is rational then $2^x \neq 3$.

2 If $2^x \neq 3$ then x is rational.

EQUIVALENCE

Some conjectures with two statements A and B involve **logical equivalence** or simply **equivalence**.

We say A *is equivalent to* B, or A is true *if and only if* B is true.

The phrase "if and only if" is often written as "iff" or $\Leftrightarrow$.

$A \Leftrightarrow B$ means $A \Rightarrow B$ *and* $B \Rightarrow A$

In order to prove an equivalence, we need to prove both implications: $A \Rightarrow B$ *and* $B \Rightarrow A$.

For example: $x^2 = 9 \iff x = 3$ is a false statement.

$\qquad\qquad x = 3 \Rightarrow x^2 = 9$ is true

but $x^2 = 9 \not\Rightarrow x = 3$ as x may be -3.

Example 11:   Prove that $(n+2)^2 - n^2$ is a multiple of 8 $\iff$ n is odd.

Proof: $(\Rightarrow)$ $(n+2)^2 - n^2$ is a multiple of 8

$\qquad\qquad \Rightarrow \ n^2 + 4n + 4 - n^2 = 8a$ for some integer a

$\qquad\qquad \Rightarrow \ 4n + 4 = 8a$

$\qquad\qquad \Rightarrow \ n + 1 = 2a$

$\qquad\qquad \Rightarrow \ n = 2a - 1$

$\qquad\qquad \Rightarrow \ n$ is odd.

$\qquad\ \ (\Leftarrow)$ n is odd

$\qquad\qquad \Rightarrow \ n = 2a - 1$ for some integer a

$\qquad\qquad \Rightarrow \ n + 1 = 2a$

$\qquad\qquad \Rightarrow \ 4n + 4 = 8a$

$\qquad\qquad \Rightarrow \ (n^2 + 4n + 4) - n^2 = 8a$

$\qquad\qquad \Rightarrow \ (n+2)^2 - n^2$ is a multiple of 8.

In the above example the $(\Rightarrow)$ argument is clearly reversible to give the $(\Leftarrow)$ argument. However, this is not always the case.

Example 12:   Prove that for all $x \in \mathbb{Z}^+$, x is not divisible by 3 $\iff$ $x^2 - 1$ is divisible by 3.

Proof: $(\Rightarrow)$ x is not divisible by 3

$\qquad\qquad \Rightarrow$ either $x = 3k + 1$ or $x = 3k + 2$ for some $k \in \mathbb{Z}^+ \cup \{0\}$

$\qquad\qquad \Rightarrow$ $x^2 - 1 = 9k^2 + 6k$ or $9k^2 + 12k + 3$

$\qquad\qquad\qquad\qquad\qquad = 3(3k^2 + 2)$ or $3(3k^2 + 4k + 1)$

$\qquad\qquad \Rightarrow$ $x^2 - 1$ is divisible by 3.

$\qquad\ \ (\Leftarrow)$ $x^2 - 1$ is divisible by 3

$\qquad\qquad \Rightarrow \ 3 \mid x^2 - 1$

$\qquad\qquad \Rightarrow \ 3 \mid (x+1)(x-1)$

$\qquad\qquad \Rightarrow \ 3 \mid (x+1)$ or $3 \mid (x-1)$ {as 3 is a prime number}

$\qquad\qquad \Rightarrow \ 3 \nmid x$

$\qquad\ $ or in other words, x is not divisible by 3.

NEGATION

For any given statement A, we write not A or $\neg A$ to represent the negation of the statement A.

For example:

	A	$\neg A$
	$x > 0$	$x \leqslant 0$
	x is prime	x is not prime
	x is an integer	x is not an integer
For $x \in \mathbb{R}$:	x is rational	x is irrational
For $z \in \mathbb{C}$:	z is real	$z = a + bi, \ a, b \in \mathbb{R}, \ b \neq 0$
For $x \in \mathbb{Z}^+ \cup \{0\}$:	x is a multiple of 3	x is not a multiple of 3 *or* $x = 3k + 1$ or $3k + 2$ for $k \in \mathbb{Z}^+ \cup \{0\}$

PROOF OF THE CONTRAPOSITIVE

To prove the statement "If A then B", we can provide a direct proof, or we can prove the logically equivalent **contrapositive** statement "If not B, then not A" which we can also write as "If $\neg B$, then $\neg A$".

For example, the statement   "If it is Jon's bicycle, then it is blue"
  is logically equivalent to   "If that bicycle is not blue, then it is not Jon's".

Example 13:   Prove that for $a, b \in \mathbb{R}$, "ab is irrational $\Rightarrow$ either a or b is irrational".

Proof using contrapositive:

$\quad a$ and b are both rational $\Rightarrow \ a = \dfrac{p}{q}$ and $b = \dfrac{r}{s}$ where $p, q, r, s \in \mathbb{Z}, \ q \neq 0, \ s \neq 0$

$\qquad\qquad\qquad\qquad\qquad \Rightarrow \ ab = \left(\dfrac{p}{q}\right)\left(\dfrac{r}{s}\right) = \dfrac{pr}{qs}$ {where $qs \neq 0$, since $q, s \neq 0$}

$\qquad\qquad\qquad\qquad\qquad \Rightarrow \ ab$ is rational   {since $pr, qs \in \mathbb{Z}$}

$\quad$ Thus ab is irrational $\Rightarrow$ either a or b is irrational.

Example 14:   Prove that if n is a positive integer of the form $3k + 2, \ k \geqslant 0, \ k \in \mathbb{Z}$, then n is not a square.

Proof using contrapositive:

$\quad$ If n is a square then
$\quad n$ has one of the forms $(3a)^2, \ (3a + 1)^2$ or $(3a + 2)^2$, where $a \in \mathbb{Z}^+ \cup \{0\}$.

$\quad \Rightarrow \ n = 9a^2, \ 9a^2 + 6a + 1$ or $9a^2 + 12a + 4$

$\quad \Rightarrow \ n = 3(3a^2), \ 3(3a^2 + 2a) + 1$ or $3(3a^2 + 4a + 1) + 1$

$\quad \Rightarrow \ n$ has the form $3k$ or $3k + 1$ only, where $k \in \mathbb{Z}^+ \cup \{0\}$

$\quad \Rightarrow \ n$ does not have form $3k + 2$.

$\quad$ Thus if n is a positive integer of the form $3k + 2, \ k \geqslant 0, \ k \in \mathbb{Z}$, then n is not a square.

USING PREVIOUS RESULTS

In mathematics we build up collections of important and useful results, each depending on previously proven statements.

Example 15:   Prove the conjecture:

"The recurring decimal $0.\overline{9} = 0.999\,999\,99....$ is exactly equal to 1".

Proof (by contradiction):

Suppose $0.\overline{9} < 1$

$\Rightarrow \quad 0.\overline{9} < \dfrac{0.\overline{9} + 1}{2}$ {We proved earlier that $a < b \ \Rightarrow \ a < \dfrac{a+b}{2}$}

$\Rightarrow \quad 0.\overline{9} < \dfrac{1.\overline{9}}{2}$ $\left\{\text{Ordinary division:} \quad \begin{array}{r} 2 \,\lfloor\, \overline{1.999\,999\,99....} \\ 0.999\,999\,99.... \end{array} \right\}$

$\Rightarrow \quad 0.\overline{9} < 0.\overline{9}$ clearly a contradiction

Therefore the supposition is false, and so $0.\overline{9} \geqslant 1$ is true.

Since $0.\overline{9} > 1$ is absurd, $0.\overline{9} = 1$.

Proof (Direct Proof):

$0.\overline{9} = 0.999\,999\,99....$

$= 0.9 + 0.09 + 0.009 + 0.0009 + ...$

$= 0.9 \left(1 + \tfrac{1}{10} + \tfrac{1}{100} + \tfrac{1}{1000} + ...\right)$

$= \tfrac{9}{10} \left(\displaystyle\sum_{i=0}^{\infty} \left(\tfrac{1}{10}\right)^{i}\right)$

$= \tfrac{9}{10} \left(\dfrac{1}{1 - \tfrac{1}{10}}\right)$ {Using the previously proved Geometric Series with $r = \tfrac{1}{10}$ and $\left|\tfrac{1}{10}\right| < 1$}

$= \tfrac{9}{10} \times \tfrac{10}{9}$

$= 1$

THEORY OF KNOWLEDGE   AXIOMS AND OCCAM'S RAZOR

In order to understand complicated concepts, we often try to break them down into simpler components. But when mathematicians try to understand the foundations of a particular branch of the subject, they consider the question "What is the minimal set of assumptions from which all other results can be deduced or proved?" The assumptions they make are called **axioms**. Whether the axioms accurately reflect properties observed in the physical world is less important to pure mathematicians than the theory which can be developed and deduced from the axioms.

Occam's razor is a principle of economy that among competing hypotheses, the one that makes the fewest assumptions should be selected.

1 What value does Occam's razor have in understanding the long-held belief that the world was flat?

2 Is the simplest explanation to something always true?

3 Is it reasonable to construct a set of mathematical axioms under Occam's razor?

One of the most famous examples of a set of axioms is given by Euclid in his set of 13 books called *Elements*. He gives five axioms, which he calls "postulates", as the basis for his study of Geometry:

1. Any two points can be joined by a straight line.

2. Any straight line segment can be extended indefinitely in a straight line.

3. Given any straight line segment, a circle can be drawn having the segment as radius and one endpoint as centre.

4. All right angles are congruent.

5. **Parallel postulate**: If two lines intersect a third in such a way that the sum of the inner angles on one side is less than two right angles, then the two lines inevitably must intersect each other on that side if extended far enough.

4 Is the parallel postulate genuinely an axiom, or can it be proved from the others?

5 What happens if you change the list of axioms or do not include the parallel postulate?

6 What other areas of mathematics can we reduce to a concise list of axioms?

APPENDIX B: FORMAL DEFINITION OF A LIMIT

The informal definition of a limit we were given in **Section B** is sufficient for our study here. However, for completeness we justify its use by considering and interpreting the formal definition:

The formal definition of a limit of a function:

Let f be a function defined in an open interval about $x = a$, except $f(a)$ need not be defined. The number l is called the **limit of f as x approaches a** if, for any value $\varepsilon > 0$, there exists a corresponding value $\delta > 0$ such that $0 < |x - a| < \delta$ ensures $|f(x) - l| < \varepsilon$.

We write $\lim\limits_{x \to a} f(x) = l$ to denote "the limit of f as x approaches a, is l".

To interpret this definition, note that l and a are constants, and x and $f(x)$ are variables.

The value $\varepsilon > 0$ is *any* positive value, but in particular we consider ε a very, very small positive value.

In this case
$$|f(x) - l| < \varepsilon$$
$$\Leftrightarrow \quad -\varepsilon < f(x) - l < \varepsilon$$
$$\Leftrightarrow \quad l - \varepsilon < f(x) < l + \varepsilon$$
$$\Leftrightarrow \quad \text{the value } f(x) \text{ is very, very close to } l$$

$f(x)$ will lie in the shaded band of values shown.

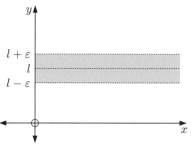

Similarly, the value $\delta > 0$ is a positive value, and in particular we consider δ a very, very small positive value.

In this case
$$0 < |x - a| < \delta$$
$$\Leftrightarrow \quad x \neq a \quad \text{and} \quad -\delta < x - a < \delta$$
$$\Leftrightarrow \quad x \neq a \quad \text{and} \quad a - \delta < x < a + \delta$$
so that x is very, very close to, **but not equal to**, the value a.

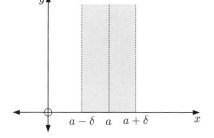

Putting this all together, we have that **f has limit l as x approaches a** if for any choice of $\varepsilon > 0$, there always exists a value $\delta > 0$ such that the value $f(x)$ will be within distance ε from l, whenever x is within distance δ from a, but not equal to a. In particular, this must be true for $\varepsilon > 0$ chosen as small as we like.

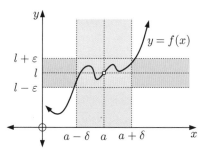

These algebraic and geometric interpretations of the formal definition lead to the informal definition of the limit of a function given in **Section B**.

ESTABLISHING LIMITS

By considering the identity function $f(x) = x$, we intuitively see that $\lim\limits_{x \to a} x = a$ for any constant $a \in \mathbb{R}$.

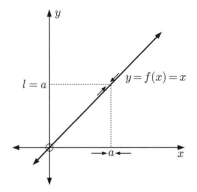

This is proved formally as follows:

Suppose $f(x) = x$ and $a \in \mathbb{R}$ is a constant. For any $\varepsilon > 0$, there exists $\delta = \varepsilon > 0$ such that

$$0 < |x - a| < \delta$$
$$\Rightarrow |x - a| < \varepsilon \qquad \{\text{since } \delta = \varepsilon\}$$
$$\Rightarrow |f(x) - a| < \varepsilon \qquad \{\text{since } f(x) = x\}$$

Since an appropriate δ can be found for any choice of $\varepsilon > 0$, by the formal definition of a limit, $\lim\limits_{x \to a} x = a$, for a any constant.

Arguments such as this can be used to establish the **limit laws** presented in **Section B**.

When we define new functions using a sum, composition, or some other combination of simpler functions, the limit laws help us calculate limits for these new functions using what we already know about the simpler functions.

Example: Determine the limit $\lim\limits_{x \to 1} \dfrac{3(x^2 - 1)}{x - 1}$.

Using Limit Laws

$\lim\limits_{x \to 1} \dfrac{3(x^2 - 1)}{x - 1}$

$= \lim\limits_{x \to 1} \dfrac{3(x-1)(x + 1)}{(x-1)}$

$= \lim\limits_{x \to 1} 3(x + 1)$ $\qquad$ $\{\text{using Limit Laws with } \dfrac{x - 1}{x - 1} = 1 \text{ a constant, since } x \neq 1\}$

$= \lim\limits_{x \to 1} (3x + 3)$

$= \left(\lim\limits_{x \to 1} 3 \right) \left(\lim\limits_{x \to 1} x \right) + \left(\lim\limits_{x \to 1} 3 \right)$ $\quad$ $\{\text{by the Limit Laws, since each limit exists}\}$

$= 3 \times 1 + 3$ $\qquad\qquad\qquad$ $\{\text{since } \lim\limits_{x \to 1} 3 = 3 \text{ from the Limit Laws}$

$= 6$ $\qquad\qquad\qquad\qquad\quad$ and $\lim\limits_{x \to 1} x = 1$ from above using $a = 1\}$

Using the formal definition directly (**not** required for this course)

From the graph of $y = \dfrac{3(x^2 - 1)}{x - 1}$ we observe that for x near 1, $f(x)$ is close to the value 6.

We conjecture that $\lim\limits_{x \to 1} \dfrac{3(x^2 - 1)}{x - 1} = 6$, and must prove this formally.

For $x \neq 1$, $\quad |f(x) - 6| < \varepsilon \quad \Leftrightarrow \quad \left| \dfrac{3(x^2 - 1)}{x - 1} - 6 \right| < \varepsilon$

$$\Leftrightarrow \quad \left| \frac{3\cancel{(x - 1)}(x + 1)}{\cancel{(x - 1)}} - 6 \right| < \varepsilon$$

$$\Leftrightarrow \quad |3(x + 1) - 6| < \varepsilon$$

$$\Leftrightarrow \quad |3x + 3 - 6| < \varepsilon$$

$$\Leftrightarrow \quad |3x - 3| < \varepsilon$$

$$\Leftrightarrow \quad 3\,|x - 1| < \varepsilon$$

$$\Leftrightarrow \quad |x - 1| < \frac{\varepsilon}{3}$$

Therefore, for all $\varepsilon > 0$, there exists $\delta = \dfrac{\varepsilon}{3} > 0$ such that $0 < |x - 1| < \delta$ implies $|f(x) - 6| < \varepsilon$.

Thus by the formal definition of the limit, $\displaystyle \lim_{x \to 1} \frac{3(x^2 - 1)}{x - 1} = 6$.

Worked Solutions

EXERCISE A

1 If $a \geqslant 0$, $|a| = a \Rightarrow |a| \geqslant 0$ .... (1)
If $a < 0$, $|a| = -a$ where $-a > 0 \Rightarrow |a| > 0$ .... (2)
From (1) and (2), $|a| \geqslant 0$ for all $a \in \mathbb{R}$.

2 $|-a| = \begin{cases} -a & \text{if } -a > 0 \\ 0 & \text{if } -a = 0 \\ -(-a) & \text{if } -a < 0 \end{cases}$

$= \begin{cases} -a & \text{if } a < 0 \\ 0 & \text{if } a = 0 \\ a & \text{if } a > 0 \end{cases}$

$= \begin{cases} a & \text{if } a \geqslant 0 \\ -a & \text{if } a < 0 \end{cases}$

$= |a|$

or $|-a| = |-1 \times a|$
$= |-1| \, |a|$ $\{|ab| = |a| \, |b|\}$
$= 1 \, |a|$
$= |a|$

3 P_n is:
$|a_1 + a_2 + a_3 + ... + a_n| \leqslant |a_1| + |a_2| + |a_3| + ... + |a_n|$
for all $n \in \mathbb{Z}^+$
Proof: (by induction)
(1) If $n = 1$, $|a_1| \leqslant |a_1|$ is true $\Rightarrow P_1$ is true.
(2) If $n = 2$, $|a_1 + a_2| \leqslant |a_1| + |a_2|$ {Triangle inequality}
(3) If P_k is true, $|a_1 + a_2 + ... + a_k| \leqslant |a_1| + |a_2| + ... + |a_k|$
$\therefore$ $|a_1 + a_2 + ... + a_k + a_{k+1}|$
$= |(a_1 + a_2 + ... + a_k) + a_{k+1}|$
$\leqslant |a_1 + a_2 + ... + a_k| + |a_{k+1}|$ {using Case 2}
$\leqslant |a_1| + |a_2| + ... + |a_k| + |a_{k+1}|$ {Truth of P_k}

Thus P_1, P_2 are true and P_{k+1} is true whenever P_k is true
$\Rightarrow P_n$ is true. {The Principle of Mathematical Induction}

4 $a < x < b$ .... (1)
$a < y < b \Rightarrow -b < -y < -a$ .... (2)
From (1) and (2), $a - b < x - y < b - a$
$\Rightarrow$ $-(b - a) < x - y < b - a$
$\Rightarrow$ $|x - y| < b - a$ as $b - a > 0$
    {Property **5**}

We have: (number line with a x y b) *or* (number line with a y x b)

If two points lie in a particular interval $[a, b]$ on the number line then the distance between them is less than the length of the interval.

5 $|a - b| = |(a - c) + (c - b)|$
$\leqslant |a - c| + |c - b|$ {Triangle inequality}

6 $|x - a| < \dfrac{a}{2} \Rightarrow -\dfrac{a}{2} < x - a < \dfrac{a}{2}$ {as $a > 0$}
$\Rightarrow \dfrac{a}{2} < x < \dfrac{3a}{2}$
$\Rightarrow x > \dfrac{a}{2}$

7 $|(x + y) - (a + b)|$
$= |(x - a) + (y - b)|$
$\leqslant |x - a| + |y - b|$ {Triangle inequality}
$\leqslant \varepsilon + \varepsilon$
$\Rightarrow |(x + y) - (a + b)| \leqslant 2\varepsilon$

8 Consider the Archimedean Property with $a = \varepsilon$ and $b = 1$ where $\varepsilon > 0$.
There exists a natural number n such that
$n\varepsilon > 1 \Rightarrow \varepsilon > \dfrac{1}{n} \Rightarrow \dfrac{1}{n} < \varepsilon$

9 P_n is: if $x > -1$ then $(1 + x)^n \geqslant 1 + nx$ for all $n \in \mathbb{Z}^+$
Proof: (by induction)
(1) If $n = 1$, $(1 + x)^1 \geqslant 1 + 1x$
$\Rightarrow$ $1 + x \geqslant 1 + x$
$\Rightarrow$ P_1 is true
(2) If P_k is true, then $(1 + x)^k \geqslant 1 + kx$, $k \in \mathbb{Z}^+$.
Now $x > -1 \Rightarrow 1 + x > 0$
$\Rightarrow (1 + x)^k (1 + x) \geqslant (1 + kx)(1 + x)$
$\Rightarrow (1 + x)^{k+1} \geqslant 1 + (k + 1)x + kx^2$
$\Rightarrow (1 + x)^{k+1} \geqslant 1 + (k + 1)x$, as $kx^2 \geqslant 0$
Thus P_1 is true and P_{k+1} is true whenever P_k is true
$\Rightarrow P_n$ is true. {Principle of Mathematical Induction}

10 Consider $A = \,]0, 1[$, a subset of $\mathbb{R}^+$.
Suppose α is the **least** element of A, $0 < \alpha < 1$.
$\Rightarrow 0 < \dfrac{\alpha}{2} < \alpha < 1$
$\Rightarrow \dfrac{\alpha}{2}$ lies in A, but is smaller than α

We have a contradiction as α was the least element of A and so A does not have a least element.

11 Suppose $r + x$ is rational
$\Rightarrow r + x = \dfrac{a}{b}$ where $a, b \in \mathbb{Z}$, $b \neq 0$
$\Rightarrow x = \dfrac{a}{b} - r$ which $\in \mathbb{Q}$, a contradiction
$\Rightarrow r + x$ is irrational.
Similarly suppose $rx = \dfrac{c}{d}$, $c, d \in \mathbb{Z}$, $d \neq 0$
$\Rightarrow x = \dfrac{c}{dr}$ which $\in \mathbb{Q}$, a contradiction
$\Rightarrow rx$ is irrational.

EXERCISE B.1

1 **a**
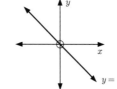
As $x \to \infty$, $-x \to -\infty$
$\therefore \lim_{x \to \infty} (-x)$ DNE.

b

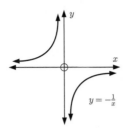

As $x \to \infty$, $-\dfrac{1}{x} \to 0^-$

$\therefore \quad \lim\limits_{x \to \infty} \left(-\dfrac{1}{x}\right) = 0$

c

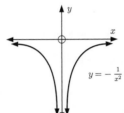

As $x \to \infty$, $-\dfrac{1}{x^2} \to 0^-$

$\therefore \quad \lim\limits_{x \to \infty} \left(-\dfrac{1}{x^2}\right) = 0$

d

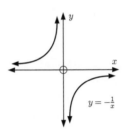

As $x \to 0^+$, $-\dfrac{1}{x} \to -\infty$

As $x \to 0^-$, $-\dfrac{1}{x} \to \infty$

$\therefore \quad \lim\limits_{x \to \infty} \left(-\dfrac{1}{x}\right)$ DNE.

2   a

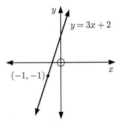

As $x \to -1^-$, $3x + 2 \to -1$ below
As $x \to -1^+$, $3x + 2 \to -1$ above
$\therefore \quad \lim\limits_{x \to -1}(3x + 2) = -1$

b $f(x) = \dfrac{x^2 + x - 2}{x + 2} = \dfrac{(x + 2)(x - 1)}{x + 2}$

$\therefore \quad f(x) = \begin{cases} x - 1 \text{ if } x \in \mathbb{R}, \ x \neq -2 \\ \text{undefined if } x = -2 \end{cases}$

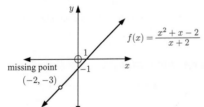

$f(x) = \dfrac{x^2 + x - 2}{x + 2}$

As $x \to -2^-$, $y \to -3$ below
As $x \to -2^+$, $y \to -3$ above

$\therefore \quad \lim\limits_{x \to -2} \dfrac{x^2 + x - 2}{x + 2} = -3$

3   a

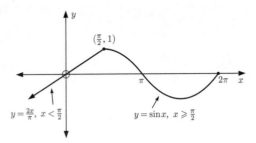

$y = \dfrac{2x}{\pi}, \ x < \dfrac{\pi}{2}$ $y = \sin x, \ x \geqslant \dfrac{\pi}{2}$

b As $x \to \dfrac{\pi}{2}^-$, $y \to 1$ below

$\therefore \quad \lim\limits_{x \to \frac{\pi}{2}^-} f(x) = 1$

As $x \to \dfrac{\pi}{2}^+$, $y \to 1$ below

$\therefore \quad \lim\limits_{x \to \frac{\pi}{2}^+} f(x) = 1$

c Since $\lim\limits_{x \to \frac{\pi}{2}^-} f(x) = \lim\limits_{x \to \frac{\pi}{2}^+} f(x) = 1$,

$\lim\limits_{x \to \frac{\pi}{2}} f(x) = 1$

4   a

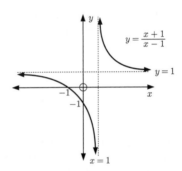

$y = \dfrac{x + 1}{x - 1}$ $y = 1$ $x = 1$

b   i As $x \to -\infty$, $y \to 1$ below $\therefore \quad \lim\limits_{x \to -\infty} f(x) = 1$

ii As $x \to \infty$, $y \to 1$ above $\therefore \quad \lim\limits_{x \to \infty} f(x) = 1$

iii $\left.\begin{array}{l} \text{As } x \to 1^-, \ y \to -\infty \\ \text{As } x \to 1^+, \ y \to \infty \end{array}\right\}$ $\therefore \quad \lim\limits_{x \to 1} f(x)$ DNE.

5   a

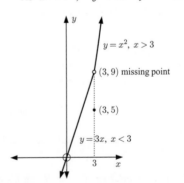

$y = x^2, \ x > 3$

$(3, 9)$ missing point

$(3, 5)$

$y = 3x, \ x < 3$

b As $x \to 3^-$, $y \to 9$ below
As $x \to 3^+$, $y \to 9$ above

c Yes the limit exists
$\lim\limits_{x \to 3} f(x) = 9$ {as both LH and RH limits are 9}

6 For $x < 0$, $\sqrt{x}$ does not exist

$\therefore \quad \lim\limits_{x \to 0^-}$ DNE.

So, although $\lim\limits_{x \to 0^+} \sqrt{x} = 0$, $\lim\limits_{x \to 0} \sqrt{x}$ DNE.

7 a

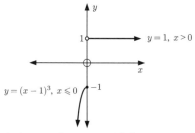

i As $x \to 0^-$, $y \to -1$ below

$\therefore \quad \lim\limits_{x \to 0^-} f(x) = -1$

ii As $x \to 0^+$, $y = 1$

$\therefore \quad \lim\limits_{x \to 0^+} f(x) = 1$

iii Since the limits in **i** and **ii** are different, $\lim\limits_{x \to 0} f(x)$ DNE.

b

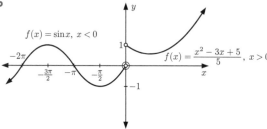

i As $x \to 0^-$, $y \to 0$ $\therefore \quad \lim\limits_{x \to 0^-} f(x) = 0$

ii As $x \to 0^+$, $y \to 1$ $\therefore \quad \lim\limits_{x \to 0^+} f(x) = 1$

iii Since the limits in **i** and **ii** are different, $\lim\limits_{x \to 0} f(x)$ DNE.

c

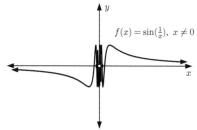

$f(x)$ does not approach any value as $x \to 0$ from above or below.

i $\lim\limits_{x \to 0^-} f(x)$ DNE   **ii** $\lim\limits_{x \to 0^+} f(x)$ DNE

iii $\lim\limits_{x \to 0} f(x)$ DNE

EXERCISE B.2

1 a $\lim\limits_{x \to 1} \dfrac{x+1}{x^2 - 2x - 3}$

$= \dfrac{2}{-4}$

$= -\dfrac{1}{2}$

b $\lim\limits_{x \to -1} \dfrac{x+1}{x^2 - 2x - 3}$

$= \lim\limits_{x \to -1} \dfrac{x+1}{(x+1)(x - 3)}$ $\{x \neq -1\}$

$= -\dfrac{1}{4}$

c $\lim\limits_{x \to 0} \dfrac{x^2 + 3x - 4}{x - 1}$

$= \dfrac{-4}{-1}$

$= 4$

d $\lim\limits_{x \to 1} \dfrac{x^2 + 3x - 4}{x - 1}$

$= \lim\limits_{x \to 1} \dfrac{(x-1)(x + 4)}{x - 1}$ $\{x \neq 1\}$

$= 5$

e $\lim\limits_{y \to 2} \dfrac{1}{y - 5} \left(\dfrac{1}{y} - \dfrac{1}{5} \right)$

$= \dfrac{1}{-3} \left(\dfrac{1}{2} - \dfrac{1}{5} \right)$

$= -\dfrac{1}{3} \times \dfrac{3}{10}$

$= -\dfrac{1}{10}$

f $\lim\limits_{y \to 5} \dfrac{1}{y - 5} \left(\dfrac{1}{y} - \dfrac{1}{5} \right)$

$= \lim\limits_{y \to 5} \dfrac{\dfrac{5 - y}{5y}}{(y - 5)^1}$ $\{y \neq 5\}$

$= \lim\limits_{y \to 5} \dfrac{-1}{5y}$

$= -\dfrac{1}{25}$

2 a $x < 2$

$\therefore \quad 2 - x > 0$

$\therefore \quad \sqrt{2 - x}$ exists.

Now $\lim\limits_{x \to 2^-} \ln x \neq 0$ but $\lim\limits_{x \to 2^-} \sqrt{2 - x} = 0$

$\therefore \quad \lim\limits_{x \to 2^-} \dfrac{\ln x}{\sqrt{2 - x}}$ DNE

b $\lim\limits_{x \to 0} \dfrac{\sin x}{e^x} = \dfrac{0}{1} = 0$

c $\lim\limits_{x \to \pi^-} \dfrac{\sin x}{1 - \cos x}$

$= \dfrac{0}{1 - (-1)}$

$= 0$

d $\lim\limits_{\theta \to 0^-} \cos \theta = 1$ but $\lim\limits_{\theta \to 0^-} \theta = 0$

$\therefore \quad \lim\limits_{\theta \to 0^-} \dfrac{\cos \theta}{\theta}$ DNE

e $\lim\limits_{x \to \frac{\pi}{2}^-} \dfrac{\tan x}{\sec x}$

$= \lim\limits_{x \to \frac{\pi}{2}^-} \dfrac{\sin x}{\cos x} \cdot \dfrac{\cos x}{1}$ $\{\cos x \neq 0\}$

$= 1$

3 a $\lim\limits_{x\to\infty}\dfrac{3+x}{x+5}$

$=\lim\limits_{x\to\infty}\dfrac{\frac{3}{x}+1}{1+\frac{5}{x}}$

$=\dfrac{0+1}{1+0}$

$=1$

b $\lim\limits_{x\to\infty}\dfrac{4x^2-5x+1}{x^2+x+1}$

$=\lim\limits_{x\to\infty}\dfrac{4-\frac{5}{x}+\frac{1}{x^2}}{1+\frac{1}{x}+\frac{1}{x^2}}$

$=\dfrac{4-0+0}{1+0+0}$

$=4$

c $\lim\limits_{x\to\infty}\sqrt{\dfrac{x^2+3}{x}}$

$=\lim\limits_{x\to\infty}\sqrt{x+\dfrac{3}{x}}$

But as $x\to\infty$,

$\sqrt{x+\dfrac{3}{x}}\to\infty$

$\therefore$ the limit DNE.

d $\lim\limits_{x\to\infty}\dfrac{1+x}{x^2+x+1}$

$=\lim\limits_{x\to\infty}\dfrac{\frac{1}{x^2}+\frac{1}{x}}{1+\frac{1}{x}+\frac{1}{x^2}}$

$=\dfrac{0+0}{1+0+0}$

$=0$

4 $\lim\limits_{x\to\infty}\sqrt{x^2+x}-x$

$=\lim\limits_{x\to\infty}\left(\sqrt{x^2+x}-x\right)\left(\dfrac{\sqrt{x^2+x}+x}{\sqrt{x^2+x}+x}\right)$

$=\lim\limits_{x\to\infty}\dfrac{x^2+x-x^2}{\sqrt{x^2+x}+x}$

$=\lim\limits_{x\to\infty}\dfrac{x}{x\sqrt{1+\frac{1}{x}}+x}$ {as $x>0$}

$=\lim\limits_{x\to\infty}\dfrac{1}{\sqrt{1+\frac{1}{x}}+1}$

$=\dfrac{1}{1+1}$

$=\dfrac{1}{2}$

5 If $\lim\limits_{x\to a}f(x)=l$ $\Leftrightarrow$ $\lim\limits_{x\to a}f(x)=\lim\limits_{x\to a}l$

$\Leftrightarrow$ $\lim\limits_{x\to a}f(x)-\lim\limits_{x\to a}l=0$

$\Leftrightarrow$ $\lim\limits_{x\to a}(f(x)-l)=0$

EXERCISE B.3

1 a $\lim\limits_{\theta\to0}\dfrac{\sin^2\theta}{\theta}$

$=\lim\limits_{\theta\to0}\left(\dfrac{\sin\theta}{\theta}\right)\sin\theta$

$=1\times0$

$=0$

b $\lim\limits_{\theta\to0}\dfrac{\sin3\theta}{\theta}$

$=\lim\limits_{\theta\to0}\left(\dfrac{\sin3\theta}{3\theta}\right)3$

$=3\lim\limits_{3\theta\to0}\left(\dfrac{\sin3\theta}{3\theta}\right)$

{as $\theta\to0$,

$3\theta\to0$ also}

$=3\times1$

$=3$

c $\lim\limits_{\theta\to0}\dfrac{\theta}{\tan\theta}$

$=\lim\limits_{\theta\to0}\dfrac{\theta}{\frac{\sin\theta}{\cos\theta}}$

$=\lim\limits_{\theta\to0}\left(\dfrac{\theta}{\sin\theta}\right)\cos\theta$

$=1\times1$

$=1$

{Since $\lim\limits_{\theta\to0}\dfrac{\sin\theta}{\theta}=1$,

$\lim\limits_{\theta\to0}\dfrac{\theta}{\sin\theta}=1$}

e $\lim\limits_{x\to0}x\cot x$

$=\lim\limits_{x\to0}x\dfrac{\cos x}{\sin x}$

$=\lim\limits_{x\to0}\left(\dfrac{x}{\sin x}\right)\cos x$

$=1\times1$

$=1$

f $\lim\limits_{x\to0}\left(\dfrac{x^2+x}{\sin2x}\right)$

$=\lim\limits_{x\to0}\left(\dfrac{x^2}{\sin2x}+\dfrac{x}{\sin2x}\right)$

$=\lim\limits_{x\to0}\left[\dfrac{x}{2}\left(\dfrac{2x}{\sin2x}\right)+\dfrac{1}{2}\left(\dfrac{2x}{\sin2x}\right)\right]$

$=0\times1+\dfrac{1}{2}\times1$

$=\dfrac{1}{2}$

g $\lim\limits_{x\to0^+}\dfrac{\sin x}{\sqrt{x}}=\lim\limits_{x\to0^+}\left(\dfrac{\sin x}{x}\right)\sqrt{x}$

$=1\times0$

$=0$

d $\lim\limits_{x\to0}\dfrac{\sin7x}{4x}$

$=\lim\limits_{x\to0}\left(\dfrac{\sin7x}{7x}\right)\dfrac{7}{4}$

$=\dfrac{7}{4}\times\lim\limits_{7x\to0}\left(\dfrac{\sin7x}{7x}\right)$

$=\dfrac{7}{4}\times1$

$=\dfrac{7}{4}$

2 a $\lim\limits_{x\to0}\dfrac{x+\sin x}{x-\sin x}=\lim\limits_{x\to0}\dfrac{1+\frac{\sin x}{x}}{1-\frac{\sin x}{x}}$

But as $x\to0$, $1-\dfrac{\sin x}{x}\to1-1=0$

$\therefore$ the limit DNE.

b $\lim\limits_{h\to0}\dfrac{\cos h-1}{h}=\lim\limits_{h\to0}\left(\dfrac{\cos h-1}{h}\right)\left(\dfrac{\cos h+1}{\cos h+1}\right)$

$=\lim\limits_{h\to0}\dfrac{\cos^2h-1}{h(\cos h+1)}$

$=\lim\limits_{h\to0}\dfrac{-\sin^2h}{h(\cos h+1)}$

$=\lim\limits_{h\to0}-h\left(\dfrac{\sin h}{h}\right)^2\dfrac{1}{\cos h+1}$

$=0\times1^2\times\dfrac{1}{2}$

$=0$

c $\lim\limits_{x \to 0} \dfrac{1 - \cos x}{x^2} = \lim\limits_{x \to 0} \left(\dfrac{1 - \cos x}{x^2} \right) \left(\dfrac{1 + \cos x}{1 + \cos x} \right)$

$\qquad = \lim\limits_{x \to 0} \dfrac{\sin^2 x}{x^2 (1 + \cos x)}$

$\qquad = \lim\limits_{x \to 0} 1 \left(\dfrac{\sin x}{x} \right)^2 \dfrac{1}{1 + \cos x}$

$\qquad = 1 \times 1^2 \times \tfrac{1}{2}$

$\qquad = \tfrac{1}{2}$

3   a As $-1 \leqslant \cos\left(\dfrac{1}{x^2} \right) \leqslant 1$, then

$\qquad -x^2 \leqslant x^2 \cos\left(\dfrac{1}{x^2} \right) \leqslant x^2$

But $\lim\limits_{x \to 0} (-x^2) = \lim\limits_{x \to 0} (x^2) = 0$

$\qquad \therefore \ \lim\limits_{x \to 0} x^2 \cos\left(\dfrac{1}{x^2} \right) = 0$ {Squeeze Theorem}

b As $-1 \leqslant \sin\left(\dfrac{1}{x} \right) \leqslant 1$, then

$\qquad -x \leqslant x \sin\left(\dfrac{1}{x} \right) \leqslant x$ {if $x > 0$}

But $\lim\limits_{x \to 0} (-x) = \lim\limits_{x \to 0} (x) = 0$

$\qquad \therefore \ \lim\limits_{x \to 0} x \sin\left(\dfrac{1}{x} \right) = 0$ {Squeeze Theorem}

However, if $x < 0$

$-1 \leqslant \sin\left(\dfrac{1}{x} \right) \leqslant 1 \ \Rightarrow \ x \leqslant x \sin\left(\dfrac{1}{x} \right) \leqslant -x$

and as $\lim\limits_{x \to 0} (-x) = \lim\limits_{x \to 0} (x) = 0$,

$\qquad \therefore \ \lim\limits_{x \to 0} x \sin\left(\dfrac{1}{x} \right) = 0$ {Squeeze Theorem}

c Consider $x \geqslant 0$

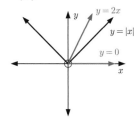

Now $0 \leqslant |x| \leqslant 2x$

$\therefore \ \dfrac{0}{1 + x^4} \leqslant \dfrac{|x|}{1 + x^4} \leqslant \dfrac{2x}{1 + x^4}$

As $x \to 0^+$, $\dfrac{2x}{1 + x^4} \to \dfrac{0}{1} = 0$

$\therefore \ \lim\limits_{x \to 0^+} \dfrac{|x|}{1 + x^4} = 0$ .... (1) {Squeeze Theorem}

Consider $x < 0$

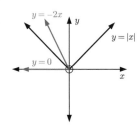

Now $0 \leqslant |x| \leqslant -2x$

$\therefore \ \dfrac{0}{1 + x^4} \leqslant \dfrac{|x|}{1 + x^4} \leqslant \dfrac{-2x}{1 + x^4}$

But, as $x \to 0^-$, $\dfrac{-2x}{1 + x^4} \to 0$

$\therefore \ \lim\limits_{x \to 0^-} \dfrac{|x|}{1 + x^4} = 0$ .... (2) {Squeeze Theorem}

From (1) and (2), $\lim\limits_{x \to 0} g(x) = 0$

4   a As $-1 \leqslant \sin x \leqslant 1$ and $e^{\frac{1}{x}} > 0$ for all $x \in \mathbb{R}$,

$\qquad -\dfrac{1}{e^{\frac{1}{x}}} \leqslant \dfrac{\sin x}{e^{\frac{1}{x}}} \leqslant \dfrac{1}{e^{\frac{1}{x}}}$

But as $x \to 0^+$, $\dfrac{1}{x} \to \infty$ and $e^{\frac{1}{x}} \to \infty$

$\qquad \therefore \ \lim\limits_{x \to 0^+} \left(-\dfrac{1}{e^{\frac{1}{x}}} \right) = \lim\limits_{x \to 0^+} \left(\dfrac{1}{e^{\frac{1}{x}}} \right) = 0$

$\qquad \therefore \ \lim\limits_{x \to 0^+} e^{\left(-\frac{1}{x} \right)} \sin x = 0$ {Squeeze Theorem}

b As $-1 \leqslant \sin x \leqslant 1$ and $e^{\frac{1}{x}} > 0$ for all $x \in \mathbb{R}$,

$\qquad -\dfrac{1}{e^{\frac{1}{x}}} \leqslant \dfrac{\sin x}{e^{\frac{1}{x}}} \leqslant \dfrac{1}{e^{\frac{1}{x}}}$

Now $\lim\limits_{x \to 0^+} e^{-\frac{1}{x}} = 0$ but $\lim\limits_{x \to 0^-} e^{-\frac{1}{x}}$ is undefined.

$\qquad \therefore \ \lim\limits_{x \to 0} e^{-\frac{1}{x}}$ is undefined.

$\qquad \therefore \ \lim\limits_{x \to 0} e^{-\frac{1}{x}} \sin x$ is undefined.

EXERCISE C.1

1   a Let $F(x) = f(x) g(x)$

As $f(x)$ and $g(x)$ are defined at $x = a$, $F(a) = f(a) g(a)$ is also defined at $x = a$.

Now $\lim\limits_{x \to a} F(x) = \lim\limits_{x \to a} [f(x) g(x)]$

$\qquad = \lim\limits_{x \to a} f(x) \times \lim\limits_{x \to a} g(x)$

$\qquad = f(a) \times g(a)$

$\qquad = F(a)$

$\therefore \ f(x) g(x)$ is continuous at $x = a$.

b Let $F(x) = f(x) \pm g(x)$

As $f(x)$ and $g(x)$ are defined at $x = a$,

$F(a) = f(a) \pm g(a)$ is also defined at $x = a$.

Now $\lim\limits_{x \to a} F(x) = \lim\limits_{x \to a} (f(x) \pm g(x))$

$\qquad = \lim\limits_{x \to a} f(x) \pm \lim\limits_{x \to a} g(x)$

$\qquad = f(a) \pm g(a)$

$\qquad = F(a)$

$\therefore \ f(x) \pm g(x)$ is continuous at $x = a$.

c Let $F(x) = \dfrac{f(x)}{g(x)}$ where $g(x) \neq 0$

Now $F(a) = \dfrac{f(a)}{g(a)}$ where $g(a) \neq 0$

$\therefore$ $F(a)$ is defined.

Now $\displaystyle\lim_{x \to a} F(x) = \lim_{x \to a} \dfrac{f(x)}{g(x)}$

$\qquad = \dfrac{\displaystyle\lim_{x \to a} f(x)}{\displaystyle\lim_{x \to a} g(x)}$

$\qquad = \dfrac{f(a)}{g(a)}$ where $g(a) \neq 0$

$\qquad = F(a)$

$\therefore$ $\dfrac{f(x)}{g(x)}$ is continuous at $x = a$.

d Let $F(x) = c\,f(x)$

$\therefore$ $F(a) = c\,f(a)$ is defined as $f(a)$ is defined and $c \in \mathbb{R}$.

Now $\displaystyle\lim_{x \to a} F(x) = \lim_{x \to a} c\,f(x)$

$\qquad = c \displaystyle\lim_{x \to a} f(x)$

$\qquad = c\,f(a)$

$\qquad = F(a)$

$\therefore$ $c\,f(x)$ is continuous at $x = a$.

e Let $F(x) = [f(x)]^n$, $n \in \mathbb{Z}^+$

$\therefore$ $F(a) = [f(a)]^n$ is defined as $f(a)$ is defined.

Now $\displaystyle\lim_{x \to a} F(x) = \lim_{x \to a} [f(x)]^n$

$\qquad = \left[\displaystyle\lim_{x \to a} f(x) \right]^n$

$\qquad = [f(a)]^n$

$\qquad = F(a)$

$\therefore$ $[f(x)]^n$ is continuous at $x = a$.

2 a   **i** f has an essential discontinuity at $x = 6$.
   ii f has a removable discontinuity at $x = 5$.
b f is continuous on $\{x \mid x \in \mathbb{R}, \ x \neq 5 \text{ or } 6\}$

3 a

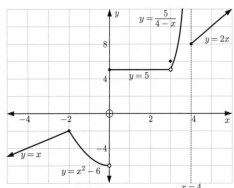

b   **i** f is continuous at $x = -2$.
   ii f has a 'jump' discontinuity at $x = 0$.
   iii f has a removable discontinuity at $x = 3$.
   iv f has a 'break' discontinuity at $x = 4$ due to the vertical asymptote at $x = 4$.

4 a

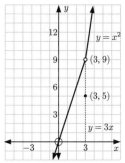

$f(x)$ is continuous for all $x \in \mathbb{R}$, $x \neq 3$.
At $x = 3$ there is a removable discontinuity.
It could be removed by defining $f(x)$ as:

$$f(x) = \begin{cases} x^2, & x \geqslant 3 \\ 3x, & x < 3 \end{cases}$$

b

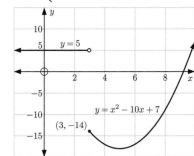

$f(x)$ is continuous for all $x \in \mathbb{R}$, $x \neq 3$.
At $x = 3$ we have a 'jump' discontinuity which is essential.

5 a $\displaystyle\lim_{x \to 1} \dfrac{x^3 - 1}{x - 1}$

$\qquad = \displaystyle\lim_{x \to 1} \dfrac{(x - 1)(x^2 + x + 1)}{x - 1}$

$\qquad = 1 + 1 + 1$

$\qquad = 3$

$\qquad \therefore$ let $k = 3$

b $\displaystyle\lim_{x \to 0} \dfrac{\sin 3x}{x}$

$\qquad = \displaystyle\lim_{x \to 0} \left(\dfrac{\sin 3x}{3x} \right) 3$

$\qquad = 3 \times \displaystyle\lim_{3x \to 0} \left(\dfrac{\sin 3x}{3x} \right)$

$\qquad = 3 \times 1 \qquad \{\text{as } x \to 0, \ 3x \to 0\}$

$\qquad = 3$

$\qquad \therefore$ let $k = 3$

c $f(2) = 2^2 = 4$
   $\therefore$ let $k = 4$

d $y = \dfrac{1}{x}$ has an essential discontinuity at $x = 0$ which cannot be removed
   $\therefore$ no value for k can be found.

e $y = kx$ represents the infinite number of lines passing through $O(0, 0)$.
   $\therefore$ $k \in \mathbb{R}$

f If $k + 2 \geqslant 0$,
then $k \geqslant -2$,
and $f(x)$ has graph:

If $k + 2 < 0$,
then $k < -2$,
and $f(x)$ has graph:

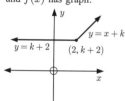

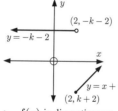

$\therefore$ $f(x)$ is continuous
for all $x \in \mathbb{R}$

$\therefore$ $f(x)$ is discontinuous
at $x = 2$

So, if $k \geqslant -2$, $k \in \mathbb{R}$, $f(x)$ is continuous
and if $k < -2$, $k \in \mathbb{R}$, $f(x)$ is continuous for all $x \neq 2$.

6 a $x_n = a + \dfrac{\sqrt{2}}{n}$, $a \in \mathbb{Q}$

Since $a \in \mathbb{Q}$, $x_n \notin \mathbb{Q}$ for all $n \in \mathbb{Z}^+$

$\therefore$ $\lim\limits_{n \to \infty} g(x_n) = 0$ {Dirichlet function}

But $g(a) = 1$ since $a \in \mathbb{Q}$

$\therefore$ $\lim\limits_{n \to \infty} g(x_n) \neq g(a)$

But $\lim\limits_{n \to \infty} x_n = a$

$\therefore$ $g(x)$ is discontinuous at $x = a$.

b If x_n is the decimal expansion of a to n decimal places then
$x_n \in \mathbb{Q}$

$\therefore$ $\lim\limits_{n \to \infty} g(x_n) = 1$ {Dirichlet function}

But $g(a) = 0$ since $a \notin \mathbb{Q}$

$\therefore$ $\lim\limits_{n \to \infty} g(x_n) \neq g(a)$

Also $\lim\limits_{n \to \infty} x_n = a$

$\therefore$ $g(x)$ is discontinuous at $x = a$.

c From **a** and **b**, the Dirichlet function is nowhere continuous.

7 a If $g(x)$ is continuous at $x = a$, then

$\lim\limits_{x \to a} g(x) = g(a) = l$ .... (1)

If $f(x)$ is continuous at $g(a)$ then

$\lim\limits_{g(x) \to g(a)} f(g(x)) = f(g(a)) = f(l)$

But $g(x) \to g(a)$ when $x \to a$

$\therefore$ $\lim\limits_{x \to a} f(g(x)) = f(l)$

b From **a**, if $\lim\limits_{x \to a} g(x)$ exists then,

$\lim\limits_{x \to a} f(g(x)) = f(l)$

$= f\left(\lim\limits_{x \to a} g(x)\right)$ {from (1)}

c If $\lim\limits_{x \to \infty} g(x)$ exists then

$\lim\limits_{x \to \infty} f(g(x)) = f(l) = f\left(\lim\limits_{x \to \infty} g(x)\right)$

8 a

$x = e^{\ln x}$

$\therefore$ $x^{\frac{1}{n}} = (e^{\ln x})^{\frac{1}{n}}$

$\Rightarrow$ $x^{\frac{1}{n}} = e^{\frac{1}{n} \ln x}$

$\Rightarrow$ $x^{\frac{1}{n}} = e^{\ln x^{\frac{1}{n}}}$

b From **a**, $x^{\frac{1}{n}} = f(g(n))$ where $f(n) = e^n$, $g(n) = \ln x^{\frac{1}{n}}$

From **7 c**, $\lim\limits_{n \to \infty} f(g(n)) = f\left(\lim\limits_{n \to \infty} g(n)\right)$

$\therefore$ $\lim\limits_{n \to \infty} x^{\frac{1}{n}} = f(\ln 1)$

$= f(0)$

$= e^0$

$= 1$

EXERCISE C.2

1 a $f(x)$ is continuous for all $x \in \mathbb{R}$ and $\therefore$ on $[0, 2]$.
$f(0) = -3$ and $f(2) = 7$
Thus, with $k = 0$, $f(0) \leqslant k \leqslant f(2)$
Hence, by the IVT, there exists $c \in [0, 2]$ such that
$f(c) = 0$
$\Rightarrow$ $f(x)$ has a zero on $[0, 2]$.

b

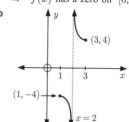

$f(x)$ has an essential discontinuity at $x = 2$
$\therefore$ the IVT will not apply.
Clearly for $[1, 2[$, $f(x) < 0$ and for $]2, 3]$, $f(x) > 0$
$\therefore$ $f(x)$ is never zero on $[1, 3]$.

2 $f(x) = x^3 - 9x^2 + 24x - 10$ has graph:

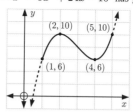

$f'(x) = 3x^2 - 18x + 24$ $\qquad$ $\therefore$ $(2, 10)$ is a local maximum
$= 3(x^2 - 6x + 8)$ $\qquad$ $(4, 6)$ is a local minimum.
$= 3(x - 2)(x - 4)$

a On $[1, 5]$, $m = 10$ and $x_m = 2$ or 5

b On $[1, 5]$, $m = 6$ and $x_m = 1$ or 4

3 As $f(a)$ and $f(b)$ have opposite signs, then $f(a) \leqslant f(b)$ or $f(b) \leqslant f(a)$
By the IVT, there exists $c \in [a, b]$ such that
$f(a) \leqslant f(c) = 0 \leqslant f(b)$ or $f(b) \leqslant f(c) = 0 \leqslant f(a)$
$\therefore$ there exists a zero $c \in [a, b]$
$\Rightarrow$ there exists at least one zero of $f(x)$.

4   a Let $f(x) = \sin x + rx - 1$, $r > 0$ for $x \in]0, \dfrac{\pi}{2}[$.

Now $f(0) = -1 < 0$ and $f\left(\dfrac{\pi}{2}\right) = r\dfrac{\pi}{2} > 0$

Since $f(0)$ and $f\left(\dfrac{\pi}{2}\right)$ are opposite in sign, by the IVT there

exists $c \in [0, \dfrac{\pi}{2}]$ such that $f(c) = 0$

b

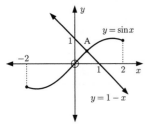

When $r = 1$,
at A, $\sin x = 1 - x$
$\therefore \ f(x) = 0$
$\therefore \ x \approx 0.511$

5   a If $f(x) = x^{15} + \dfrac{1}{1 + \sin^2 x + (r + 1)^2}$

where $\sin^2(x) \approx 0.7081$ for $x = \pm 1$

and $(r + 1)^2 \geqslant 0$ for $r \in \mathbb{R}$

$\therefore \ 0 \leqslant \dfrac{1}{1 + \sin^2 x + (r + 1)^2} \leqslant 0.5854$

for $x = \pm 1$ and $r \in \mathbb{R}$.

So, for $r \in \mathbb{R}$,

$f(1) = (1)^{15} + \dfrac{1}{1 + \sin^2(1) + (r + 1)^2}$

$= 1 + \dfrac{1}{1 + \sin^2(1) + (r + 1)^2}$

$\therefore \ 1 \leqslant f(1) \leqslant 1.5854$

and also

$f(-1) = (-1)^{15} + \dfrac{1}{1 + \sin^2(-1) + (r + 1)^2}$

$= -1 + \dfrac{1}{1 + \sin^2(-1) + (r + 1)^2}$

$\therefore \ -1 \leqslant f(-1) \leqslant -0.4146$

Since f is continuous for all x, $r \in \mathbb{R}$, f is also continuous

on $[-1, 1]$ and since $f(-1) < 0 < f(1)$

$\therefore \ $ there exists an $x \in [-1, 1]$ such that $f(x) = 0$.

b If $g(x) = rx^{17} + \dfrac{1}{5x}$, where $r \in \mathbb{R}$, $r > 0$, there is a

discontinuity at $x = 0$.
f is not continuous on the interval $[-1, 1]$, so the IVT
cannot be used to prove the existence of a zero.

EXERCISE D

1 If $f(x) = \cos x$

$f'(x) = \displaystyle\lim_{h \to 0} \dfrac{\cos(x + h) - \cos x}{h}$

$= \displaystyle\lim_{h \to 0} \dfrac{\cos x \cos h - \sin x \sin h - \cos x}{h}$

$= \displaystyle\lim_{h \to 0} \cos x \left(\dfrac{\cos h - 1}{h}\right) - \sin x \left(\dfrac{\sin h}{h}\right)$

$\therefore \ f'(x) = \cos x \times 0 - \sin x \times 1$

$= -\sin x$

$\left\{\displaystyle\lim_{h \to 0} \dfrac{\sin h}{h} = 1 \text{ and } \lim_{h \to 0} \dfrac{\cos h - 1}{h} = 0 \quad \{\textbf{Example 6}\}\right\}$

2 $f(5) = 0$ is defined.

$\displaystyle\lim_{x \to 5^-} f(x) = \lim_{x \to 5^-} (5 - x) = 0$ and

$\displaystyle\lim_{x \to 5^+} f(x) = \lim_{x \to 5^+} (x - 5) = 0$

$\therefore \ \displaystyle\lim_{x \to 5} f(x) = 0 = f(5)$

Thus $f(x)$ is continuous at $x = 5$.

Now $f(x) = \begin{cases} x - 5, & x \geqslant 5 \\ 5 - x, & x < 5 \end{cases}$

$\therefore \ f'_-(x) = -1$ and $f'_+(x) = 1$

Hence $f'_-(5) = -1$ and $f'_+(5) = 1$, $\therefore \ f'_-(5) \neq f'_+(5)$

$\Rightarrow f(x)$ is not differentiable at $x = 5$

3 $f(x) = \begin{cases} x + 2, & x \geqslant 0 \\ x^2 + 3x, & x < 0 \end{cases}$

has an essential 'jump' discontinuity at $x = 0$

$\therefore \ f(x)$ is not continuous at $x = 0$

$\Rightarrow f(x)$ is not differentiable at $x = 0$

Note: $f'_+(0) = 0$ and $f'_-(0) = 2(0) + 3 = 3$ and

$f'_+(0) \neq f'_-(0)$

4 $f(x) = \begin{cases} -x^2 + 5x + 6, & x \geqslant 1 \\ 3x + 10, & x < 1 \end{cases}$

a

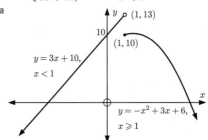

b   i $f'_-(1) = 3$

ii $f'_+(1) = -2(1) + 5 = 3$

c No, although $f'_-(1) = f'_+(1)$, $f(x)$ is not continuous at
$x = 1$.

5   a

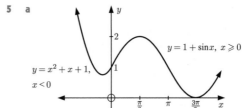

$f(0) = 1 + \sin 0 = 1$ is defined

$\displaystyle\lim_{x \to 0^-} f(x) = \lim_{x \to 0^-} (x^2 + x + 1) = 1$

$\displaystyle\lim_{x \to 0^+} f(x) = \lim_{x \to 0^-} (1 + \sin x) = 1$

$\therefore \ \displaystyle\lim_{x \to 0} f(x) = 1 = f(0)$

$\Rightarrow f(x)$ is continuous at $x = 0$

Now $f'_-(0) = 2(0) + 1 = 1$ and $f'_+(0) = \cos 0 = 1$

$\therefore$ $f'_-(0) = f'_+(0) = 1$

$\Rightarrow$ $f(x)$ is differentiable at $x = 0$

b

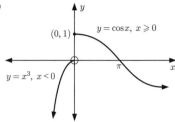

As $f(x)$ is discontinuous at $x = 0$, it is not differentiable at $x = 0$.

c

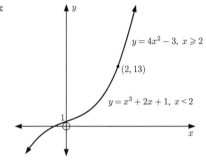

$f(2) = 4(2)^2 - 3 = 13$ is defined

$\lim\limits_{x \to 2^-} f(x) = 2^3 + 2(2) + 1 = 13$

$\lim\limits_{x \to 2^+} f(x) = 4(2)^2 - 3 = 13$

$\therefore$ $\lim\limits_{x \to 2} f(x) = 13 = f(2)$

$\Rightarrow$ $f(x)$ is continuous at $x = 2$

Now $f'_-(2) = 3(2)^2 + 2 = 14$ and

$f'_+(2) = 8(2) = 16$

$\therefore$ $f'_-(2) \neq f'_+(2)$

$\Rightarrow$ $f(x)$ is not differentiable at $x = 2$

6 $f(0) = k \sin 0 = 0$

$\therefore$ $f(0)$ is defined.

Also, $\lim\limits_{x \to 0^-} f(x) = \lim\limits_{x \to 0^-} (\tan x) = \tan 0 = 0$

and $\lim\limits_{x \to 0^+} f(x) = \lim\limits_{x \to 0^+} (k \sin x) = k(0) = 0$

$\therefore$ $\lim\limits_{x \to 0} f(x) = 0 = f(0)$

$\Rightarrow$ $f(x)$ is continuous at $x = 0$ for all $k \in \mathbb{R}$.

Now $f'_-(0) = \sec^2(0) = \dfrac{1}{1^2} = 1$ and

$f'_+(0) = k \cos(0) = k$

$\therefore$ $f'_-(0) = f'_+(0) \Leftrightarrow k = 1$

$\therefore$ $f(x)$ is differentiable at $x = 0 \Leftrightarrow k = 1$

7 a $f(x) = \begin{cases} x^2, & x \leqslant 1 \\ cx + d, & x > 1 \end{cases}$

$f(1) = 1^2 = 1$ is defined.

Also, $\lim\limits_{x \to 1^-} f(x) = \lim\limits_{x \to 1^-} x^2 = 1$

and $\lim\limits_{x \to 1^+} f(x) = \lim\limits_{x \to 1^+} (cx + d) = c + d$

$\therefore$ $\lim\limits_{x \to 1} f(x) = f(1) \Leftrightarrow c + d = 1$ .... (1)

Now $f'_-(1) = 2(1) = 2$ and $f'_+(1) = c$

$\therefore$ $f'(1)$ exists $\Leftrightarrow c = 2$

But from (1), $c + d = 1$ $\therefore$ $d = -1$

$\therefore$ $c = 2, \ d = -1$

b $f(x) = \begin{cases} \sin(x - 1) + cx, & x \geqslant 1 \\ x^2 - x + d, & x < 1 \end{cases}$

$f(1) = \sin 0 + c = c$ is defined.

Also, $\lim\limits_{x \to 1^-} f(x) = \lim\limits_{x \to -1^-} (x^2 - x + d) = d$

and $\lim\limits_{x \to 1^+} f(x) = \lim\limits_{x \to 1^+} (\sin(x - 1) + cx) = c$

$\therefore$ $\lim\limits_{x \to 1} f(x) = f(1) \Leftrightarrow c = d$ .... (1)

Now $f'_-(1) = 2(1) - 1 = 1$

and $f'_+(1) = \cos(0) + c(1) = 1 + c$

$\therefore$ $f'(1)$ exists $\Leftrightarrow 1 + c = 1 \Leftrightarrow c = 0$

Thus, from (1), $c = d = 0$

8 $f(x) = \begin{cases} x^3 \sin\left(\dfrac{1}{x}\right), & x \neq 0 \\ 0, & x = 0 \end{cases}$

a $f(0) = 0$ is defined.

<u>For $x \neq 0$,</u> $|f(x)| = \left| x^3 \sin\left(\dfrac{1}{x}\right) \right| \leqslant \left| x^3 \right|$

$\therefore$ $-\left| x^3 \right| \leqslant f(x) \leqslant \left| x^3 \right|$

and $\lim\limits_{x \to 0} -\left| x^3 \right| = \lim\limits_{x \to 0} \left| x^3 \right| = 0$

$\Rightarrow$ $\lim\limits_{x \to 0} f(x) = 0$ {Squeeze Theorem}

$\Rightarrow$ $\lim\limits_{x \to 0} f(x) = f(0)$

$\Rightarrow$ $f(x)$ is continuous at $x = 0$

<u>Consider $x > 0$</u>

$f'(x) = 3x^2 \sin\left(\dfrac{1}{x}\right) - x \cos\left(\dfrac{1}{x}\right)$

where

$-1 \leqslant \sin\left(\dfrac{1}{x}\right) \leqslant 1 \Rightarrow -3x^2 \leqslant 3x^2 \sin\left(\dfrac{1}{x}\right) \leqslant 3x^2$

and

$-1 \leqslant \cos\left(\dfrac{1}{x}\right) \leqslant 1 \Rightarrow x \geqslant -x \cos\left(\dfrac{1}{x}\right) \geqslant -x$

$\Rightarrow -x \leqslant -x \cos\left(\dfrac{1}{x}\right) \leqslant x$

Thus,

$-3x^2 - x \leqslant 3x^2 \sin\left(\dfrac{1}{x}\right) - x \cos\left(\dfrac{1}{x}\right) \leqslant 3x^2 + x$

or $-3x^2 - x \leqslant f'(x) \leqslant 3x^2 + x$

But $\lim\limits_{x \to 0^+} (-3x^2 - x) = 0 = \lim\limits_{x \to 0^+} (3x^2 + x)$

$\therefore$ $\lim\limits_{x \to 0^+} f'(x) = 0$ .... (1) {Squeeze Theorem}

Consider $x < 0$

as $3x^2 > 0$,

$$-3x^2 \leqslant 3x^2 \sin\left(\frac{1}{x}\right) \leqslant 3x^2$$

and as $-x > 0$,

$$x \leqslant -x \cos\left(\frac{1}{x}\right) \leqslant -x$$

Thus,

$$-3x^2 + x \leqslant 3x^2 \sin\left(\frac{1}{x}\right) - x\cos\left(\frac{1}{x}\right) \leqslant 3x^2 - x$$

or $-3x^2 + x \leqslant f(x) \leqslant 3x^2 - x$

But $\lim_{x \to 0^-}(-3x^2 + x) = 0 = \lim_{x \to 0^-}(3x^2 - x)$

$\therefore \quad \lim_{x \to 0^-} f'(x) = 0 \quad .... \ (2) \quad \{$Squeeze Theorem$\}$

So, for $x \neq 0$, $\lim_{x \to 0} f'(x) = 0$

b $f'(x) = \begin{cases} 3x^2 \sin\left(\dfrac{1}{x}\right) - x\cos\left(\dfrac{1}{x}\right), & x \neq 0 \\ 0, & x = 0 \end{cases}$

c From (1) and (2) above,

$\lim_{x \to 0^+} f'(x) = 0 = f'(0) \quad$ and

$\lim_{x \to 0^-} f'(x) = 0 = f'(0)$

$\therefore \quad \lim_{x \to 0} f'(x) = f'(0)$

$\Rightarrow \ f'(x)$ is continuous for all x

EXERCISE E

1 a As $x \to 0$, $1 - \cos x \to 0$ and $x^2 \to 0$

The limit has type $\frac{0}{0}$, so we can use l'Hôpital's Rule.

$$\therefore \quad \lim_{x \to 0} \frac{1 - \cos x}{x^2} = \lim_{x \to 0} \frac{\sin x}{2x}$$
$$= \tfrac{1}{2}\lim_{x \to 0} \frac{\sin x}{x}$$
$$= \tfrac{1}{2} \times 1$$
$$= \tfrac{1}{2}$$

b As $x \to 0$, $e^x - 1 - x \to 1 - 1 - 0 = 0$ and $x^2 \to 0$

The limit has type $\frac{0}{0}$, so we can use l'Hôpital's Rule.

$$\lim_{x \to 0} \frac{e^x - 1 - x}{x^2} = \lim_{x \to 0} \frac{e^x - 1}{2x}$$

This limit also has type $\frac{0}{0}$, so we again use l'Hôpital's Rule.

$$\therefore \quad \lim_{x \to 0} \frac{e^x - 1 - x}{x^2} = \lim_{x \to 0} \frac{e^x}{2}$$
$$= \tfrac{1}{2}$$

c As $x \to 1$, $\ln x \to 0$ and $x - 1 \to 0$

The limit has type $\frac{0}{0}$, so we can use l'Hôpital's Rule.

$$\therefore \quad \lim_{x \to 1} \frac{\ln x}{x - 1} = \lim_{x \to 1} \frac{\frac{1}{x}}{1} = \lim_{x \to 1} \frac{1}{x} = 1$$

d As $x \to \infty$, $e^x \to \infty$

The limit has type $\frac{\infty}{\infty}$, so we can use l'Hôpital's Rule.

$\therefore \quad \lim_{x \to \infty} \frac{e^x}{x} = \lim_{x \to \infty} \frac{e^x}{1}$ which does not exist

$\therefore \quad \lim_{x \to \infty} \dfrac{e^x}{x} \quad$ DNE

e As $x \to 0^+$, $x \to 0$, $\ln x \to -\infty$

The limit has type $0 \times \infty$, so we can use l'Hôpital's Rule.

$$\therefore \quad \lim_{x \to 0^+} x \ln x = \lim_{x \to 0^+} \frac{\ln x}{x^{-1}}$$
$$= \lim_{x \to 0^+} \frac{\frac{1}{x}}{-x^{-2}}$$
$$= \lim_{x \to 0^+} (-x)$$
$$= 0$$

f As $x \to 0$, $\arctan x \to 0$

The limit has type $\frac{0}{0}$, so we can use l'Hôpital's Rule.

$$\therefore \quad \lim_{x \to 0} \frac{\arctan x}{x} = \lim_{x \to 0}\left(\frac{\frac{1}{1+x^2}}{1}\right) = 1$$

g As $x \to 0$, $x^2 + x \to 0$ and $\sin 2x \to 0$

The limit has type $\frac{0}{0}$, so we can use l'Hôpital's Rule.

$$\therefore \quad \lim_{x \to 0} \frac{x^2 + x}{\sin 2x} = \lim_{x \to 0} \frac{2x + 1}{2\cos 2x}$$
$$= \tfrac{1}{2}$$

h As $x \to 0^+$, $\sin x \to 0$ and $\sqrt{x} \to 0$

The limit has type $\frac{0}{0}$, so we can use l'Hôpital's Rule.

$$\therefore \quad \lim_{x \to 0^+} \frac{\sin x}{\sqrt{x}} = \lim_{x \to 0^+} \frac{\cos x}{\frac{1}{2}x^{-\frac{1}{2}}}$$
$$= \lim_{x \to 0^+} 2\sqrt{x}\cos x$$
$$= 2(0)(1)$$
$$= 0$$

Note: $\lim_{x \to 0^+} \dfrac{\sin x}{\sqrt{x}} = \lim_{x \to 0^+} \sqrt{x}\left(\dfrac{\sin x}{x}\right)$
$$= 0 \times 1$$
$$= 0$$

i As $x \to 0$, $x + \sin x \to 0$ and $x - \sin x \to 0$

The limit has type $\frac{0}{0}$, so we can use l'Hôpital's Rule.

$$\therefore \quad \lim_{x \to 0} \frac{x + \sin x}{x - \sin x} = \lim_{x \to 0} \frac{1 + \cos x}{1 - \cos x}$$

which DNE as $1 + \cos x \to 2$ and $1 - \cos x \to 0$

j As $x \to 0^+$, $x^2 \to 0$ and $\ln x \to -\infty$

The limit has type $0 \times \infty$, so we can use l'Hôpital's Rule.

$$\therefore \quad \lim_{x \to 0^+} x^2 \ln x = \lim_{x \to 0^+} \frac{\ln x}{x^{-2}}$$
$$= \lim_{x \to 0^+} \frac{\frac{1}{x}}{-2x^{-3}}$$
$$= \lim_{x \to 0^+} -\tfrac{1}{2}x^2$$
$$= 0$$

k As $x \to 0$, $a^x - b^x \to 0$ and $\sin x \to 0$

The limit has type $\frac{0}{0}$, so we can use l'Hôpital's Rule.

$$\therefore \lim_{x \to 0} \frac{a^x - b^x}{\sin x} = \lim_{x \to 0} \frac{a^x \ln a - b^x \ln b}{\cos x}$$

$$= \frac{\ln a - \ln b}{1}$$

$$= \ln\left(\frac{a}{b}\right) \quad \text{provided } a > 0, \ b > 0$$

2 As $x \to \frac{\pi}{2}^-$, $\tan x \to \infty$ and $\sec x \to \infty$

The limit has type $\frac{\infty}{\infty}$, so we can use l'Hôpital's Rule.

$$\therefore \lim_{x \to \frac{\pi}{2}^-} \frac{\tan x}{\sec x} = \lim_{x \to \frac{\pi}{2}^-} \frac{\sec^2 x}{\sec x \tan x}$$

$$= \lim_{x \to \frac{\pi}{2}^-} \frac{\sec x}{\tan x}$$

$$= \lim_{x \to \frac{\pi}{2}^-} \frac{\sec x \tan x}{\sec^2 x}$$

{using l'Hôpital's Rule again}

$$= \lim_{x \to \frac{\pi}{2}^-} \frac{\tan x}{\sec x}$$

which is back to where we started.
So, l'Hôpital's Rule was no use here.

Note: $\dfrac{\tan x}{\sec x} = \dfrac{\frac{\sin x}{\cos x}}{\frac{1}{\cos x}} = \sin x \quad$ provided $\cos x \neq 0$

that is, $x \neq \dfrac{\pi}{2}$

$$\therefore \lim_{x \to \frac{\pi}{2}^-} \frac{\tan x}{\sec x} = \lim_{x \to \frac{\pi}{2}^-} \sin x = 1$$

3 As $x \to 0$, $\frac{\pi}{2} - \arccos x - x \to \frac{\pi}{2} - \frac{\pi}{2} - 0$

that is, $\frac{\pi}{2} - \arccos x - x \to 0$ and $x^3 \to 0$

The limit has type $\frac{0}{0}$, so we can use l'Hôpital's Rule.

$$\therefore \lim_{x \to 0} \frac{\frac{\pi}{2} - \arccos x - x}{x^3}$$

$$= \lim_{x \to 0} \frac{0 + \frac{1}{\sqrt{1-x^2}} - 1}{3x^2}$$

$$= \lim_{x \to 0} \frac{1 - \sqrt{1-x^2}}{3x^2 \sqrt{1-x^2}} \left(\frac{1 + \sqrt{1-x^2}}{1 + \sqrt{1-x^2}}\right)$$

$$= \lim_{x \to 0} \frac{1 - (1-x^2)}{3x^2 \sqrt{1-x^2}(1 + \sqrt{1-x^2})}$$

$$= \lim_{x \to 0} \frac{1}{3\sqrt{1-x^2}(1 + \sqrt{1-x^2})}$$

$$= \frac{1}{3(1)(2)}$$

$$= \frac{1}{6}$$

4 a As $x \to 0^+$, $\ln(\cos 5x) \to 0$ and $\ln(\cos 3x) \to 0$

The limit has type $\frac{0}{0}$, so we can use l'Hôpital's Rule.

$$\therefore \lim_{x \to 0^+} \frac{\ln(\cos 5x)}{\ln(\cos 3x)} = \lim_{x \to 0^+} \frac{\frac{-5\sin 5x}{\cos 5x}}{\frac{-3\sin 3x}{\cos 3x}}$$

which is

$$\lim_{x \to 0^+} \frac{5}{3}\left(\frac{\sin 5x}{\sin 3x}\right)\left(\frac{\cos 3x}{\cos 5x}\right)$$

$$= \lim_{x \to 0^+} \frac{5}{3}\left(\frac{\sin 5x}{5x}\right)5\left(\frac{3x}{\sin 3x}\right)\frac{1}{3}\left(\frac{\cos 3x}{\cos 5x}\right)$$

$$= \frac{25}{9} \times \lim_{5x \to 0^+}\left(\frac{\sin 5x}{5x}\right) \times \lim_{3x \to 0^+}\left(\frac{3x}{\sin 3x}\right) \times \frac{1}{1}$$

$$= \frac{25}{9} \times 1 \times 1 \times 1$$

$$= \frac{25}{9}$$

b $\dfrac{\ln(\sin 2x)}{\ln(\sin 3x)}$ is not defined when $\sin 3x < 0$

that is, when $\pi \leqslant 3x \leqslant 2\pi$

$$\Rightarrow \frac{\pi}{3} \leqslant x \leqslant \frac{2\pi}{3}$$

and $\frac{\pi}{2}$ lies in this interval

$$\therefore \lim_{x \to \frac{\pi}{2}^-} \frac{\ln(\sin 2x)}{\ln(\sin 3x)} \quad \text{DNE}$$

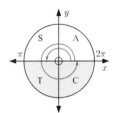

5 a $\dfrac{1}{x} - \dfrac{1}{\sin x} = \dfrac{\sin x - x}{x \sin x}$

$$\therefore \lim_{x \to 0^+}\left(\frac{1}{x} - \frac{1}{\sin x}\right) = \lim_{x \to 0^+}\left(\frac{\sin x - x}{x \sin x}\right)$$

The limit has type $\frac{0}{0}$, so we can use l'Hôpital's Rule.

$$\therefore \lim_{x \to 0^+}\left(\frac{1}{x} - \frac{1}{\sin x}\right) = \lim_{x \to 0^+} \frac{\cos x - 1}{\sin x + x \cos x}$$

The limit also has type $\frac{0}{0}$, so we again use l'Hôpital's Rule.

$$\therefore \lim_{x \to 0^+}\left(\frac{1}{x} - \frac{1}{\sin x}\right) = \lim_{x \to 0^+} \frac{-\sin x}{\cos x + [\cos x + x(-\sin x)]}$$

$$= \lim_{x \to 0^+} \frac{-\sin x}{2\cos x - x \sin x}$$

$$= \frac{0}{2 - 0}$$

$$= 0$$

b $\dfrac{1}{x} - \dfrac{1}{\sin 2x} = \dfrac{\sin 2x - x}{x \sin 2x}$

$$\therefore \lim_{x \to 0^+}\left(\frac{1}{x} - \frac{1}{\sin 2x}\right) = \lim_{x \to 0^+} \frac{\sin 2x - x}{x \sin 2x}$$

The limit has type $\frac{0}{0}$, so we can use l'Hôpital's Rule.

$$\therefore \lim_{x \to 0^+}\left(\frac{1}{x} - \frac{1}{\sin 2x}\right) = \lim_{x \to 0^+} \frac{2\cos 2x - 1}{\sin 2x + x(2\cos 2x)}$$

$$= \frac{2(1) - 1}{0 + 0}$$

$\therefore$ the limit DNE.

c $\sec^2 x - \tan x = \dfrac{1}{\cos^2 x} - \dfrac{\sin x}{\cos x}$

$$= \dfrac{1 - \sin x \cos x}{\cos^2 x}$$

$$= \dfrac{1 - \frac{1}{2}\sin 2x}{\cos^2 x}$$

$\therefore \quad \lim\limits_{x \to \frac{\pi}{2}^-} (\sec^2 x - \tan x) = \dfrac{1 - \frac{1}{2}(1)}{0}$

$\therefore \quad$ the limit DNE.

6　a For all $k \in \mathbb{Z}^+$, as $x \to \infty$, $x^k \to \infty$ and $e^x \to \infty$.

The limit has type $\frac{\infty}{\infty}$, so we can use l'Hôpital's Rule.

$\therefore \quad \lim\limits_{x \to \infty} \dfrac{x^k}{e^x} = \lim\limits_{x \to \infty} \dfrac{kx^{k-1}}{e^x}$

And, by using l'Hôpital's Rule repeatedly

$$= \lim\limits_{x \to \infty} \dfrac{k(k-1)x^{k-2}}{e^x}$$

$$= \lim\limits_{x \to \infty} \dfrac{k(k-1)(k-2)x^{k-3}}{e^x}$$

$$\vdots$$

$$= \lim\limits_{x \to \infty} \dfrac{k!x^0}{e^x}$$

$$= 0 \quad \{k \text{ is fixed}, \ e^x \to \infty\}$$

b The result in **a** implies that for large x, e^x is greater than x^k for any fixed $k \in \mathbb{Z}^+$.

$\therefore \quad e^x$ increases more rapidly than any fixed positive power of x.

7 Consider $\lim\limits_{x \to \infty} \dfrac{\ln x}{x^k}, \ k \in \mathbb{Z}^+$

As $x \to \infty$, $\ln x \to \infty$ and $x^k \to \infty$

The limit has type $\frac{\infty}{\infty}$, so we can use l'Hôpital's Rule.

$\therefore \quad \lim\limits_{x \to \infty} \dfrac{\ln x}{x^k} = \lim\limits_{x \to \infty} \dfrac{\frac{1}{x}}{kx^{k-1}}$

$$= \lim\limits_{x \to \infty} \dfrac{1}{kx^k}$$

$$= 0$$

$\therefore \quad$ for large x, x^k is very much greater than $\ln x$

$\Rightarrow \ \ln x$ increases more slowly than any fixed power of x.

8　a As $x \to \infty$, $\ln\left(1 + \dfrac{1}{x}\right) \to \ln 1 = 0$

that is, $\lim\limits_{x \to \infty} \ln\left(1 + \dfrac{1}{x}\right) = 0$

Consider $x \ln\left(1 + \dfrac{1}{x}\right)$

As $x \to \infty$, $\ln\left(1 + \dfrac{1}{x}\right) \to 0$

The limit has type $0 \times \infty$, so we can use l'Hôpital's Rule.

Now $\lim\limits_{x \to \infty} x \ln\left(1 + \dfrac{1}{x}\right)$

$$= \lim\limits_{x \to \infty} \dfrac{\ln(1 + x^{-1})}{x^{-1}}$$

$$= \lim\limits_{x \to \infty} \left(\dfrac{\frac{-x^{-2}}{1+x^{-1}}}{-x^{-2}}\right)$$

$$= \lim\limits_{x \to \infty} \dfrac{1}{1 + x^{-1}}$$

$$= 1 \quad \left\{x^{-1} = \dfrac{1}{x} \to 0\right\}$$

b $1 + \dfrac{1}{x} = e^{\ln\left(1 + \frac{1}{x}\right)} \quad \{a = e^{\ln a}\}$

$\Rightarrow \ \left(1 + \dfrac{1}{x}\right)^x = e^{x \ln\left(1 + \frac{1}{x}\right)}$

$\therefore \quad \lim\limits_{x \to \infty} \left(1 + \dfrac{1}{x}\right)^x = \lim\limits_{x \to \infty} e^{x \ln\left(1 + \frac{1}{x}\right)}$

$$= e^{\left(\lim\limits_{x \to \infty} x \ln\left(1 + \frac{1}{x}\right)\right)}$$

$$= e^1 \quad \{\text{from } \textbf{a}\}$$

$$= e$$

c $\lim\limits_{x \to \infty} \left(1 + \dfrac{a}{x}\right)^x = \lim\limits_{x \to \infty} \left[\left(1 + \dfrac{1}{\left(\frac{x}{a}\right)}\right)^{\frac{x}{a}}\right]^a$

$$= \lim\limits_{\frac{x}{a} \to \infty} \left[\left(1 + \dfrac{1}{\left(\frac{x}{a}\right)}\right)^{\frac{x}{a}}\right]^a$$

$$= e^a \quad \{\text{from } \textbf{b}\}$$

9 $x = e^{\ln x} \quad \therefore \quad x^{\sin x} = (e^{\ln x})^{\sin x}$

$$= e^{\sin x \ln x}$$

$$= e^{\frac{\ln x}{[\sin x]^{-1}}} \quad .... \ (1)$$

Now consider $\dfrac{\ln x}{[\sin x]^{-1}}$ as $x \to 0^+$

As $x \to 0^+$, $\ln x \to -\infty$ and $[\sin x]^{-1} \to \infty$

The limit has type $\frac{\infty}{\infty}$, so we can use l'Hôpital's Rule.

$\therefore \quad \lim\limits_{x \to 0^+} \dfrac{\ln x}{[\sin x]^{-1}} = \lim\limits_{x \to 0^+} \dfrac{\frac{1}{x}}{-[\sin x]^{-2} \cos x}$

$$= \lim\limits_{x \to 0^+} \dfrac{-[\sin x]^2}{x \cos x}$$

The limit has type $\frac{0}{0}$, so we can use l'Hôpital's Rule.

$\therefore \quad \lim\limits_{x \to 0^+} \dfrac{\ln x}{[\sin x]^{-1}} = \lim\limits_{x \to 0^+} \dfrac{-2 \sin x \cos x}{\cos x + x(-\sin x)}$

$$= \dfrac{-2(0)(1)}{1 - 0}$$

$$= 0$$

Hence, $\displaystyle\lim_{x\to 0^+} x\sin x = \lim_{x\to 0^+} e^{\frac{\ln x}{[\sin x]^{-1}}}$

$$= e^0$$
$$= 1$$

10 $x^{\frac{1}{x}} = (e^{\ln x})^{\frac{1}{x}} = e^{\frac{\ln x}{x}}$

Consider $\displaystyle\lim_{x\to\infty} \frac{\ln x}{x}$.

As $x\to\infty$, $\ln x\to\infty$

The limit has type $\frac{\infty}{\infty}$, so we can use l'Hôpital's Rule.

$\therefore \displaystyle\lim_{x\to\infty} \frac{\ln x}{x} = \lim_{x\to\infty} \frac{\frac{1}{x}}{1} = 0$

$\therefore \displaystyle\lim_{x\to\infty} e^{\frac{\ln x}{x}} = e^0 = 1$

$\therefore \displaystyle\lim_{x\to\infty} x^{\frac{1}{x}} = 1$

EXERCISE F

1 a $f(x) = 3x^3 + 5x^2 - 43x + 35$ on $[-5, 2\frac{1}{3}]$

$f(-5) = f(2\frac{1}{3}) = 0$

$f'(x) = 9x^2 + 10x - 43$ for all $x \in \mathbb{R}$

$\therefore$ $f(x)$ is continuous and differentiable for all $x \in [-5, 2\frac{1}{3}]$ and $f(-5) = f(2\frac{1}{3}) = 0$

$\Rightarrow$ Rolle's Theorem applies

$f'(c) = 0 \iff c = \dfrac{-5 \pm 2\sqrt{103}}{9}$

both of which lie in $]-5, 2\frac{1}{3}[$

b $f(x) = |x| - 5$ on $[-5, 5]$.

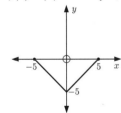

$f(x)$ is not differentiable at $x = 0$.

$\begin{cases} \text{If } x \geqslant 0, & f'_+(x) = 1 \\ \text{If } x < 0, & f'_-(x) = -1 \end{cases}$

Thus $f(x)$ is not differentiable for all $x \in [-5, 5]$

$\therefore$ Rolle's Theorem does not apply.

c $f(x) = 2 - \dfrac{1}{x+1}$ on $[-\frac{1}{2}, 7]$.

$f(x)$ is continuous for all $x \in \mathbb{R}$, $x \neq -1$

$\therefore$ is continuous on $[-\frac{1}{2}, 7]$

$f'(x) = \dfrac{1}{(x+1)^2}$ exists for all $x \in \mathbb{R}$, $x \neq -1$

$\therefore$ is differentiable on $[-\frac{1}{2}, 7]$

$f(-\frac{1}{2}) = 0$ and $f(7) = 1\frac{7}{8} \neq 0$

$\therefore$ Rolle's Theorem does not apply.

d $f(x) = \begin{cases} -2x - 5, & x < -1 \\ x^2 - 4, & x \geqslant -1 \end{cases}$ on $[-2\frac{1}{2}, 2]$

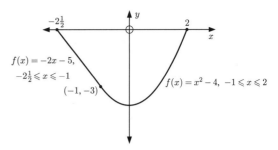

$f(x) = -2x - 5,$
$-2\frac{1}{2} \leqslant x \leqslant -1$
$(-1, -3)$

$f(x) = x^2 - 4, \ -1 \leqslant x \leqslant 2$

$f'(x) = \begin{cases} -2, & x < -1 \\ 2x, & x \geqslant -1 \end{cases}$

$\therefore$ $f'_-(-1) = f'_+(-1) = -2$

$\therefore$ $f'(-1) = -2$

$f(-1\frac{1}{2}) = f(2) = 0$ and $f(x)$ is continuous and differentiable on $[-2\frac{1}{2}, 2]$.

$\therefore$ Rolle's Theorem applies and $f'(c) = 0 \iff c = 0$ which lies in $]-2\frac{1}{2}, 2[$.

2 a i $f(x) = (x-1)(x-2)(x-4)(x-5)$

has zeros: 1, 2, 4, and 5

As $f(x)$ is a real polynomial, continuous and differentiable for all $x \in \mathbb{R}$, by Rolle's Theorem, there exist zeros of $f'(x)$ in the intervals $]1, 2[$ and $]2, 4[$ and $]4, 5[$.

So at least 3 real zeros exist for $f'(x)$.

ii $f(x)$ has sign diagram and graph:

We see that there are 3 turning points

$\therefore$ there are exactly 3 real distinct zeros of $f'(x)$.

b i $f(x) = (x-1)^2(x^2-9)(x-2)$
$= (x+3)(x-1)^2(x-2)(x-3)$

which has zeros: -3, 1, 2, and 3.

As $f(x)$ is a polynomial, continuous and differentiable for all $x \in \mathbb{R}$, by Rolle's Theorem, there exist zeros of $f'(x)$ in the intervals $]-3, 1[$ and $]1, 2[$ and $]2, 3[$.

So at least 3 zeros exist for $f'(x)$.

ii $f(x)$ has sign diagram and graph:

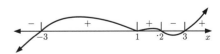

As $y = f(x)$ has 4 turning points, $f'(x)$ has 4 distinct real zeros, 3 guaranteed by Rolle's Theorem and $x = 1$.

c i $f(x) = (x-1)^2(x^2+9)(x-2)$

has two real zeros: 1 and 2.

As $f(x)$ is a polynomial, continuous and differentiable for all $x \in \mathbb{R}$, by Rolle's Theorem, there exists a zero of $f(x)$ in $]1, 2[$.

So at least one zero exists for $f'(x)$.

ii $f(x)$ has sign diagram and graph:

$\therefore$ $f'(x)$ has exactly 2 real distinct zeros, the one guaranteed by Rolle's Theorem and the one at $x = 1$.

3 **a** $f(x) = x^3$ is continuous on $[-2, 2]$ and differentiable on $]-2, 2[$.

Thus, by the MVT, there exists c in $[-2, 2]$ such that
$f(2) - f(-2) = f'(c)(2 - -2)$
$\Rightarrow$ $8 - (-8) = f'(c) \times 4$
$\quad \Rightarrow$ $f'(c) = 4$

As $f'(x) = 3x^2$, $f'(c) = 4$ $\Leftrightarrow$ $3c^2 = 4$
$\Leftrightarrow$ $c = \pm\dfrac{2}{\sqrt{3}}$

b

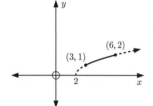

$f(x) = \sqrt{x - 2}$ is continuous on $[3, 6]$ and differentiable on $]3, 6[$.

$\therefore$ by the MVT, there exists c on $[3, 6]$ such that
$f(6) - f(3) = f'(c)(6 - 3)$
$\therefore$ $2 - 1 = f'(c) \times 3$
$\therefore$ $f'(c) = \frac{1}{3}$

Now $f'(x) = \dfrac{1}{2\sqrt{x - 2}}$

$\therefore$ $\dfrac{1}{2\sqrt{c - 2}} = \frac{1}{3}$

$\therefore$ $\sqrt{c - 2} = \frac{3}{2}$

$\therefore$ $c - 2 = \frac{9}{4}$

$\therefore$ $c = 4\frac{1}{4}$

c $f(x) = x + \dfrac{1}{x}$ has $f'(x) = 1 - \dfrac{1}{x^2}$

$\therefore$ $f(x)$ is continuous and differentiable for all $x \in \mathbb{R}$, $x \neq 0$

$\therefore$ $f(x)$ is continuous on $[1, 3]$ and differentiable on $]1, 3[$ {as $0 \notin$ these intervals}

$\therefore$ by the MVT, there exists $c \in [1, 3]$ such that
$f(3) - f(1) = f'(c)(3 - 1)$
$\Rightarrow$ $3\frac{1}{3} - 2 = 2f'(c)$
$\quad \Rightarrow$ $f'(c) = \frac{2}{3}$

and $1 - \dfrac{1}{c^2} = \frac{2}{3}$ $\Leftrightarrow$ $\dfrac{1}{c^2} = \frac{1}{3}$
$\Leftrightarrow$ $c = \pm\sqrt{3}$
$\Leftrightarrow$ $c = \sqrt{3}$, as $c > 0$

4 **a** $f(x) = \sqrt{x}$ $\therefore$ $f'(x) = \dfrac{1}{2\sqrt{x}}$

$f(x)$ is continuous for all $x \geqslant 0$ and $f'(x)$ exists for all $x > 0$

Thus, on $[49, 51]$ $f(x)$ is continuous and differentiable. Hence, by the MVT, there exists $c \in [49, 51]$ such that
$$\sqrt{51} - \sqrt{49} = f'(c)(51 - 49)$$
$\Rightarrow$ $\sqrt{51} - 7 = 2 \times \dfrac{1}{2\sqrt{c}}$

$\Rightarrow$ $\sqrt{51} - 7 = \dfrac{1}{\sqrt{c}}$

b

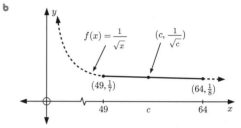

c From the graph $\frac{1}{8} < \dfrac{1}{\sqrt{c}} < \frac{1}{7}$

$\therefore$ $\frac{1}{8} < \sqrt{51} - 7 < \frac{1}{7}$

EXERCISE G.1

1

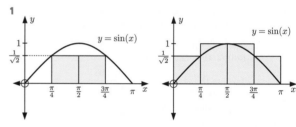

$L_4 = \frac{1}{\sqrt{2}} \times \frac{\pi}{2}$
$\quad = \frac{\pi}{2\sqrt{2}}\left(\dfrac{\sqrt{2}}{\sqrt{2}}\right)$
$\quad = \frac{\pi}{4}(\sqrt{2})$

$U_4 = \frac{\pi}{4}\left(2\left(\dfrac{1}{\sqrt{2}}\right) + 2(1)\right)$
$\quad = \frac{\pi}{4}(\sqrt{2} + 2)$

2 **a**

$\Delta x = \dfrac{4 - 1}{n} = \dfrac{3}{n}$

$x_i = x_0 + i\Delta x$

$\therefore$ $x_i = 1 + i\left(\dfrac{3}{n}\right)$

where $n = 1, 2, 3, ..., n$

b $m_i = f(x_{i-1}) = f\left(1 + \dfrac{3(i - 1)}{n}\right)$

$\therefore$ $m_i = 2 + \dfrac{6(i - 1)}{n}$

$\Rightarrow$ $L_n = \dfrac{3}{n}\displaystyle\sum_{i=1}^{n} m_i = \dfrac{3}{n}\left[\displaystyle\sum_{i=1}^{n} 2 + \dfrac{6}{n}\displaystyle\sum_{i=1}^{n}(i - 1)\right]$

$\quad = \dfrac{3}{n}\left[2n + \dfrac{6}{n}\dfrac{(n - 1)n}{2}\right]$

$\therefore\ L_n = 6 + 9\left(1 - \dfrac{1}{n}\right)$

$= 15 - \dfrac{9}{n}$

$m_i = f(x_i) = f\left(1 + \dfrac{3i}{n}\right) = 2 + \dfrac{6i}{n}$

$\Rightarrow\ U_n = \dfrac{3}{n}\displaystyle\sum_{i=1}^{n} M_i$

$= \dfrac{3}{n}\left[\displaystyle\sum_{i=1}^{n} 2 + \dfrac{6}{n}\displaystyle\sum_{i=1}^{n} i\right]$

$= \dfrac{3}{n}\left[2n + \dfrac{6}{n}\dfrac{n(n+1)}{2}\right]$

$= 6 + 9\left(1 + \dfrac{1}{n}\right)$

$= 15 + \dfrac{9}{n}$

c From **b**, $15 - \dfrac{9}{n} \leqslant A \leqslant 15 + \dfrac{9}{n},\ n \in \mathbb{Z}^+$ and as $n \to \infty$,

$\dfrac{9}{n} \to 0$

$\therefore\ A = 15$ units^2 {Squeeze Theorem}

3 **a** $f(x) = x^2$ on $[1, 2]$.

$\Delta x = \dfrac{2-1}{n} = \dfrac{1}{n}$ and

$x_i = 1 + i\left(\dfrac{1}{n}\right)$ for $i = 1, 2, 3, 4, ..., n$.

b $m_i = f(x_{i-1}) = \left(1 + \dfrac{i-1}{n}\right)^2$

$\therefore\ L_n = \dfrac{1}{n}\displaystyle\sum_{i=1}^{n} m_i$

$= \dfrac{1}{n}\displaystyle\sum_{i=1}^{n}\left[1 + \dfrac{2(i-1)}{n} + \dfrac{(i-1)^2}{n^2}\right]$

$= \dfrac{1}{n}\left[n + \dfrac{2}{n}\dfrac{(n-1)n}{2} + \dfrac{1}{n^2}\dfrac{(n-1)n(2n-1)}{6}\right]$

$= \dfrac{1}{n}\left[n + n - 1 + \dfrac{n}{6}\left(1 - \dfrac{1}{n}\right)\left(2 - \dfrac{1}{n}\right)\right]$

$= 2 - \dfrac{1}{n} + \tfrac{1}{6}\left(1 - \dfrac{1}{n}\right)\left(2 - \dfrac{1}{n}\right)$

$M_i = f(x_i) = \left(1 + \dfrac{i}{n}\right)^2$

$\therefore\ U_n = \dfrac{1}{n}\displaystyle\sum_{i=1}^{n}\left[1 + \dfrac{2i}{n} + \dfrac{i^2}{n^2}\right]$

$= \dfrac{1}{n}\left[n + \dfrac{2}{n}\dfrac{n(n+1)}{2} + \dfrac{1}{n^2}\dfrac{n(n+1)(2n+1)}{6}\right]$

$= \dfrac{1}{n}\left[n + n + 1 + \dfrac{n}{6}\left(1 + \dfrac{1}{n}\right)\left(2 + \dfrac{1}{n}\right)\right]$

$= 2 + \dfrac{1}{n} + \tfrac{1}{6}\left(1 + \dfrac{1}{n}\right)\left(2 + \dfrac{1}{n}\right)$

c But $L_n \leqslant A \leqslant U_n$ where $\displaystyle\lim_{n\to\infty} L_n = \lim_{n\to\infty} U_n = \tfrac{7}{3}$

$\therefore\ A = \tfrac{7}{3}$ units^2 {Squeeze Theorem}

EXERCISE G.2

1 **a** **i** $\displaystyle\int_1^6 f(x)\,dx = \int_1^3 f(x)\,dx + \int_3^6 f(x)\,dx$

$= 2 + -2$

$= 0$

ii $\displaystyle\int_5^7 f(x)\,dx = \int_5^2 f(x)\,dx + \int_2^7 f(x)\,dx$

$= -\displaystyle\int_2^5 f(x)\,dx + \int_2^7 f(x)\,dx$

$= \tfrac{1}{2} + \tfrac{1}{2}$

$= 1$

iii $\displaystyle\int_7^5 f(x)\,dx = -\int_5^7 f(x)\,dx$

$= -1$

iv $\displaystyle\int_4^4 f(x)\,dx = 0$

v $\displaystyle\int_3^5 f(x)\,dx - \int_1^2 f(x)\,dx$

$= \displaystyle\int_2^5 f(x)\,dx - \cancel{\int_2^3 f(x)\,dx}$

$\quad - \left[\displaystyle\int_1^3 f(x)\,dx - \cancel{\int_2^3 f(x)\,dx}\right]$

$= -\tfrac{1}{2} - 2$

$= -2\tfrac{1}{2}$

vi $\displaystyle\int_2^3 f(x)\,dx + \int_6^7 f(x)\,dx$

$= \displaystyle\int_2^7 f(x)\,dx - \int_3^6 f(x)\,dx$

$= \tfrac{1}{2} - (-2)$

$= 2\tfrac{1}{2}$

b

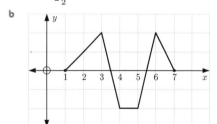

2 $f(x) = \begin{cases} 3x, & 0 \leqslant x < 1 \\ 4, & x = 1 \\ 4 - 2x, & 1 < x \leqslant 3 \end{cases}$

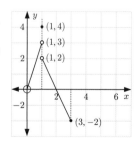

a $\displaystyle\int_0^3 f(x)\,dx = \int_0^1 f(x)\,dx + \int_1^3 f(x)\,dx$

$$= \frac{1 \times 3}{2} + 0$$

$$= 1\tfrac{1}{2}$$

b $\displaystyle\int_0^3 |f(x)|\,dx = \int_0^1 f(x) + 2\int_1^2 f(x)\,dx$

$$= \frac{1 \times 3}{2} + 2\left(\frac{1 \times 2}{2}\right)$$

$$= 3\tfrac{1}{2}$$

3 a $\displaystyle\int_a^c f(x)\,dx + \int_c^b f(x)\,dx$

$$= \lim_{n \to \infty}\left[\frac{c-a}{n}\sum_{i=1}^n f(x_i)\right] + \lim_{n \to \infty}\left[\frac{b-c}{n}\sum_{i=1}^n f(x_i)\right]$$

$$= \lim_{n \to \infty}\left[\frac{c-a}{n}\sum_{i=1}^n f(x_i) + \frac{b-c}{n}\sum_{i=1}^n f(x_i)\right]$$

$$= \lim_{n \to \infty}\left[\frac{c-a+b-c}{n}\right]\sum_{i=1}^n f(x_i)$$

$$= \lim_{n \to \infty}\frac{b-a}{n}\sum_{i=1}^n f(x_i)$$

$$= \int_a^b f(x)\,dx$$

b $\displaystyle\int_a^b [f(x) + g(x)]\,dx$

$$= \lim_{n \to \infty}\left[\frac{b-a}{n}\sum_{i=1}^n (f(x_i) + g(x_i))\right]$$

$$= \lim_{n \to \infty}\frac{b-a}{n}\sum_{i=1}^n f(x_i) + \lim_{n \to \infty}\frac{b-a}{n}\sum_{i=1}^n g(x_i)$$

$$= \int_a^b f(x)\,dx + \int_a^b g(x)\,dx$$

EXERCISE H

1 a $\displaystyle F(x) = \int_1^x \sin^4 t\,dx$ where $f(t) = \sin^4 t$ which is

continuous for all $t \in \mathbb{R}$

$\therefore\ F'(x) = f(x) = \sin^4 x$ {FTOC}

b $\displaystyle F(x) = \int_0^x \frac{1}{(t^2+2)^{15}}\,dx$ where $f(t) = \dfrac{1}{(t^2+2)^{15}}$ is

continuous for all $t \in \mathbb{R}$

$\therefore\ F'(x) = \dfrac{1}{(x^2+2)^{15}}$ {FTOC}

c $\displaystyle F(x) = \int_x^4 e^{t^2}\,dt$ where $f(t) = e^{t^2}$ is continuous for

all $x \in \mathbb{R}$

Now $\displaystyle F'(x) = -\int_4^x e^{t^2}\,dt$

$\Rightarrow F'(x) = -f(x)$ {FTOC}

$\Rightarrow F'(x) = -e^{x^2}$

d $\displaystyle F(x) = \int_{-1}^{x^2} e^{\sin t}\,dt$ where $f(t) = e^{\sin t}$ is continuous

for all $x \in \mathbb{R}$

$\therefore\ F'(x) = \dfrac{d}{dx}\left(\displaystyle\int_{-1}^{x^2} e^{\sin t}\,dt\right)$

$$= \frac{d}{du}\left(\int_{-1}^u e^{\sin t}\,dt\right)\frac{du}{dx}\qquad \{u = x^2\}$$

$$= e^{\sin u}(2x)$$

$$= 2x\,e^{\sin(x^2)}$$

2 $f(x) = \dfrac{1}{x^2}$ has a discontinuity at $x = 0$ and $0 \in\ ]{-1},\,2[$,

the range of integration.

$\therefore$ the FTOC does not apply and $\displaystyle\int_{-1}^2 \frac{1}{x^2}\,dx$ is meaningless.

3 a $f(t) = \dfrac{1}{t}$ is discontinuous at $t = 0$

$\therefore\ \dfrac{d}{dx}\left(\displaystyle\int_{-1}^x \frac{1}{t}\,dt\right)$ cannot be found if $0 \in\ ]{-1},\,x[$.

b However, <u>if $x < 0$</u>, $\dfrac{d}{dx}\left(\displaystyle\int_{-1}^x \frac{1}{t}\,dt\right)$ can be determined

using the FTOC.

4 a $f(t) = \dfrac{t}{\sqrt{1+t^4}}$ is continuous on $\mathbb{R}$.

$$\frac{d}{dx}\left(\int_1^{2x} \frac{t}{\sqrt{1+t^4}}\,dt\right)$$

$$= \frac{d}{dx}\left(\int_1^u \frac{t}{\sqrt{1+t^4}}\,dt\right)\qquad \text{where } u = 2x$$

$$= \frac{d}{du}\left(\int_1^u \frac{t}{\sqrt{1+t^4}}\,dt\right)\frac{du}{dx}$$

$$= \frac{u}{\sqrt{1+u^4}} \times 2\qquad \text{\{FTOC\}}$$

$$= \frac{4x}{\sqrt{1+16x^4}}\qquad \{u = 2x\}$$

b $f(t) = \sin(e^t)$ is continuous for all $x \in \mathbb{R}$.

$$\frac{d}{dx}\left(\int_x^{x^2} \sin(e^t)\,dt\right)$$

$$= \frac{d}{dx}\left[\int_c^{x^2} \sin(e^t)\,dt + \int_x^c \sin(e^t)\,dt\right]$$

$$= \frac{d}{dx} \left(\int_c^u \sin(e^t)\,dt \right) - \int_c^x \sin(e^t)\,dt \quad \{u = x^2\}$$

$$= \frac{d}{du} \left(\int_c^u \sin(e^t)\,dt \right) \frac{du}{dx} - \sin(e^x) \qquad \{\text{FTOC}\}$$

$$= \sin(e^u) \times 2x - \sin(e^x) \qquad\qquad \{\text{FTOC again}\}$$

$$= 2x\sin(e^{x^2}) - \sin(e^x)$$

c $f(t) = \dfrac{1}{1+t^2}$ is continuous for all $t \in \mathbb{R}$.

$$\frac{d}{dx} \left(\int_{x^3}^{\sin x} \frac{1}{1+t^2}\,dt \right)$$

$$= \frac{d}{dx} \left(\int_c^{\sin x} \frac{1}{1+t^2}\,dt + \int_{x^3}^c \frac{1}{1+t^2}\,dt \right)$$

$$= \frac{d}{dx} \left(\int_c^u \frac{1}{1+t^2}\,dt - \int_c^v \frac{1}{1+t^2}\,dt \right)$$

where $u = \sin x$ and $v = x^3$

$$= \frac{d}{du} \left(\int_c^u \frac{1}{1+t^2}\,dt \right) \frac{du}{dx} - \frac{d}{dv} \left(\int_c^v \frac{1}{1+t^2}\,dt \right) \frac{dv}{dx}$$

$$= \frac{1}{1+u^2}\cos x - \frac{1}{1+v^2}3x^2$$

$$= \frac{\cos x}{1+\sin^2 x} - \frac{3x^2}{1+x^6}$$

5 $\displaystyle\int_{-3}^{10} |x|\,dx$

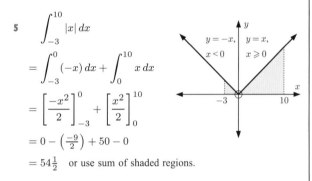

$$= \int_{-3}^0 (-x)\,dx + \int_0^{10} x\,dx$$

$$= \left[\frac{-x^2}{2} \right]_{-3}^0 + \left[\frac{x^2}{2} \right]_0^{10}$$

$$= 0 - \left(\frac{-9}{2} \right) + 50 - 0$$

$$= 54\tfrac{1}{2} \quad \text{or use sum of shaded regions.}$$

6 $f(x) = \begin{cases} \sin x, & 0 \leqslant x \leqslant \frac{\pi}{2} \\ 2x, & \frac{\pi}{2} \leqslant x < 3 \\ \dfrac{1}{x}, & 3 < x \leqslant 5 \end{cases}$

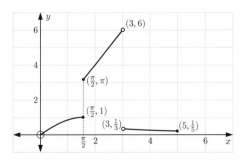

$$\int_0^5 f(x)\,dx = \int_0^{\frac{\pi}{2}} f(x)\,dx + \int_{\frac{\pi}{2}}^3 f(x)\,dx + \int_3^5 f(x)\,dx$$

$$\therefore \quad \int_0^5 f(x)\,dx = \left[-\cos x \right]_0^{\frac{\pi}{2}} + \left[x^2 \right]_{\frac{\pi}{2}}^3 + \left[\ln|x| \right]_3^5$$

$$= 0 - (-1) + 9 - \frac{\pi^2}{4} + \ln 5 - \ln 3$$

$$= 10 + \ln\left(\frac{5}{3} \right) - \frac{\pi^2}{4}$$

7 a The average value of f on $[2, 5]$

$$= \frac{1}{5-2} \int_2^5 x^{-3}\,dx$$

$$= \frac{1}{3} \left[\frac{x^{-2}}{-2} \right]_2^5$$

$$= \frac{1}{3} \left(-\frac{1}{50} + \frac{1}{8} \right)$$

$$= \frac{7}{200}$$

b

The average value of f on $[-2, 5]$

$$= \frac{1}{5-(-2)} \int_{-2}^5 f(x)\,dx$$

$$= \frac{1}{7} \left(\int_{-2}^1 f(x)\,dx + \int_1^5 f(x)\,dx \right)$$

$$= \frac{1}{7} \left(\left[\frac{x^3}{3} \right]_{-2}^1 + \left[e^x \right]_1^5 \right)$$

$$= \frac{1}{7} \left(\frac{1}{3} - \frac{-8}{3} + e^5 - e^1 \right)$$

$$= \frac{1}{7}(3 + e^5 - e)$$

8 $F(x) = \displaystyle\int_1^x \cos(e^{t^2})\,dt, \quad x > 1$

a $F'(x) = \cos(e^{x^2}), \quad x > 1 \qquad \{\text{FTOC}\}$

b $F'(2) = \cos(e^4)$

c $F'\left(\sqrt{\ln \pi} \right) = \cos\left(e^{\ln \pi} \right)$

$$= \cos \pi$$

$$= -1$$

d $F''(x) = -\sin(e^{x^2})\,e^{x^2}\,2x$

$$= -2x\,e^{x^2}\sin(e^{x^2})$$

e $F''(2) = -4e^4 \sin(e^4)$

9 $g(x) = \int_0^x f(t)\,dt, \ x \in [0, 4].$

a $g(1) = \int_0^1 f(t)\,dt$

$= \left(\dfrac{1+3}{2}\right) \times 1$

$= 2$

{area of trapezium}

b $g(3)$

$= \int_0^3 f(t)\,dt$

$= \left(\dfrac{1+5}{2}\right) \times 2 + \tfrac{1}{4}\pi(1)^2$

$= 6 + \tfrac{\pi}{4}$

c $g'(x)$

$= \dfrac{d}{dx}\int_0^x f(t)\,dt$

$= f(x) \quad$ {FTOC}

$\therefore \ g'(1) = f(1) = 3$

d $g'(3)$

$= f(3)$

$= 1$

e $g''(x) = f'(x), \ \therefore \ g''(3) = f'(3) = 0$
{tangent at $(3, 1)$ is horizontal}

10 a $F(x) = \int_1^{g(x)} f(t-2)\,dt$

$\therefore \ F'(x) = \dfrac{d}{dx}\left(\int_1^{g(x)} f(t-2)\,dt\right)$

$= \dfrac{d}{dx}\left(\int_1^{u} f(t-2)\,dt\right) \quad$ where $u = g(x)$

$= \dfrac{d}{du}\left(\int_1^{u} f(t-2)\,dt\right)\dfrac{du}{dx} \quad$ {Chain rule}

$= f(u-2)\,g'(x)$

$= f(g(x) - 2)\,g'(x)$

$\therefore \ F'(3) = f(g(3) - 2) \times g'(3)$

$= f(4-2) \times 5$

$= 5f(2)$

$= -5$

b *Assumptions:*

- f is continuous for all $x > 1$.
- g is continuous and differentiable for all $x > 1$.

EXERCISE I.1

1 a $\dfrac{x}{2x^5 + 3x^2 + 1} < \dfrac{x}{2x^5} < \dfrac{1}{x^4} \quad$ for all $x \geqslant 1$

$\therefore \ 0 < \dfrac{x}{2x^5 + 3x^2 + 1} < \dfrac{1}{x^4} \quad$ for all $x \geqslant 1$

$\Rightarrow \ 0 < \int_1^{\infty} \dfrac{x}{2x^5 + 3x^2 + 1}\,dx < \int_1^{\infty} \dfrac{1}{x^4}\,dx$

where $\int_1^{\infty} \dfrac{1}{x^4}\,dx$ converges

$\left\{\int_1^{\infty} \dfrac{1}{x^p}\,dx \text{ converges for all } p > 1\right\}$

$\therefore$ by the Comparison Test $\int_1^{\infty} \dfrac{x}{2x^5 + 3x^2 + 1}\,dx$
converges.

b For all $x \geqslant 2$, $\dfrac{x^2 - 1}{\sqrt{x^7 + 1}} < \dfrac{x^2}{\sqrt{x^7}} = \dfrac{1}{x^{1.5}}$

$\therefore \ 0 < \dfrac{x^2 - 1}{\sqrt{x^7 + 1}} < \dfrac{1}{x^{1.5}} \quad \{x \geqslant 2\}$

$\therefore \ 0 < \int_1^{\infty} \dfrac{x^2 - 1}{\sqrt{x^7 + 1}}\,dx < \int_1^{\infty} \dfrac{1}{x^{1.5}}\,dx$

where $\int_1^{\infty} \dfrac{1}{x^{1.5}}\,dx$ converges

$\left\{\int_1^{\infty} \dfrac{1}{x^p}\,dx \text{ converges for } p > 1\right\}$

$\therefore \ \int_1^{\infty} \dfrac{x^2 - 1}{\sqrt{x^7 + 1}}\,dx$ converges   {Comparison Test}

$\Rightarrow \ \int_2^{\infty} \dfrac{x^2 - 1}{\sqrt{x^7 + 1}}\,dx$ converges

$\left\{\int_1^{2} \dfrac{x^2 - 1}{\sqrt{x^7 + 1}}\,dx \text{ is a positive constant}\right\}$

2 For all $x \geqslant 1$, $0 \leqslant \left|\dfrac{\sin x}{x^3}\right| \leqslant \dfrac{1}{x^3}$

$\therefore \ 0 \leqslant \int_1^{\infty} \left|\dfrac{\sin x}{x^3}\right|\,dx \leqslant \int_1^{\infty} \dfrac{1}{x^3}\,dx$

where $\int_1^{\infty} \dfrac{1}{x^3}\,dx$ converges

$\left\{\int_1^{\infty} \dfrac{1}{x^p}\,dx \text{ converges for } p > 1\right\}$

$\therefore \ \int_1^{\infty} \left|\dfrac{\sin x}{x^3}\right|\,dx$ converges for all $x \geqslant 1$

{Comparison Test}

$\Rightarrow \ \int_1^{\infty} \dfrac{\sin x}{x^3}\,dx$ converges

3 a $0 < \dfrac{x^2 + 1}{x^4 + 1} < \dfrac{x^2 + 1}{x^4} = \dfrac{1}{x^2} + \dfrac{1}{x^4}$

$\therefore \ 0 < \int_1^{\infty} \dfrac{x^2 + 1}{x^4 + 1}\,dx < \int_1^{\infty} \dfrac{1}{x^2}\,dx + \int_1^{\infty} \dfrac{1}{x^4}\,dx$

where $\int_1^{\infty} \dfrac{1}{x^2}\,dx$ and $\int_1^{\infty} \dfrac{1}{x^4}\,dx$ converge

$\left\{\int_1^{\infty} \dfrac{1}{x^p}\,dx \text{ converges for } p > 1\right\}$

$\Rightarrow \ \int_1^{\infty} \dfrac{x^2 + 1}{x^4 + 1}\,dx$ converges   {Comparison Test}

b For $x \geqslant 1$, $x^2 \geqslant x \ \Rightarrow \ -x^2 \leqslant -x$

$\Rightarrow \ e^{-x^2} \leqslant e^{-x}$

$\therefore \ 0 \leqslant e^{-x^2} \leqslant e^{-x} \quad$ for all $x \in \mathbb{R}, \ x \geqslant 1$

$\therefore \ 0 \leqslant \int_1^{\infty} e^{-x^2}\,dx \leqslant \int_{-1}^{\infty} e^{-x}\,dx$

Now $\displaystyle\int_1^\infty e^{-x}\,dx = \lim_{b\to\infty}\int_1^b e^{-x}\,dx$

$\displaystyle = \lim_{b\to\infty}\left[-e^{-x}\right]_1^b$

$\displaystyle = \lim_{b\to\infty}\left(-e^{-b}+e^{-1}\right)$

$\displaystyle = 0 + \frac{1}{e}$

$\displaystyle = \frac{1}{e}$

$\displaystyle \therefore\ 0 \leqslant \int_1^\infty e^{-x^2}\,dx \leqslant \frac{1}{e}$

$\displaystyle \Rightarrow\ \int_1^\infty e^{-x^2}\,dx \ \text{converges}\qquad\text{\{Comparison Test\}}$

But $\displaystyle\int_0^\infty e^{-x^2}\,dx = \underbrace{\int_0^1 e^{-x^2}\,dx}_{\substack{\text{a positive}\\\text{constant}}} + \underbrace{\int_1^\infty e^{-x^2}\,dx}_{\text{convergent}}$

$\displaystyle \therefore\ \int_0^\infty e^{-x^2}\,dx \ \text{converges}$

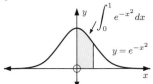

c $\displaystyle\int \frac{\ln x}{x}\,dx = \int [\ln x]\,\frac{1}{x}\,dx$

$\displaystyle = \int u\,\frac{du}{dx}\,dx \qquad \{u = \ln x\}$

$\displaystyle = \int u\,du$

$\displaystyle = \frac{u^2}{2} + c$

$\displaystyle \therefore\ \int_1^\infty \frac{\ln x}{x}\,dx = \lim_{b\to\infty}\left(\int_1^b \frac{\ln x}{x}\,dx\right)$

$\displaystyle = \lim_{b\to\infty}\left[\frac{[\ln x]^2}{2}\right]_1^b$

$\displaystyle = \lim_{b\to\infty}\left(\tfrac{1}{2}(\ln b)^2 - 0\right)\quad\text{which DNE}$

$\displaystyle \therefore\ \int_1^\infty \frac{\ln x}{x}\,dx \ \text{is divergent.}$

d

For $x > 1,\ \ln x < x$

$\displaystyle \therefore\ 0 < \frac{\ln x}{e^x} < \frac{x}{e^x}$

$\displaystyle \therefore\ 0 < \int_1^\infty \frac{\ln x}{e^x}\,dx < \int_1^\infty \frac{x}{e^x}\,dx$

Using $\begin{cases} u' = e^{-x}, & v = x \\ u = -e^{-x}, & v' = 1, \end{cases}$

$\displaystyle \int xe^{-x}\,dx = -xe^{-x} - \int -e^{-x}\,dx$

$\displaystyle = -xe^{-x} + -e^{-x} + c$

$\displaystyle = -(x+1)e^{-x} + c$

$\displaystyle \therefore\ \int_1^\infty \frac{x}{e^x}\,dx = \lim_{b\to\infty}\int_1^b \frac{x}{e^x}\,dx$

$\displaystyle = \lim_{b\to\infty}\left[-(x+1)e^{-x}\right]_1^b$

$\displaystyle = \lim_{b\to\infty}\left(\frac{-(b+1)}{e^b} + \frac{2}{e}\right)$

$\displaystyle = \frac{2}{e}$

$\displaystyle \therefore\ 0 < \int_1^\infty \frac{\ln x}{e^x}\,dx < \frac{2}{e}$

$\displaystyle \Rightarrow\ \int_1^\infty \frac{\ln x}{e^x}\,dx \ \text{is convergent.}$

4 Since $-1 \leqslant \cos x \leqslant 1$ for all $x \in \mathbb{R}$, and $e^x > 0$ for all $x \in \mathbb{R}$,

$\displaystyle -\frac{1}{e^x} \leqslant \frac{\cos x}{e^x} \leqslant \frac{1}{e^x}\quad \text{for all}\ x \geqslant 0$

$\displaystyle \therefore\ -\int_0^\infty \frac{1}{e^x}\,dx \leqslant \int_0^\infty \frac{\cos x}{e^x}\,dx \leqslant \int_0^\infty \frac{1}{e^x}\,dx \quad....\ (1)$

But $\displaystyle\int_0^\infty \frac{1}{e^x}\,dx = \lim_{b\to\infty}\left(\int_0^b e^{-x}\,dx\right)$

$\displaystyle = \lim_{b\to\infty}\left[-e^{-x}\right]_0^b$

$\displaystyle = \lim_{b\to\infty} -e^{-b} - (-e^0)$

$\displaystyle = 1$

$\displaystyle \therefore\ \text{from (1)}\ -1 \leqslant \int_0^\infty \frac{\cos x}{e^x}\,dx \leqslant 1$

$\displaystyle \Rightarrow\ \int_0^\infty \frac{\cos x}{e^x}\,dx \ \text{is convergent.}$

5 a $\displaystyle\int_a^\infty \frac{dx}{x^2 + a^2} = \lim_{b\to\infty}\left(\int_a^b \frac{1}{x^2 + a^2}\,dx\right)$

$\displaystyle = \lim_{b\to\infty}\left[\frac{1}{a}\arctan\left(\frac{x}{a}\right)\right]_a^b$

$\displaystyle = \frac{1}{a}\lim_{b\to\infty}\left(\arctan\left(\frac{b}{a}\right) - \arctan 1\right)$

$\displaystyle = \frac{1}{a}\left(\frac{\pi}{2} - \frac{\pi}{4}\right) = \frac{\pi}{4a}$

b $\int_{\frac{1}{\pi}}^{\infty} \frac{1}{x^2} \sin\left(\frac{1}{x}\right) dx$

$= \lim_{b \to \infty} \left(-\int_{\frac{1}{\pi}}^{b} \sin(x^{-1})(-x^{-2}) \, dx \right)$

$= \lim_{b \to \infty} \left(-\int_{\frac{1}{\pi}}^{b} \sin u \, \frac{du}{dx} \, dx \right)$

$= \lim_{b \to \infty} \left(-\int_{\pi}^{\frac{1}{b}} \sin u \, du \right)$

$= \lim_{b \to \infty} \left[\cos u \right]_{\pi}^{\frac{1}{b}}$

$= \lim_{b \to \infty} \left(\cos\left(\frac{1}{b}\right) - \cos(\pi) \right)$

$= 1 - (-1)$

$= 2$

6 $\int \frac{dx}{e^x + e^{-x}}$

$= \int \frac{1}{u + \frac{1}{u}} \, dx$ {letting $u = e^x$}

$= \int \frac{1}{\left(u + \frac{1}{u}\right)} \frac{1}{u} \, du$ {since $x = \ln u, \ \frac{dx}{du} = \frac{1}{u}$}

$= \int \frac{1}{1 + u^2} \, du$

$= \arctan u + c$

$= \arctan(e^x) + c$

$\therefore \ \int_a^{\infty} \frac{dx}{e^x + e^{-x}} = \lim_{b \to \infty} \left(\int_a^b \frac{dx}{e^x + e^{-x}} \right)$

$\qquad = \lim_{b \to \infty} \left[\arctan(e^x) \right]_a^b$

$\qquad = \lim_{b \to \infty} \left(\arctan(e^b) - \arctan(e^a) \right)$

$\qquad = \frac{\pi}{2} - \arctan(e^a)$

7 $\int_1^{\infty} \left(\frac{1}{\sqrt{x}} - \frac{1}{\sqrt{x+3}} \right) dx$

$= \int_1^{\infty} \frac{1}{\sqrt{x}} \, dx - \int_1^{\infty} \frac{1}{\sqrt{x+3}} \, dx$

$= \int_1^{\infty} \frac{1}{\sqrt{x}} \, dx - \int_4^{\infty} \frac{1}{\sqrt{u}} \, du$ $\left\{ \begin{array}{l} u = x + 3 \\ \frac{du}{dx} = 1 \end{array} \right.$

$= \int_1^{\infty} \frac{1}{\sqrt{x}} \, dx - \int_4^{\infty} \frac{1}{\sqrt{x}} \, dx$

$= \int_1^4 x^{-\frac{1}{2}} \, dx$

$= \left[2x^{\frac{1}{2}} \right]_1^4$

$= 4 - 2$

$= 2$

8

Area $= \int_0^{\infty} \frac{1}{x^2 + 6x + 10} \, dx$

$= \int_0^{\infty} \frac{1}{(x+3)^2 + 1} \, dx$

$= \lim_{b \to \infty} \left(\int_0^b \frac{1}{1 + u^2} \, dx \right)$ where $u = x + 3$

$= \lim_{b \to \infty} \left(\int_3^{b+3} \frac{1}{1 + u^2} \, du \right)$

$\left\{ \begin{array}{l} \text{When } x = 0, \ u = 3 \\ \text{When } x = b, \ u = b + 3 \\ \frac{du}{dx} = 1 \end{array} \right\}$

$= \lim_{b \to \infty} \left[\arctan u \right]_3^{b+3}$

$= \lim_{b \to \infty} \left(\arctan(b+3) - \arctan 3 \right)$

$= \frac{\pi}{2} - \arctan 3$

9 Consider $\int_e^{\infty} \frac{\ln x}{x^p} \, dx$ for $p \leqslant 1$.

From **3 c**, when $\underline{p = 1}$, $\int_1^{\infty} \frac{\ln x}{x} \, dx$ is divergent

Now $\int_1^{\infty} \frac{\ln x}{x} \, dx = \int_1^e \frac{\ln x}{x} \, dx + \int_e^{\infty} \frac{\ln x}{x} \, dx$

$\qquad = \frac{1}{2} + \int_e^{\infty} \frac{\ln x}{x} \, dx$

$\therefore \ \int_e^{\infty} \frac{\ln x}{x} \, dx$ is divergent

For $\underline{p < 1}$, we use Integration by Parts with

$\left\{ \begin{array}{ll} u' = x^{-p}, & v = \ln x \\ u = \dfrac{x^{1-p}}{1 - p}, & v' = \dfrac{1}{x} \end{array} \right.$

$\therefore \ \int \frac{\ln x}{x^p} \, dx = \left(\frac{x^{1-p}}{1-p} \right) \ln x - \int \frac{x^{1-p}}{1-p} \times \frac{1}{x} \, dx$

$\qquad = \frac{1}{1-p} \left(x^{1-p} \ln x - \int x^{-p} \, dx \right)$

$\qquad = \frac{1}{1-p} \left(x^{1-p} \ln x - \frac{x^{1-p}}{1-p} \right)$

$\qquad = \frac{x^{1-p}}{1-p} \left(\ln x - \frac{1}{1-p} \right)$

$\therefore \ \int_e^{\infty} \frac{\ln x}{x^p} \, dx = \lim_{b \to \infty} \left[\frac{x^{1-p}}{1-p} \left(\ln x - \frac{1}{1-p} \right) \right]_e^b$

$\therefore \ \int_e^{\infty} \frac{\ln x}{x} \, dx$ is divergent

10 a If $n = 0$, $\displaystyle\int_0^\infty e^{-x}\,dx = \lim_{b\to\infty}\left(\int_0^b e^{-x}\,dx\right)$

$$= \lim_{b\to\infty}\left[-e^{-x}\right]_0^b$$

$$= \lim_{b\to\infty}\left(-\frac{1}{e^b} - (-1)\right)$$

$$= 1 - 0$$

$$= 1$$

If $n = 1$, we need to find $\displaystyle\int_0^\infty xe^{-x}\,dx$

Using Integration by Parts with $u' = e^{-x}$, $\quad v = x$

$\qquad\qquad\qquad\qquad\qquad u = -e^{-x}$, $\quad v' = 1$

$$\int xe^{-x}\,dx = -xe^{-x} - \int -e^{-x}\,dx$$

$$= -xe^{-x} + (-e^{-x}) + c$$

$$= -e^{-x}(x + 1) + c$$

$\therefore \displaystyle\int_0^\infty xe^{-x}\,dx = \lim_{b\to\infty}\int_0^b xe^{-x}\,dx$

$$= \lim_{b\to\infty}\left[-e^{-x}(x + 1)\right]_0^b$$

$$= \lim_{b\to\infty}\left(\frac{b+1}{-e^b} + 1\right)$$

$$= 1$$

If $n = 2$, we need to find $\displaystyle\int_0^\infty x^2 e^{-x}\,dx$

If $u' = e^{-x}$, $\quad v = x^2$

$\quad u = -e^{-x}$, $\quad v' = 2x$

$\therefore \displaystyle\int x^2 e^{-x}\,dx = -x^2 e^{-x} - \int -2xe^{-x}\,dx$

$$= -x^2 e^{-x} + 2\int xe^{-x}\,dx$$

$$= -x^2 e^{-x} + 2(-e^{-x}(x + 1)) + d$$

$$= -e^{-x}(x^2 + 2x + 2) + d$$

$\therefore \displaystyle\int_0^\infty x^2 e^{-x}\,dx = \lim_{b\to\infty}\left[\frac{-(x^2 + 2x + 2)}{e^x}\right]_0^b$

$$= \lim_{b\to\infty}\left(\frac{-(b^2 + 2b + 2)}{e^b} - (-2)\right)$$

$$= 2$$

If $n = 3$, we need to find $\displaystyle\int_0^\infty x^3 e^{-x}\,dx$

If $u' = e^{-x}$, $\quad v = x^3$

$\quad u = -e^{-x}$, $\quad v' = 3x^2$

$\therefore \displaystyle\int x^3 e^{-x}\,dx$

$$= -x^3 e^{-x} - \int -3x^2 e^{-x}\,dx$$

$$= -x^3 e^{-x} + 3(-e^{-x}(x^2 + 2x + 2)) + e$$

$$= -e^{-x}(x^3 + 3x^2 + 6x + 6) + e$$

$\therefore \displaystyle\int_0^\infty x^3 e^{-x}\,dx$

$$= \lim_{b\to\infty}\left[\frac{-(x^3 + 3x^2 + 6x + 6)}{e^x}\right]_0^b$$

$$= \lim_{b\to\infty}\left(\frac{-(b^3 + 3b^2 + 6b + 6)}{e^b} - (-6)\right)$$

$$= 6$$

b $\displaystyle\int_0^\infty x^0 e^{-x}\,dx = 1 = 0!$

$\displaystyle\int_0^\infty x^1 e^{-x}\,dx = 1 = 1!$

$\displaystyle\int_0^\infty x^2 e^{-x}\,dx = 2 = 2!$

$\displaystyle\int_0^\infty x^3 e^{-x}\,dx = 6 = 3!$

So, we predict $\displaystyle\int_0^\infty x^n e^{-x}\,dx = n!$ for all $n \in \mathbb{Z}$, $n \geq 0$

c P_n is: $\displaystyle\int_0^\infty x^n e^{-x}\,dx = n!$ for all $n \geq 0$, $n \in \mathbb{Z}$.

(1) P_0 was proved in **a**.

(2) Assuming the truth of P_k, $\displaystyle\int_0^\infty x^k e^{-x}\,dx = k!$

Now

$$\int_0^\infty x^{k+1} e^{-x}\,dx$$

$$= \lim_{b\to\infty}\int_0^b x^{k+1} e^{-x}\,dx$$

$$\begin{cases} u' = e^{-x}, & v = x^{k+1} \\ u = -e^{-x}, & v' = (k+1)x^k \end{cases}$$

$$= \lim_{b\to\infty}\left(\left[-e^{-x}x^{k+1}\right]_0^b - \int_0^b -e^{-x}(k+1)x^k\,dx\right)$$

$$= \lim_{b\to\infty}\left(\frac{-b^{k+1}}{e^b} - (0) + (k+1)\int_0^b e^{-x}x^k\,dx\right)$$

$$= 0 + (k+1)\int_0^\infty e^{-x}x^k\,dx$$

$$= (k+1)k!$$

$$= (k+1)!$$

Thus P_0 is true and P_{k+1} is true whenever P_k is true.

$\Rightarrow$ P_n is true   {POMI}

EXERCISE 1.2

1 a $\displaystyle\int_0^\infty \frac{1}{\sqrt{x+1}}\,dx \approx \sum_{i=0}^\infty \frac{1}{\sqrt{i+1}}$

b $\displaystyle\int_4^\infty e^{-x}\,dx \approx \sum_{i=4}^\infty e^{-i}$

2 a $f(x) = e^{-x^2}$ $\quad\therefore\quad f'(x) = -2xe^{-x^2} = \dfrac{-2x}{e^{x^2}}$

For $x > 0$, $-2x < 0$ and $e^{x^2} > 0$ $\Rightarrow$ $f'(x) < 0$

$\therefore$ $f(x)$ is decreasing for $x > 0$.

b $U = \sum_{i=0}^{\infty} f(i) = \sum_{i=0}^{\infty} e^{-i^2}$

$L = \sum_{i=0}^{\infty} f(i+1) = \sum_{i=0}^{\infty} e^{-(i+1)^2}$

c $\sum_{i=0}^{\infty} e^{-(i+1)^2} < \int_{0}^{\infty} e^{-x^2}\,dx < \sum_{i=0}^{\infty} e^{-i^2}$

3 a $f(x) = -\dfrac{1}{x^2} = -x^{-2}$

$\therefore$ $f'(x) = 2x^{-3} = \dfrac{2}{x^3}$

$\Rightarrow$ $f'(x) > 0$ for all $x > 0$

$\Rightarrow$ $f(x)$ is increasing for all $x > 0$

b $U = \sum_{i=1}^{\infty} \dfrac{-1}{(i+1)^2}$, $L = \sum_{i=1}^{\infty} \dfrac{-1}{i^2}$

c $\sum_{i=1}^{\infty} \dfrac{-1}{i^2} < \int_{1}^{\infty} \dfrac{-1}{x^2}\,dx < \sum_{i=1}^{\infty} \dfrac{-1}{(i+1)^2}$

EXERCISE J.1

1 a $a_n = \dfrac{1}{n + n^3}$ As $n \to \infty$, $n + n^3 \to \infty$

$\therefore$ $\dfrac{1}{n + n^3} \to 0$

$\therefore$ $\lim_{n\to\infty} a_n = 0$

b $a_n = \ln(1+n) - \ln(n)$

$= \ln\left(\dfrac{n+1}{n}\right)$

$= \ln\left(1 + \dfrac{1}{n}\right)$

As $n \to \infty$, $a_n \to \ln 1$

$\therefore$ $\lim_{n\to\infty} a_n = 0$

c $a_n = \dfrac{3n^2 - 5n}{5n^2 + 2n - 6} = \dfrac{3 - \frac{5}{n}}{5 + \frac{2}{n} - \frac{6}{n^2}}$

As $n \to \infty$, $\dfrac{5}{n} \to 0$, $\dfrac{2}{n} \to 0$, and $\dfrac{6}{n^2} \to 0$

$\therefore$ $\lim_{n\to\infty} a_n = \dfrac{3}{5}$

d $a_n = \dfrac{n(n+2)}{n+1} - \dfrac{n^3}{n^2+1}$

$= \dfrac{(n^2+2n)(n^2+1) - n^3(n+1)}{(n+1)(n^2+1)}$

$= \dfrac{\cancel{n^4} + 2n^3 + n^2 + 2n - \cancel{n^4} - n^3}{n^3 + n^2 + n + 1}$

$= \dfrac{n^3 + n^2 + 2n}{n^3 + n^2 + n + 1}$

$= \dfrac{1 + \frac{1}{n} + \frac{2}{n^2}}{1 + \frac{1}{n} + \frac{1}{n^2} + \frac{1}{n^3}}$

As $n \to \infty$, $\dfrac{1}{n} \to 0$, $\dfrac{2}{n^2} \to 0$, $\dfrac{1}{n^2} \to 0$, $\dfrac{1}{n^3} \to 0$

$\therefore$ $\lim_{n\to\infty} a_n = 1$

e $a_n = \sqrt{n+1} - \sqrt{n}$

$= \left(\sqrt{n+1} - \sqrt{n}\right)\left(\dfrac{\sqrt{n+1} + \sqrt{n}}{\sqrt{n+1} + \sqrt{n}}\right)$

$= \dfrac{n+1-n}{\sqrt{n+1} + \sqrt{n}}$

$= \dfrac{1}{\sqrt{n+1} + \sqrt{n}}$

As $\sqrt{n} \to \infty$, $\sqrt{n+1} \to \infty$

$\therefore$ $\lim_{n\to\infty} a_n = 0$

f $a_n = \left(\dfrac{2n-3}{3n+7}\right)^4 = \left(\dfrac{2 - \frac{3}{n}}{3 + \frac{7}{n}}\right)^4$

As $n \to \infty$, $\dfrac{-3}{n} \to 0$, and $\dfrac{7}{n} \to 0$

$\therefore$ $\lim_{n\to\infty} a_n = \left(\dfrac{2}{3}\right)^4 = \dfrac{16}{81}$

2 a $a_n = \dfrac{n!}{(n+3)!} = \dfrac{1}{(n+3)(n+2)(n+1)}$

As $n \to \infty$, $(n+3)(n+2)(n+1) \to \infty$

$\therefore$ $a_n \to 0$

$\Rightarrow$ $\{a_n\}$ converges to 0.

b $a_n = \dfrac{1}{\sqrt{n^2+1} - n}$

$= \left(\dfrac{1}{\sqrt{n^2+1} - n}\right)\left(\dfrac{\sqrt{n^2+1} + n}{\sqrt{n^2+1} + n}\right)$

$\therefore$ $a_n = \dfrac{\sqrt{n^2+1} + n}{n^2 + 1 - n^2}$

$= \sqrt{n^2+1} + n$

and as $n \to \infty$, $\sqrt{n^2+1} \to \infty$

$\therefore$ $\{a_n\}$ is divergent.

c $a_n = \dfrac{\sqrt{n}-1}{\sqrt{n}+1} = \dfrac{1 - \frac{1}{\sqrt{n}}}{1 + \frac{1}{\sqrt{n}}}$ {dividing each term by $\sqrt{n}$}

As $n \to \infty$, $\dfrac{1}{\sqrt{n}} \to 0$

$\therefore$ $\{a_n\}$ converges to 1.

d $a_n = \dfrac{\cos^2 n}{2^n}$

Now $0 \leqslant \left|\dfrac{\cos^2 n}{2^n}\right| \leqslant \dfrac{1}{2^n}$, $n \in \mathbb{Z}^+$

As $n \to \infty$, $\dfrac{1}{2^n} \to 0$

$\therefore$ $|a_n|$ is convergent to 0   {Squeeze Theorem}

$\therefore$ $\{a_n\}$ converges to 0.

e $a_n = (-1)^n \sin\left(\dfrac{1}{n}\right)$

Now $0 \leqslant |a_n| \leqslant \left|\sin\left(\dfrac{1}{n}\right)\right|$

But $\left|\sin\left(\dfrac{1}{n}\right)\right| \leqslant \dfrac{1}{n}$

$\{\sin\theta \leqslant \theta, \text{ for } \theta \text{ close to } 0\}$

$\therefore\ \ 0 \leqslant |a_n| \leqslant \dfrac{1}{n}$

As $n \to \infty$, $\dfrac{1}{n} \to 0$

$\therefore$ $|a_n|$ is convergent to 0 {Squeeze Theorem}

$\therefore$ $\{a_n\}$ is convergent to 0.

f $a_n = \dfrac{\sqrt[3]{2n^5 - n^2 + 4}}{n^2 + 1}$

$= \sqrt[3]{\dfrac{2n^5 - n^2 + 4}{(n^2 + 1)^3}}$

$= \sqrt[3]{\dfrac{2n^5 - n^2 + 4}{n^6 + 3n^4 + 3n^2 + 1}}$

$= \sqrt[3]{\dfrac{\dfrac{2}{n} - \dfrac{1}{n^4} + \dfrac{4}{n^6}}{1 + \dfrac{3}{n^2} + \dfrac{3}{n^4} + \dfrac{1}{n^6}}}$

As $n \to \infty$, $a_n \to \sqrt[3]{\dfrac{0}{1}} = 0$

$\therefore$ $\{a_n\}$ is convergent to 0.

3 $a_n = \dfrac{1}{n^2} + \dfrac{2}{n^2} + \dfrac{3}{n^2} + \ldots + \dfrac{n}{n^2}$

$= \dfrac{1 + 2 + 3 + \ldots + n}{n^2}$

$= \dfrac{\frac{n(n+1)}{2}}{n^2}$ $\left\{\displaystyle\sum_{i=1}^{n} i = \dfrac{n(n+1)}{2}\right\}$

$= \tfrac{1}{2}\left(\dfrac{n+1}{n}\right)$

$= \tfrac{1}{2}\left(1 + \dfrac{1}{n}\right)$

As $n \to \infty$, $\dfrac{1}{n} \to 0$ $\therefore\ a_n \to \tfrac{1}{2}$

So, $\{a_n\}$ converges to 0.

4 a As $n > 0$, $\quad n + 1 > n$

$\Rightarrow \qquad \dfrac{1}{n+1} < \dfrac{1}{n}$

$\Rightarrow \qquad 0 < \dfrac{1}{n+1} < \dfrac{1}{n}$

$\Rightarrow \quad 0 < \left(\dfrac{1}{n+1}\right)^n < \left(\dfrac{1}{n}\right)^n$

$\Rightarrow \quad 0 < \left(\dfrac{1}{n+1}\right)^n < \dfrac{1}{n^n}$

As $n \to \infty$, $\dfrac{1}{n^n} \to 0$ $\therefore\ \displaystyle\lim_{n \to \infty}\left(\dfrac{1}{n+1}\right)^n = 0$

b As $n > 0$, $\ 2 + \dfrac{1}{n} > 2$

$\therefore\ \left(2 + \dfrac{1}{n}\right)^n > 2^n$ for all $n \in \mathbb{Z}^+$

But $\{2^n\}$ diverges

$\therefore\ \displaystyle\lim_{n \to \infty}\left(2 + \dfrac{1}{n}\right)^n$ does not exist.

5 Since $\displaystyle\lim_{n \to \infty} a_n = a$ and $\displaystyle\lim_{n \to \infty} b_n = b$, for given $\varepsilon > 0$,

there exists N such that $|a_n - a| < \dfrac{\varepsilon}{2}$ and $|b_n - b| < \dfrac{\varepsilon}{2}$ for

all $n \in \mathbb{Z}^+$.

But $|(a_n + b_n) - (a + b)|$

$= |(a_n - a) + (b_n - b)|$

$\leqslant |a_n - a| + |b_n - b|$

$< \dfrac{\varepsilon}{2} + \dfrac{\varepsilon}{2}$

Thus $|(a_n + b_n) - (a + b)| < \varepsilon$ for all $n \geqslant N$

$\therefore\ \displaystyle\lim_{n \to \infty}(a_n + b_n) = a + b$

6 $\left|\dfrac{3n + 5}{7n - 4} - \dfrac{3}{7}\right| = \left|\dfrac{21n + 35 - 21n + 12}{7(7n - 4)}\right|$

$= \left|\dfrac{47}{7(7n - 4)}\right|$

$< \left|\dfrac{49}{7(7n - 7)}\right|$

$= \dfrac{1}{|n - 1|}$

$\therefore\ \left|\dfrac{3n + 5}{7n - 4} - \dfrac{3}{7}\right| < \varepsilon$ provided $\dfrac{1}{|n - 1|} < \varepsilon$

Now $n \in \mathbb{Z}^+$, so $n - 1 > 0$

$\therefore\ |n - 1| = n - 1$

$\therefore$ we require $n - 1 > \dfrac{1}{\varepsilon}$

$\therefore\ \left|\dfrac{3n + 5}{7n - 4} - \dfrac{3}{7}\right| < \varepsilon$ provided $n > 1 + \dfrac{1}{\varepsilon}$

$\therefore\ \displaystyle\lim_{n \to \infty}\dfrac{3n + 5}{7n - 4} = \dfrac{3}{7}$ for all $n \geqslant N = 1 + \dfrac{1}{\varepsilon}$

7 Since $\displaystyle\lim_{n \to \infty} a_n = a$ and $\displaystyle\lim_{n \to \infty} b_n = b$,

$\displaystyle\lim_{n \to \infty}\alpha a_n = \alpha a$ and $\displaystyle\lim_{n \to \infty}\beta b_n = \beta b$

Hence, $\displaystyle\lim_{n \to \infty}(\alpha a_n + \beta b_n)$

$= \displaystyle\lim_{n \to \infty}\alpha a_n + \lim_{n \to \infty}\beta b_n$ {Limit Law}

$= \alpha \displaystyle\lim_{n \to \infty} a_n + \beta \lim_{n \to \infty} b_n$ {as α, β are constants}

$= \alpha a + \beta b$

For $\alpha = 1$, $\beta = -1$, $\displaystyle\lim_{n \to \infty}(a_n - b_n) = a - b$

EXERCISE J.2

1 a i $u_n = \dfrac{2n - 7}{3n + 2}$

$u_{n+1} - u_n$

$= \dfrac{2(n+1) - 7}{3(n+1) + 2} - \dfrac{2n - 7}{3n + 2}$

$= \dfrac{2n - 5}{3n + 5} - \dfrac{2n - 7}{3n + 2}$

$= \dfrac{(2n - 5)(3n + 2) - (2n - 7)(3n + 5)}{(3n + 5)(3n + 2)}$

$= \dfrac{6n^2 - 11n - 10 - [6n^2 - 11n - 35]}{(3n + 5)(3n + 2)}$

$= \dfrac{25}{(3n + 5)(3n + 2)}$

> 0 for all $n \in \mathbb{Z}^+$

$\Rightarrow$ $u_{n+1} > u_n$ for all $n \in \mathbb{Z}^+$

$\Rightarrow$ $\{u_n\}$ is monotonic (increasing)

ii As $\{u_n\}$ is monotonic increasing $u_1 = -1$ is its greatest lower bound.

Also, as $u_n = \dfrac{2n - 7}{3n + 2} < \dfrac{3n + 2}{3n + 2}$

$\therefore$ $u_n < 1$ for all $n \in \mathbb{Z}^+$

Thus $\{u_n\}$ has an upper bound of 1

So $-1 \leqslant u_n < 1 \Rightarrow \{u_n\}$ is bounded.

b i If $b_n = \dfrac{3^n}{1 + 3^n}$,

$b_{n+1} - b_n = \dfrac{3^{n+1}}{1 + 3^{n+1}} - \dfrac{3^n}{1 + 3^n}$

$= \dfrac{3^{n+1} + 3^{2n+1} - 3^n - 3^{2n+1}}{(1 + 3^{n+1})(1 + 3^n)}$

$= \dfrac{3^n(3 - 1)}{(1 + 3^{n+1})(1 + 3^n)}$

> 0 for all $n \in \mathbb{Z}^+$

$\therefore$ $b_{n+1} > b_n$ for all $n \in \mathbb{Z}^+$

$\Rightarrow$ $\{b_n\}$ is monotonic (increasing)

Hence its smallest member is $b_1 = \frac{3}{4}$

$\therefore$ $b_n \geqslant \frac{3}{4}$ for all $n \in \mathbb{Z}^+$.

Also $b_n = \dfrac{3^n}{1 + 3^n} = \dfrac{1 + 3^n - 1}{1 + 3^n}$

$\therefore$ $b_n = 1 - \dfrac{1}{1 + 3^n}$ .... (1)

$\therefore$ $b_n < 1$ for all $n \in \mathbb{Z}^+$

So, $\frac{3}{4} \leqslant b_n < 1$ for all $n \in \mathbb{Z}^+$

$\therefore$ $\{b_n\}$ is bounded

From (1), as $n \to \infty$, $\dfrac{1}{1 + 3^n} \to 0$

$\therefore$ $\lim\limits_{n \to \infty} b_n = 1$

ii Let $c_n = \dfrac{1}{e^n - e^{-n}} = \dfrac{e^n}{e^{2n} - 1}$

$\therefore$ $c_{n+1} - c_n = \dfrac{e^{n+1}}{e^{2n+2} - 1} - \dfrac{e^n}{e^{2n} - 1}$

$= \dfrac{e^{3n+1} - e^{n+1} - e^{3n+2} + e^n}{(e^{2n+2} - 1)(e^{2n} - 1)}$

$= \dfrac{e^{3n+1}(1 - e) + e^n(1 - e)}{(e^{2n+2} - 1)(e^{2n} - 1)}$

$= \dfrac{(1 - e)(e^{3n+1} + e^n)}{(e^{2n+2} - 1)(e^{2n} - 1)}$

Now $1 - e < 0$, $e^{3n+1} + e^n > 0$, $e^{2n+2} > 1$,
and $e^{2n} > 1$

$\therefore$ $c_{n+1} - c_n < 0$ for all $n \in \mathbb{Z}^+$

$\therefore$ $c_{n+1} < c_n$ for all $n \in \mathbb{Z}^+$

$\Rightarrow$ $\{c_n\}$ is monotonic (decreasing)

Thus $c_1 = \dfrac{e}{e^2 - 1}$ is its least upper bound.

Also, $c_n > 0$ for all $n \in \mathbb{Z}^+$ $\{e^n > 0, \ e^{2n} > 1\}$

Thus $0 < c_n \leqslant \dfrac{e}{e^2 - 1}$ for all $n \in \mathbb{Z}^+$

$\Rightarrow$ $\{c_n\}$ is bounded

As $\{c_n\}$ is monotonic and bounded

$\therefore$ $\{c_n\}$ is convergent.

Now as $n \to \infty$, $e^n \to \infty$, and $e^{-n} \to 0$

$\therefore$ $\dfrac{1}{e^n - e^{-n}} \to 0$

$\therefore$ $\lim\limits_{n \to \infty} \dfrac{1}{e^n - e^{-n}} = 0$

2 Let $u_n = \dfrac{1 \times 3 \times 5 \times 7 \times \ldots \times (2n - 1)}{2^n n!}$

$\therefore$ $\dfrac{u_{n+1}}{u_n} = \dfrac{1 \times 3 \times 5 \times 7 \times \ldots \times (2n - 1)(2n + 1)2^n n!}{1 \times 3 \times 5 \times 7 \times \ldots \times (2n - 1)2^{n+1}(n + 1)!}$

$= \dfrac{2n + 1}{2(n + 1)}$

$= \dfrac{2n + 1}{2n + 2}$

< 1 for all $n \in \mathbb{Z}^+$

$\therefore$ $u_{n+1} < u_n$ for all $n \in \mathbb{Z}^+$ $\{u_n > 0\}$

$\Rightarrow$ $\{u_n\}$ is monotonic (decreasing)

Thus $u_1 = \frac{1}{2}$ is its greatest lower bound.

Also $u_n > 0 \Rightarrow 0 < u_n < 1$

$\Rightarrow$ $\{u_n\}$ is bounded

Thus $\{u_n\}$ is convergent.

3 $x_1 = 0$ and $x_{n+1} = \sqrt{4 + 3x_n}$, $n \in \mathbb{Z}^+$

a P_n: $\{x_n\}$ is monotonic increasing,
that is, $x_{n+1} \geqslant x_n$ for all $n \in \mathbb{Z}^+$

Proof: (by induction)

(1) $x_2 = \sqrt{4 + 3(0)} = 2$

$\therefore$ $x_2 \geqslant x_1$

$\therefore$ P_1 is true.

(2) If P_k is true, then $x_{k+1} \geqslant x_k, \ k \in \mathbb{Z}^+ \quad \dots \ (*)$

Now $x_{k+2}^2 - x_{k+1}^2 = 4 + 3x_{k+1} - (4 + 3x_k)$

$$= 3(x_{k+1} - x_k)$$

$$\geqslant 0 \qquad \{\text{from } * \}$$

$$\Rightarrow \ x_{k+2}^2 \geqslant x_{k+1}^2$$

$$\Rightarrow \ x_{k+2} \geqslant x_{k+1} \quad \{\text{as } x_{k+2}, x_{k+1} \geqslant 0\}$$

Thus P_1 is true and P_{k+1} is true whenever P_k is true

$\Rightarrow P_n$ is true   {POMI}

b $x_1 = 0$ $\qquad x_5 \approx 3.8752$ $\qquad x_9 \approx 3.9975$

$x_2 = 2$ $\qquad x_6 \approx 3.9529$ $\qquad x_{10} \approx 3.9991$

$x_3 \approx 3.1623$ $\qquad x_7 \approx 3.9823$ $\qquad x_{11} \approx 3.9996$

$x_4 \approx 3.6724$ $\qquad x_8 \approx 3.9934$

The experimentation suggests that 4 may be an upper bound.

c P_n: If $x_1 = 0$ and $x_{n+1} = \sqrt{4 + 3x_n}$ for all $n \in \mathbb{Z}^+$

then $x_n < 4$.

Proof: (by induction)

(1) If $n = 1$, $0 < 4$ $\therefore$ P_1 is true

(2) If P_k is true then $x_k < 4$ for $k \in \mathbb{Z}^+$

Now $x_{k+1}^2 = 4 + 3x_k$

$\therefore \ x_{k+1}^2 < 4 + 3(4)$ {using P_k}

$\Rightarrow x_{k+1}^2 < 16$

$\Rightarrow x_{k+1} < 4$ $\qquad \{\text{as } x_{k+1} > 0\}$

Thus P_1 is true and P_{k+1} is true whenever P_k is true

$\Rightarrow P_n$ is true   {POMI}

Hence, $0 \leqslant x_n < 4$, so $\{x_n\}$ is bounded.

d From **a** and **c**, $\{x_n\}$ is convergent.

If $\lim\limits_{n\to\infty} x_n = L$ say, then $\lim\limits_{n\to\infty} x_{n+1} = L$ also.

Since $\lim\limits_{n\to\infty} x_{n+1} = \sqrt{4 + 3\left(\lim\limits_{n\to\infty} x_n\right)}$,

$$L = \sqrt{4 + 3L}$$

$$\therefore \ L^2 = 4 + 3L$$

$$\therefore \ L^2 - 3L - 4 = 0$$

$$\therefore \ (L - 4)(L + 1) = 0$$

$$\therefore \ L = 4 \text{ or } -1$$

$$\therefore \ L = 4 \quad \{\text{as } x_n \geqslant 0\}$$

$$\therefore \ \lim\limits_{n\to\infty} x_n = 4$$

4 a $u_1 = 2 = \frac{2}{1}$ $\qquad$ **b** u_n is defined by:

$u_2 = \frac{3}{2}$ $\qquad\qquad u_1 = 2$ and $u_{n+1} = 1 + \dfrac{1}{u_n}$

$u_3 = \frac{5}{3}$ $\qquad\qquad$ for all $n \in \mathbb{Z}^+$.

$u_4 = \frac{8}{5}$

c $\{u_n\}$ is not monotonic as $u_2 < u_1$ but $u_3 > u_2$.

All terms of the sequence $\{u_n\}$ are clearly positive.

So, as $u_{n-1} > 0$ and $u_n = 1 + \dfrac{1}{u_{n-1}}$, we deduce

$u_n > 1$ for all $n \in \mathbb{Z}^+$.

Thus $u_{n-1} > 1$ and $\dfrac{1}{u_{n-1}} < 1$, for $n - 1 \geqslant 1$

$\therefore \ u_n \leqslant 2$

$\therefore \ 1 < u_n \leqslant 2$ for all $n \in \mathbb{Z}^+$

$\therefore \ \{u_n\}$ is bounded.

d Given $\{u_n\}$ converges, then

$$\lim\limits_{n\to\infty} u_n = \lim\limits_{n\to\infty} u_{n+1} = L, \text{ say}$$

$$\therefore \quad L = 1 + \frac{1}{L}$$

$$\therefore \quad L^2 = L + 1$$

$$\therefore \ L^2 - L - 1 = 0$$

$$\therefore \quad L = \frac{1 \pm \sqrt{5}}{2}$$

But $L > 0$, so $\lim\limits_{n\to\infty} u_n = \dfrac{1 + \sqrt{5}}{2}$

5 $u_{n+1} = \frac{1}{2}\left(u_n + \dfrac{2}{u_n}\right)$

a   **i** $u_1 = 5$ $\qquad$ **ii** $u_1 = 1$ $\qquad$ **iii** $u_1 = 7$

$u_2 = 2.7$ $\qquad\quad u_2 = 1.5$ $\qquad\quad u_2 \approx 3.642\,90$

$u_3 \approx 1.720\,37$ $\quad u_3 \approx 1.416\,67$ $\quad u_3 \approx 2.095\,94$

$u_4 \approx 1.441\,46$ $\quad u_4 \approx 1.414\,22$ $\quad u_4 \approx 1.525\,08$

$u_5 \approx 1.414\,47$ $\quad u_5 \approx 1.414\,21$ $\quad u_5 \approx 1.418\,24$

$u_6 \approx 1.414\,21$ $\quad u_6 \approx 1.414\,21$ $\quad u_6 \approx 1.414\,21$

$u_7 \approx 1.414\,21$ $\quad u_7 \approx 1.414\,21$ $\quad u_7 \approx 1.414\,21$

$u_8 \approx 1.414\,21$ $\quad u_8 \approx 1.414\,21$ $\quad u_8 \approx 1.414\,21$

b No, as in **a** where $u_1 = 1$, $u_2 > u_1$ but $u_3 < u_2$.

c Yes, and if $\lim\limits_{n\to\infty} u_n = L$ then $\lim\limits_{n\to\infty} u_{n+1} = L$ also.

$$\therefore \quad L = \frac{1}{2}\left(L + \frac{2}{L}\right)$$

$$\therefore \quad 2L = L + \frac{2}{L}$$

$$\therefore \quad L = \frac{2}{L}$$

$$\therefore \quad L^2 = 2$$

$$\therefore \quad L = \sqrt{2} \quad \{\text{as } L > 0\}$$

d Suppose $u_1 = a$, $a > 0$, and $u_{n+1} = \frac{1}{2}\left(u_n + \dfrac{3}{u_n}\right)$.

If $\lim\limits_{n\to\infty} u_n = L$ then $\lim\limits_{n\to\infty} u_{n+1} = L$ also.

$$\therefore \quad L = \frac{1}{2}\left(L + \frac{3}{L}\right)$$

$$\therefore \quad 2L = L + \frac{3}{L}$$

$$\therefore \quad L = \frac{3}{L}$$

$$\therefore \quad L^2 = 3$$

$$\therefore \quad L = \sqrt{3} \quad \{\text{as } L > 0\}$$

$$\therefore \ \lim\limits_{n\to\infty} u_n = \sqrt{3}.$$

e If $u_1 = 6$ and $u_{n+1} = \frac{1}{2}\left(u_n + \dfrac{k}{u_n}\right)$ then

$$\lim\limits_{n\to\infty} u_n = \sqrt{k}.$$

f Suppose $u_1 = a$, $a > 0$, and $u_{n+1} = \frac{1}{2}\left(u_n + \dfrac{k}{u_n^2}\right)$.

If $\lim\limits_{n\to\infty} u_n = L$ then $\lim\limits_{n\to\infty} u_{n+1} = L$ also.

$$\therefore \quad L = \frac{1}{2}\left(L + \frac{k}{L^2}\right)$$

$$\therefore \quad 2L = L + \frac{k}{L^2}$$

$$\therefore \quad L = \frac{k}{L^2}$$

$$\therefore \quad L^3 = k$$

$$\therefore \quad L = \sqrt[3]{k}$$

$$\therefore \quad \lim_{n \to \infty} u_n = \sqrt[3]{k}.$$

6 a $\left(1 + \dfrac{1}{n}\right)^n$

$$= 1 + \binom{n}{1}\frac{1}{n} + \binom{n}{2}\frac{1}{n^2} + \binom{n}{3}\frac{1}{n^3}$$

$$+ .... + \binom{n}{n-1}\frac{1}{n^{n-1}} + \binom{n}{n}\frac{1}{n^n}$$

b $e^n = 1 + n\left(\dfrac{1}{n}\right) + \dfrac{n(n-1)}{2!}\left(\dfrac{1}{n^2}\right)$

$$+ \frac{n(n-1)(n-2)}{3!}\left(\frac{1}{n^3}\right) + ...$$

$$+ \frac{n(n-1)(n-2)....(n-[n-1])}{n!}\left(\frac{1}{n^n}\right)$$

$$\therefore \quad e^n = 1 + 1 + \frac{1}{2!}\left(\frac{n-1}{n}\right) + \frac{1}{3!}\left(\frac{n-1}{n}\right)\left(\frac{n-2}{2}\right)$$

$$+ .... + \frac{1}{n!}\left(\frac{n-1}{n}\right) .... \left(\frac{n-[n-1]}{n}\right)$$

$$\therefore \quad e^n = 1 + 1 + \frac{1}{2!}\left(1 - \frac{1}{n}\right) + \frac{1}{3!}\left(1 - \frac{1}{n}\right)\left(1 - \frac{2}{n}\right)$$

$$+ .... + \frac{1}{n!}\left(1 - \frac{1}{n}\right) .... \left(1 - \frac{n-1}{n}\right)$$

c i From **b**, $e^n = 1 + 1 +$ many other positive terms

$$\Rightarrow \quad e^n \geqslant 2 \quad .... \ (1)$$

To prove that $e_{n+1} > e_n$ for all $n \in \mathbb{Z}^+$, consider

$$f(x) = \left(1 + \frac{1}{x}\right)^x, \quad x > 0, \ x \in \mathbb{R}.$$

Now $f(x) = e^{x\ln(1+x^{-1})}$

$$\therefore \quad f'(x)$$

$$= e^{x\ln(1+x^{-1})}\left[1\ln(1+x^{-1}) + x\frac{-x^{-2}}{1+x^{-1}}\right]$$

$$= f(x)\left[\ln(1+x^{-1}) - \frac{x^{-1}}{1+x^{-1}}\right]$$

$$= f(x)\left[\ln(1+x^{-1}) - \frac{1}{x+1}\right]$$

$$= f(x)\,g(x), \text{ say.}$$

Now $g'(x) = \dfrac{-x^{-2}}{1+x^{-1}}\left(\dfrac{x^2}{x^2}\right) + (x+1)^{-2}$

$$= \frac{-1}{x^2 + x} + \frac{1}{(x+1)^2}$$

$$= \frac{-1}{x(x+1)} + \frac{1}{(x+1)^2}$$

$$\therefore \quad g'(x) = \frac{-(x+1) + x}{x(x+1)^2}$$

$$= \frac{-1}{x(x+1)^2}$$

$\Rightarrow \quad g'(x) < 0$ for all $x > 0$

$\Rightarrow \quad g(x) > \lim\limits_{x \to \infty} g(x) = \ln 1 - 0$

$\Rightarrow \quad g(x) > 0$

Since $f'(x) = f(x)\,g(x)$ where $f(x) > 0$, $g(x) > 0$ for all $x > 0$, we deduce $f'(x) > 0$ for all $x > 0$

$\therefore \quad f(x)$ is strictly increasing for all $x > 0$

$$\Rightarrow \quad \left(1 + \frac{1}{n+1}\right)^{n+1} > \left(1 + \frac{1}{n}\right)^n, \quad n > 0$$

$\Rightarrow \quad e_{n+1} > e_n$ for all $n \geqslant 1$

Hence, from (1), $2 \leqslant e^n < e_{n+1}$

ii Using **b**, since

$$1 - \frac{1}{n} < 1, \ 1 - \frac{2}{n} < 1, \ 1 - \frac{3}{n} < 1, \ ...., \ 1 - \frac{n-1}{n} < 1,$$

$$e_n < 1 + 1 + \frac{1}{2!} + \frac{1}{3!} + \frac{1}{4!} + ... + \frac{1}{n!}$$

We now need to show that $\dfrac{1}{n!} < \dfrac{1}{2^{n-1}}$ for all $n \geqslant 3$,

$n \in \mathbb{Z}^+$ *or* $n! > 2^{n-1}$.

P_n: $n! > 2^{n-1}$ for all $n \geqslant 3$, $n \in \mathbb{Z}^+$

Proof: (by induction)

(1) If $n = 3$, $3! > 2^2 \Rightarrow 6 > 4$

$\qquad \therefore \ P_3$ is true

(2) If P_k is true, then $k! > 2^{k-1}$, $k \in \mathbb{Z}^+$

$$\therefore \quad (k+1)! = (k+1)k!$$

$$> 2 \times 2^{k-1}$$

$$= 2^k$$

Thus P_3 is true and P_{k+1} is true whenever P_k is true.

$\qquad \Rightarrow \ P_n$ is true {POMI}

So, as $e_n = 1 + 1 + \dfrac{1}{2!} + \dfrac{1}{3!} + \dfrac{1}{4!} + ... + \dfrac{1}{n!}$,

$$e_n < 1 + 1 + \frac{1}{2} + \frac{1}{2^2} + \frac{1}{2^3} + ... + \frac{1}{2^{n-1}}$$

iii Thus $e_n < 1 + \dfrac{1\left(1 - \left(\frac{1}{2}\right)^n\right)}{1 - \frac{1}{2}}$ {sum of a GS}

$$\therefore \quad e_n < 1 + 2\left(1 - \left(\tfrac{1}{2}\right)^n\right)$$

$$\Rightarrow \quad e_n < 3 - \left(\tfrac{1}{2}\right)^{n-1}$$

$$\Rightarrow \quad e_n < 3 \text{ for all } n \in \mathbb{Z}^+, \ n \geqslant 3$$

Thus $2 \leqslant e_n < 3 \Rightarrow \{e_n\}$ is bounded.

So, e_n is monotonic (increasing) and bounded

$\Rightarrow \{e_n\}$ is convergent.

d i $\lim\limits_{n \to \infty}\left(1 + \dfrac{1}{n}\right)^n = e$

$$\therefore \quad \lim_{n \to \infty}\left(\frac{n+1}{n}\right)^n = e$$

$$\lim_{n \to \infty} \left(1 - \frac{1}{n}\right)^n$$

$$= \lim_{n \to \infty} \left(\frac{n-1}{n}\right)^n$$

$$= \lim_{m \to \infty} \left(\frac{m}{m+1}\right)^{m+1} \quad \{\text{replacing } n \text{ by } m+1\}$$

$$= \frac{\lim\limits_{m \to \infty} \frac{m}{m+1}}{\lim\limits_{m \to \infty} \left(\frac{m+1}{m}\right)^m}$$

$$= \frac{1}{e}$$

ii $\quad \dfrac{n!}{n^n} = \dfrac{n(n-1)(n-2) \times \dots \times 3 \times 2 \times 1}{n \times n \times n \times \dots \times n \times n \times n}$

$$\therefore \quad \frac{n!}{n^n} = \underbrace{\left(\frac{n-1}{n}\right)\left(\frac{n-2}{n}\right) \dots \left(\frac{3}{n}\right)\left(\frac{2}{n}\right)\left(\frac{1}{n}\right)}_{n-2 \text{ of these}}$$

$$\therefore \quad \frac{n!}{n^n} \leqslant \left(\frac{n-1}{n}\right)^{n-2}\left(\frac{1}{n}\right)$$

$$\therefore \quad 0 < \frac{n!}{n^n} \leqslant \left(1 - \frac{1}{n}\right)^n \left(\frac{n}{n-1}\right)^2 \left(\frac{1}{n}\right)$$

But

$$\lim_{n \to \infty} \left(1 - \frac{1}{n}\right)^n \left(\frac{n}{n-1}\right)^2 \left(\frac{1}{n}\right) = \frac{1}{e} \times 1 \times 0 = 0$$

$$\therefore \quad \lim_{n \to \infty} \frac{n!}{n^n} = 0$$

EXERCISE K.1

1 a $\quad e^{2n} = (e^2)^n > 4^n \quad \Rightarrow \quad \dfrac{1}{e^{2n}} < \left(\dfrac{1}{4}\right)^n$

$$\therefore \quad \sum_{n=1}^{\infty} \frac{1}{e^{2n}} < \sum_{n=1}^{\infty} \left(\frac{1}{4}\right)^n$$

But $\dfrac{1}{e^{2n}}$ is positive and $\displaystyle\sum_{n=1}^{\infty} \left(\frac{1}{4}\right)^n$ is a convergent geometric series

$$\Rightarrow \quad \sum_{n=1}^{\infty} \frac{1}{e^{2n}} \text{ converges } \{\text{Comparison test}\}$$

b $\quad \displaystyle\lim_{n \to \infty} \frac{n^2}{3(n+1)(n+2)} = \lim_{n \to \infty} \frac{1}{3\left(1 + \frac{1}{n}\right)\left(1 + \frac{2}{n}\right)}$

$$= \frac{1}{3}$$
$$\neq 0$$

$$\therefore \quad \sum_{n=1}^{\infty} \frac{n^2}{3(n+1)(n+2)} \text{ diverges } \{\text{Test of divergence}\}$$

c $\quad \displaystyle\sum_{n=1}^{\infty} \frac{3^n + 2^n}{6^n} = \sum_{n=1}^{\infty} \left(\frac{1}{2}\right)^n + \sum_{n=1}^{\infty} \left(\frac{1}{3}\right)^n$ where these two series are convergent geometric series.

Hence, $\displaystyle\sum_{n=1}^{\infty} \frac{3^n + 2^n}{6^n}$ converges.

d Suppose $\displaystyle\sum_{n=1}^{\infty} \left(\frac{1}{n} - \frac{1}{n^2}\right)$ converges

$$\therefore \quad \sum_{n=1}^{\infty} \left(\frac{1}{n} - \frac{1}{n^2}\right) + \sum_{n=1}^{\infty} \frac{1}{n^2} = \sum_{n=1}^{\infty} \frac{1}{n} \text{ converges}$$

This is false $\therefore \quad \displaystyle\sum_{n=1}^{\infty} \left(\frac{1}{n} - \frac{1}{n^2}\right)$ diverges.

2 Let $a_n = \dfrac{2n^2 + 3n}{\sqrt{5 + n^7}}$ and $b_n = \dfrac{2}{\sqrt{n^3}}$

$$\therefore \quad \frac{a_n^2}{b_n^2} = \frac{4n^4 + 12n^3 + 9n^2}{5 + n^7} \times \frac{n^3}{4}$$

$$= \frac{4n^7 + 12n^6 + 9n^5}{4n^7 + 20}$$

$$= \frac{4n^7 \left(1 + \frac{3}{n} + \frac{9}{4n^2}\right)}{4n^7 \left(1 + \frac{5}{n^7}\right)}$$

$$\therefore \quad \lim_{n \to \infty} \frac{a_n^2}{b_n^2} = 1$$

Since $a_n > 0$ and $b_n > 0$, $\displaystyle\lim_{n \to \infty} \frac{a_n}{b_n} = 1$

$$\Rightarrow \quad \sum_{n=1}^{\infty} a_n \text{ and } \sum_{n=1}^{\infty} b_n \text{ either both converge or both diverge}$$

$$\{\text{Limit comparison test}\}$$

But $\displaystyle\sum_{n=1}^{\infty} \frac{2}{\sqrt{n^3}} = 2\sum_{n=1}^{\infty} \frac{1}{n^{1.5}}$ which converges using the p-series test $(p > 1)$.

Thus $\displaystyle\sum_{n=1}^{\infty} \frac{2n^2 + 3n}{\sqrt{5 + n^7}}$ converges.

3 Consider $\displaystyle\sum_{n=1}^{\infty} \frac{1}{n^n}: \quad 0 < \frac{1}{n^n} \leqslant \frac{1}{n^2}$ for all $n \in \mathbb{Z}^+$

$$\therefore \quad \sum_{n=1}^{\infty} \frac{1}{n^n} \leqslant \sum_{n=1}^{\infty} \frac{1}{n^2}$$

where $\displaystyle\sum_{n=1}^{\infty} \frac{1}{n^2}$ converges $\{p\text{-series test}\}$

$$\Rightarrow \quad \sum_{n=1}^{\infty} \frac{1}{n^n} \text{ converges } \{\text{Comparison test}\}$$

Consider $\displaystyle\sum_{n=1}^{\infty} \frac{1}{n!}:$

$$\frac{1}{n!} = \frac{1}{n(n-1)(n-2)\dots(3)(2)(1)}$$

$$\Rightarrow \quad \frac{1}{n!} \leqslant \underbrace{\frac{1}{2 \times 2 \times 2 \times \dots \times 2 \times 2 \times 1}}_{n-1 \text{ of these}}$$

$$\Rightarrow \quad 0 < \frac{1}{n!} < \frac{1}{2^{n-1}} \text{ for all } n \in \mathbb{Z}^+$$

But $\displaystyle\sum_{n=1}^{\infty} \frac{1}{2^{n-1}}$ is a convergent geometric series.

Hence, $\displaystyle\sum_{n=1}^{\infty} \frac{1}{n!}$ converges $\{\text{Comparison test}\}$

4 a $\dfrac{1}{\sqrt{n(n+1)(n+2)}} < \dfrac{1}{\sqrt{n^3}} = \dfrac{1}{n^{1.5}}$ and

$\displaystyle\sum_{n=1}^{\infty} \dfrac{1}{n^{1.5}}$ converges   {p-series test}

$\therefore\ \displaystyle\sum_{n=1}^{\infty} \dfrac{1}{\sqrt{n(n+1)(n+2)}}$ converges

{Comparison test}

b $n(n+1)(n-1) = n^3 - n < n^3$

$\therefore\ \sqrt[3]{n(n+1)(n-1)} < n$

$\therefore\ \dfrac{1}{\sqrt[3]{n(n+1)(n-1)}} > \dfrac{1}{n}$ where $\displaystyle\sum_{n=2}^{\infty} \dfrac{1}{n}$ diverges

$\therefore\ \displaystyle\sum_{n=2}^{\infty} \dfrac{1}{\sqrt[3]{n(n+1)(n-1)}}$ diverges

{Comparison test}

c As $0 \leqslant \sin^2 \theta \leqslant 1$ for all $\theta \in \mathbb{R}$,

$\dfrac{\sin^2 n}{n\sqrt{n}} \leqslant \dfrac{1}{n^{1.5}}$

Since $\displaystyle\sum_{n=1}^{\infty} \dfrac{1}{n^{1.5}}$ converges   {p-series test}

$\Rightarrow\ \displaystyle\sum_{n=1}^{\infty} \dfrac{\sin^2 n}{n\sqrt{n}}$ also converges   {Comparison test}

d Since $\dfrac{\sqrt{n}}{n-1} > \dfrac{\sqrt{n}}{n}$ for all $n \in \mathbb{Z}^+$,

$\dfrac{\sqrt{n}}{n-1} > \dfrac{1}{n^{0.5}}$

But $\displaystyle\sum_{n=2}^{\infty} \dfrac{1}{n^{0.5}}$ diverges   {p-series test}

$\Rightarrow\ \displaystyle\sum_{n=2}^{\infty} \dfrac{\sqrt{n}}{n-1}$ also diverges   {Comparison test}

e Since $\dfrac{1 + 2^n}{1 + 3^n} < \dfrac{2^n + 2^n}{3^n}$, then

$\dfrac{1 + 2^n}{1 + 3^n} < \dfrac{2 \times 2^n}{3^n} = 2\left(\dfrac{2}{3}\right)^n$

But $\displaystyle\sum_{n=1}^{\infty} \left(\dfrac{2}{3}\right)^n$ converges   {geometric series, $|r| < 1$}

$\Rightarrow\ 2\displaystyle\sum_{n=1}^{\infty} \left(\dfrac{2}{3}\right)^n$ converges

Hence $\displaystyle\sum_{n=1}^{\infty} \dfrac{1 + 2^n}{1 + 3^n}$ converges   {Comparison test}

f

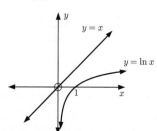

From the graphs of $y = x$ and $y = \ln x$

$\ln x < x$ for all $x > 0$

$\therefore\ \dfrac{1}{\ln x} > \dfrac{1}{x}$ for all $x > 0$

$\therefore\ \dfrac{1}{\ln n} > \dfrac{1}{n}$ for all $n \in \mathbb{Z}^+,\ n \geqslant 2$

But $\displaystyle\sum_{n=2}^{\infty} \dfrac{1}{n}$ diverges   {p-series test}

$\therefore\ \displaystyle\sum_{n=2}^{\infty} \dfrac{1}{\ln n}$ diverges also   {Comparison test}

5 $\displaystyle\sum_{n=0}^{\infty} 2^n |\sin^n x| = \displaystyle\sum_{n=0}^{\infty} |2\sin x|^n$ which is a geometric series,

converging for $|r| < 1$

$\therefore\ \ |2\sin x| < 1$

$\therefore\ \ -1 < 2\sin x < 1$

$\therefore\ \ -\tfrac{1}{2} < \sin x < \tfrac{1}{2}$

$\therefore\ \ 0 \leqslant x < \dfrac{\pi}{6}$

or $\dfrac{5\pi}{6} < x < \dfrac{7\pi}{6}$

or $\dfrac{11\pi}{6} < x \leqslant 2\pi$

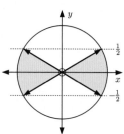

6 If $\displaystyle\sum_{n=2}^{\infty} (1+c)^{-n} = 2$, then $\displaystyle\sum_{n=2}^{\infty} \left(\dfrac{1}{1+c}\right)^n = 2$

where $\displaystyle\sum_{n=2}^{\infty} \left(\dfrac{1}{1+c}\right)^n$ is a geometric series with $S_\infty = 2$.

Since $u_1 = \left(\dfrac{1}{1+c}\right)^2$ and $S_\infty = \dfrac{u_1}{1 - r}$

$$2 = \dfrac{\left(\dfrac{1}{1+c}\right)^2}{1 - \left(\dfrac{1}{1+c}\right)} \times \dfrac{(1+c)^2}{(1+c)^2}$$

$\therefore\ \ 2 = \dfrac{1}{(1+c)^2 - (1+c)}$

$\therefore\ \ 2[1 + 2c + c^2 - 1 - c] = 1$

$\therefore\ \ 2c^2 + 2c - 1 = 0$

$\therefore\ \ c = \dfrac{-1 \pm \sqrt{3}}{2}$ {quadratic formula}

But $|r| < 1$

$\therefore\ \ \dfrac{1}{|1+c|} < 1$

$\therefore\ \ |1+c| > 1$

$\therefore\ \ 1 + c > 1$ or $1 + c < -1$

$\therefore\ \ c > 0$ or $c < -2$

Thus $c = \dfrac{\sqrt{3} - 1}{2}$

7 a $f(x) = \dfrac{x}{x^2 + 1}$ is continuous for all $x \geqslant 1$ .... (1)

         {$x^2 \geqslant 0 \ \Rightarrow\ x^2 + 1$ cannot be 0}

$f'(x) = \dfrac{1(x^2 + 1) - x(2x)}{(x^2 + 1)^2} = \dfrac{1 - x^2}{(x^2 + 1)^2}$

But $x \geqslant 1 \ \Rightarrow\ x^2 \geqslant 1 \ \Rightarrow\ 1 - x^2 \leqslant 0$

Thus $f'(x) \leqslant 0$ for all $x \geqslant 1$

$\Rightarrow \quad f(x)$ is decreasing for all $x \geqslant 1$ .... (2)

And as $x \geqslant 1$, $f(x) > 0$ for all $x \geqslant 1$

$\therefore \quad f(x)$ is positive for all $x \geqslant 1$ .... (3)

From (1), (2), and (3) we can apply the Integral Test.

Now $\displaystyle\int_1^\infty \frac{x}{x^2+1} \, dx$

$= \displaystyle\lim_{b \to \infty} \left(\int_1^b \frac{x}{x^2+1} \, dx \right)$

$= \displaystyle\lim_{b \to \infty} \left(\frac{1}{2} \int_1^b \frac{2x}{x^2+1} \, dx \right)$

$= \displaystyle\lim_{b \to \infty} \left(\frac{1}{2} \left[\ln(x^2+1) \right]_1^b \right)$

$= \displaystyle\lim_{b \to \infty} \frac{1}{2} (\ln(b^2+1) - \ln 2)$

which DNE, $\{$as $b \to \infty$, $\ln(b^2+1) \to \infty\}$

$\Rightarrow \displaystyle\sum_{n=1}^\infty \frac{n}{n^2+1}$ diverges $\{$Integral Test$\}$

b $f(x) = xe^{-x^2} = \dfrac{x}{e^{x^2}}$ is continuous for all $x \geqslant 1$ .... (1)

$\{e^{x^2} \neq 0 \text{ for all } x \geqslant 1\}$

$f'(x) = 1e^{-x^2} + xe^{-x^2}(-2x) = e^{-x^2}(1 - 2x^2)$

$\therefore \quad f'(x) = \dfrac{1 - 2x^2}{e^{x^2}} < 0$ for all $x \geqslant 1$

Now if $x \geqslant 1$ then $\qquad 2x^2 > 1$

$\therefore \quad 1 - 2x^2 < 0$

$\therefore \quad f'(x) = \dfrac{1 - 2x^2}{e^{x^2}} < 0$

$\therefore \quad f(x)$ is decreasing for all $x \geqslant 1$ .... (2)

And $f(x)$ is positive for all $x \geqslant 1$ .... (3)

From (1), (2), and (3) we can apply the Integral Test.

Now $\displaystyle\int_1^\infty xe^{-x^2} = \lim_{b \to \infty} \left(\int_1^b xe^{-x^2} \, dx \right)$

$= \displaystyle\lim_{b \to \infty} \left(\int_1^b -\frac{1}{2} e^{-x^2} (-2x) \, dx \right)$

$= \displaystyle\lim_{b \to \infty} \left(-\frac{1}{2} \left[e^{-x^2} \right]_1^b \right)$

$= \displaystyle\lim_{b \to \infty} \left(-\frac{1}{2} \left(e^{-b^2} - \frac{1}{e} \right) \right)$

$= \dfrac{1}{2e}$

$\Rightarrow \displaystyle\sum_{n=1}^\infty ne^{-n^2}$ is convergent.

c For $x \geqslant 2$, $f(x) = \dfrac{\ln x}{x}$ is positive .... (1)

and $f'(x) = \dfrac{\left(\frac{1}{x} \right) x - \ln x (1)}{x^2} = \dfrac{1 - \ln x}{x^2}$

$\Rightarrow \quad f(x)$ is decreasing when $\ln x > 1 \quad \{f'(x) < 0\}$

that is, when $\quad x > e$

$\therefore \quad f(x)$ is decreasing for $x \geqslant 3$ .... (2)

Also $f(x) = \dfrac{\ln x}{x}$ is continuous for $x \geqslant 1$ .... (3)

From (1), (2), and (3), the Integral Test applies for $x \geqslant 3$.

Now $\displaystyle\int_3^\infty \frac{\ln x}{x} \, dx = \lim_{b \to \infty} \left(\int_3^b \frac{\ln x}{x} \, dx \right)$

$= \displaystyle\lim_{b \to \infty} \left(\int_3^b [\ln x]^1 \left(\frac{1}{x} \right) dx \right)$

$\qquad\qquad\qquad \underset{f(x)}{\uparrow} \quad \underset{f'(x)}{\uparrow}$

$= \displaystyle\lim_{b \to \infty} \left[\frac{[\ln x]^2}{2} \right]_3^b$

$= \displaystyle\lim_{b \to \infty} \left(\frac{[\ln b]^2}{2} - \frac{[\ln 3]^2}{2} \right)$

which DNE $\{$as $b \to \infty$, $\dfrac{[\ln b]^2}{2} \to \infty\}$

Thus $\displaystyle\sum_{n=3}^\infty \frac{\ln n}{n}$ diverges.

Since $\displaystyle\sum_{n=1}^\infty \frac{\ln n}{n} = \frac{\ln 1}{1} + \frac{\ln 2}{2} + \sum_{n=3}^\infty \frac{\ln n}{n}$,

$\displaystyle\sum_{n=1}^\infty \frac{\ln n}{n}$ diverges also.

d $f(x) = \dfrac{1}{x \ln x}$ is positive for $x \geqslant 2$ .... (1)

$\{\ln x \geqslant 0 \text{ for } x \geqslant 1\}$

$f'(x) = \dfrac{0(x \ln x) - 1 \left(1 \ln x + x \left(\frac{1}{x} \right) \right)}{[x \ln x]^2} = \dfrac{-(\ln x + 1)}{[x \ln x]^2}$

$\therefore \quad f'(x) < 0$ when $\ln x + 1 < 0$,

which is when $x > e^{-1}$

$\therefore \quad f'(x)$ is decreasing for $x \geqslant 2$ .... (2)

Also $f(x)$ is continuous for all $x \geqslant 2$ .... (3)

From (1), (2), and (3), the Integral Test applies for $x \geqslant 2$.

Now $\displaystyle\int_2^\infty \frac{1}{x \ln x} \, dx = \lim_{b \to \infty} \left(\int_2^b \frac{1}{u} \frac{du}{dx} \, dx \right)$

$\{$letting $u = \ln x$, $\dfrac{du}{dx} = \dfrac{1}{x} \}$

$= \displaystyle\lim_{b \to \infty} \left(\int_{\ln 2}^{\ln b} \frac{1}{u} \, du \right)$

$= \displaystyle\lim_{b \to \infty} \left[\ln u \right]_{\ln 2}^{\ln b}$

$= \displaystyle\lim_{b \to \infty} (\ln(\ln b) - \ln(\ln 2))$

which DNE $\{$as $b \to \infty$, $\ln(\ln b) \to \infty\}$

$\therefore \displaystyle\sum_{n=2}^\infty \frac{1}{n \ln n}$ diverges.

8 $f(x) = \dfrac{1}{1 + x^2}$ is positive for all x .... (1)

$\therefore$ $f'(x) = -(1 + x^2)^{-2}(2x)$

$\qquad = \dfrac{-2x}{(1 + x^2)^2}$

$\therefore$ $f'(x) < 0$ for all $x \geqslant 1$ .... (2)

Also $f(x)$ is continuous for all $x \in \mathbb{R}$ .... (3)

From (1), (2), and (3), the Integral Test applies for $x \geqslant 1$.

Now $\displaystyle\int_1^\infty \dfrac{1}{1 + x^2} \, dx < \sum_{n=1}^\infty \dfrac{1}{1 + n^2} < a_1 + \int_1^\infty \dfrac{1}{1 + x^2} \, dx$

where $a_1 = f(1) = \frac{1}{2}$.   .... (*)

Now $\displaystyle\int_1^\infty \dfrac{1}{1 + x^2} \, dx = \lim_{b \to \infty} \left(\int_1^b \dfrac{1}{1 + x^2} \, dx \right)$

$\qquad = \displaystyle\lim_{b \to \infty} \Big[\arctan x \Big]_1^b$

$\qquad = \displaystyle\lim_{b \to \infty} (\arctan b - \arctan 1)$

$\qquad = \frac{\pi}{2} - \frac{\pi}{4}$

$\qquad = \frac{\pi}{4}$

So, in *, $\dfrac{\pi}{4} < \displaystyle\sum_{n=1}^\infty \dfrac{1}{1 + n^2} < \dfrac{1}{2} + \dfrac{\pi}{4}$.

9 If $p = 1$, we showed in **7 d** that $\displaystyle\sum_{n=2}^\infty \dfrac{1}{n \ln n}$ diverges.

If $p < 1$, $n^p < n$ $\therefore$ $n^p \ln n < n \ln n$

$\Rightarrow \qquad \dfrac{1}{n^p \ln n} > \dfrac{1}{n \ln n}$

$\Rightarrow \qquad \displaystyle\sum_{n=2}^\infty \dfrac{1}{n^p \ln n} > \sum_{n=2}^\infty \dfrac{1}{n \ln n}$

$\Rightarrow \qquad \displaystyle\sum_{n=2}^\infty \dfrac{1}{n^p \ln n}$ diverges {Comparison test}

If $p > 1$, and $n \geqslant 3$, $\ln n > 1$

$\Rightarrow \qquad n^p \ln n > n^p$

$\Rightarrow \qquad \dfrac{1}{n^p \ln n} < \dfrac{1}{n^p}$

$\Rightarrow \qquad \displaystyle\sum_{n=3}^\infty \dfrac{1}{n^p \ln n} < \sum_{n=3}^\infty \dfrac{1}{n^p}$

But $\displaystyle\sum_{n=3}^\infty \dfrac{1}{n^p}$ converges for $p > 1$ {p-series test}

$\Rightarrow \displaystyle\sum_{n=3}^\infty \dfrac{1}{n^p \ln n}$ also converges {Comparison test}

$\Rightarrow \displaystyle\sum_{n=2}^\infty \dfrac{1}{n^p \ln n} = \dfrac{1}{2^p \ln 2} + \sum_{n=3}^\infty \dfrac{1}{n^p \ln n}$ converges.

10 $\displaystyle\sum_{n=1}^\infty a_n$ is convergent $\Rightarrow$ $\displaystyle\lim_{n \to \infty} a_n = 0$

$\Rightarrow \displaystyle\lim_{n \to \infty} \dfrac{1}{a_n}$ DNE

$\Rightarrow \displaystyle\sum_{n=1}^\infty \dfrac{1}{a_n}$ is divergent

11 **a** As $n \to \infty$, $\sqrt{n} \to \infty$

$\therefore$ $\displaystyle\lim_{n \to \infty} \dfrac{1}{\sqrt{n}} = 0$

b $S_n = \displaystyle\sum_{i=1}^n \dfrac{1}{\sqrt{i}}$

$\qquad = \dfrac{1}{\sqrt{1}} + \dfrac{1}{\sqrt{2}} + \dfrac{1}{\sqrt{3}} + \dots + \dfrac{1}{\sqrt{n}}$

$\qquad \geqslant \dfrac{1}{\sqrt{n}} + \dfrac{1}{\sqrt{n}} + \dfrac{1}{\sqrt{n}} + \dots + \dfrac{1}{\sqrt{n}}$

$\qquad\qquad$ {since $\dfrac{1}{\sqrt{k}} > \dfrac{1}{\sqrt{n}}$ if $k < n$}

$\qquad = \dfrac{n}{\sqrt{n}}$

c $S_n \geqslant \dfrac{n}{\sqrt{n}} = \sqrt{n}$ {as $n \neq 0$}

Since $0 \leqslant \sqrt{n} \leqslant S_n$,

and $\displaystyle\lim_{n \to \infty} \sqrt{n}$ DNE,

by the Comparison test $\{S_n\}$ diverges.

d Even though $\displaystyle\lim_{n \to \infty} \dfrac{1}{\sqrt{n}} = 0$ (from **a**), this has no bearing on the convergence or otherwise of the series.

$\displaystyle\sum_{n=1}^\infty \dfrac{1}{\sqrt{n}} = \lim_{n \to \infty} S_n$ if this limit exists,

but from **c** the sequence of partial sums diverges

$\therefore$ the series diverges (by definition).

12 **a** P_n: $S_n = \displaystyle\sum_{i=1}^n \dfrac{i^2}{3^i} = \dfrac{1^2}{3^1} + \dfrac{2^2}{3^2} + \dfrac{3^2}{3^3} + \dfrac{4^2}{3^4} + \dots + \dfrac{n^2}{3^n}$

$\qquad = \dfrac{3 - 3^{-n}(n^2 + 3n + 3)}{2}$, $n \in \mathbb{Z}^+$

Proof: (By the Principle of Mathematical Induction)

(1) If $n = 1$, LHS $= \frac{1}{3}$ and

$\qquad$ RHS $= \dfrac{3 - 3^{-1}(1^2 + 3(1) + 3)}{2}$

$\qquad\qquad = \dfrac{3 - \frac{1}{3}(7)}{2} = \dfrac{9 - 7}{3 \times 2} = \dfrac{2}{3 \times 2} = \frac{1}{3}$

$\qquad \therefore$ P_1 is true.

(2) If P_k is true, then $\dfrac{1^2}{3^1} + \dfrac{2^2}{3^2} + \dfrac{3^2}{3^3} + \dfrac{4^2}{3^4} + \dots + \dfrac{k^2}{3^k}$

$\qquad\qquad = \dfrac{3 - 3^{-k}(k^2 + 3k + 3)}{2}$ (*)

$\therefore$ $\dfrac{1^2}{3^1} + \dfrac{2^2}{3^2} + \dfrac{3^2}{3^3} + \dfrac{4^2}{3^4} + \dots + \dfrac{k^2}{3^k} + \dfrac{(k+1)^2}{3^{(k+1)}}$

$\qquad = \dfrac{3 - 3^{-k}(k^2 + 3k + 3)}{2} + \dfrac{(k+1)^2}{3^{(k+1)}}$ {using *}

$\qquad = \dfrac{3 - 3^{-(k+1)}(3k^2 + 9k + 9) + 3^{-(k+1)}2(k^2 + 2k + 1)}{2}$

$\qquad = \dfrac{3 - 3^{-(k+1)}[(3k^2 + 9k + 9) - (2k^2 + 4k + 2)]}{2}$

$$= \frac{3 - 3^{-(k+1)}(k^2 + 5k + 7)}{2}$$

$$= \frac{3 - 3^{-(k+1)}(k^2 + 2k + 1 + 3k + 3 + 3)}{2}$$

$$= \frac{3 - 3^{-(k+1)}[(k+1)^2 + 3(k+1) + 3]}{2}$$

Thus P_{k+1} is true whenever P_k is true, and P_1 is true.

$\therefore$ P_n is true   {POMI}

b $\displaystyle\lim_{n\to\infty} S_n = \lim_{n\to\infty} \frac{3 - 3^{-n}(n^2 + 3n + 3)}{2}$

$$= \lim_{n\to\infty} \frac{3}{2} - \frac{n^2 + 3n + 3}{2 \times 3^n}$$

since 2×3^n grows much faster than $n^2 + 3n + 3$,

$\dfrac{n^2 + 3n + 3}{2 \times 3^n} \to 0$ as $n \to \infty$

$\therefore$ $\displaystyle\lim_{n\to\infty} S_n = \lim_{n\to\infty} \frac{3}{2} = \frac{3}{2}$

c Yes, $\displaystyle\sum_{n=1}^{\infty} \frac{n^2}{3^n}$ converges, by definition, since from **b** the

corresponding sequence of partial sums converges to limit $\frac{3}{2}$.

Hence $\displaystyle\sum_{n=1}^{\infty} \frac{n^2}{3^n} = \frac{3}{2}$.

EXERCISE K.2

1 a $\displaystyle\int_{k+1}^{\infty} f(x)\,dx < R_k < \int_{k}^{\infty} f(x)\,dx$ .... (1)

If $f(x) = \dfrac{1}{5x^2} = \dfrac{1}{5}x^{-2}$, $\displaystyle\int f(x)\,dx = \frac{1}{5} \frac{x^{-1}}{-1} + c$

$$= \frac{-1}{5x} + c$$

From (1),

$$\lim_{b\to\infty} \left(\int_{13}^{b} f(x)\,dx \right) < R_{12} < \lim_{b\to\infty} \left(\int_{12}^{b} f(x)\,dx \right)$$

$\therefore$ $\displaystyle\lim_{b\to\infty} \left(\left[\frac{-1}{5x} \right]_{13}^{b} \right) < R_{12} < \lim_{b\to\infty} \left(\left[\frac{-1}{5x} \right]_{12}^{b} \right)$

$\therefore$ $\displaystyle\lim_{b\to\infty} \left(\frac{-1}{5b} + \frac{1}{65} \right) < R_{12} < \lim_{b\to\infty} \left(\frac{-1}{5b} + \frac{1}{60} \right)$

$\therefore$ $\dfrac{1}{65} < R_{12} < \dfrac{1}{60}$

b Consider $R_k < \displaystyle\int_{k}^{\infty} \frac{1}{x^4}\,dx$

$\therefore$ $R_k < \displaystyle\lim_{b\to\infty} \left(\int_{k}^{b} x^{-4}\,dx \right)$

$\therefore$ $R_k < \displaystyle\lim_{b\to\infty} \left(\left[\frac{x^{-3}}{-3} \right]_{k}^{b} \right)$

$\therefore$ $R_k < \displaystyle\lim_{b\to\infty} \left(\frac{-1}{3b^3} + \frac{1}{3k^3} \right)$

$\therefore$ $R_k < \dfrac{1}{3k^3}$

To be correct to 6 decimal places, we require

$$\frac{1}{3k^3} < 0.000\,000\,5$$

$\therefore$ $3k^3 > 2 \times 10^6$

$\therefore$ $k^3 > \dfrac{2 \times 10^6}{3}$

$\therefore$ $k > \sqrt[3]{\dfrac{2 \times 10^6}{3}}$

$\therefore$ $k > 87.36$

$\therefore$ $k \geqslant 88$

$\therefore$ at least 88 terms are required.

2 a $S_1 = a_1 = \dfrac{0}{2} \Rightarrow a_1 = 0$

Now $a_n = S_n - S_{n-1}$ for all $n \geqslant 2$

$\therefore$ $a_n = \dfrac{n-1}{n+1} - \dfrac{n-2}{n}$

$$= \frac{n^2 - n - [n^2 - n - 2]}{n(n+1)}$$

$$= \frac{2}{n(n+1)}, \quad n \geqslant 2, \ n \in \mathbb{Z}^+$$

b $a_1 + a_2 + a_3 + a_4 + ...$

$$= 0 + \frac{2}{2 \times 3} + \frac{2}{3 \times 4} + \frac{2}{4 \times 5} + ...$$

$\therefore$ $\displaystyle\sum_{n=1}^{\infty} a_n = \frac{2}{2 \times 3} + \frac{2}{3 \times 4} + \frac{2}{4 \times 5} + ...$ and its sum

is $\displaystyle\lim_{n\to\infty} S_n = \lim_{n\to\infty} \frac{1 - \frac{1}{n}}{1 + \frac{1}{n}} = 1$

3 a $S_1 = \dfrac{1}{2!} = \frac{1}{2}$

$S_2 = \dfrac{1}{2!} + \dfrac{2}{3!} = \dfrac{5}{6}$

$S_3 = \dfrac{5}{6} + \dfrac{3}{4!} = \dfrac{23}{24}$

$S_4 = \dfrac{23}{24} + \dfrac{4}{5!} = \dfrac{119}{120}$

$S_5 = \dfrac{119}{120} + \dfrac{5}{6!} = \dfrac{719}{720}$

$S_6 = \dfrac{719}{720} + \dfrac{6}{7!} = \dfrac{5039}{5040}$

The denominator for S_n seems to be $(n+1)!$ and

$\therefore$ the numerator $(n+1)! - 1$.

b *Conjecture*: $S_n = \dfrac{(n+1)! - 1}{(n+1)!}, \quad n \in \mathbb{Z}^+$.

c **Proof:** (by induction)

(1) If $n = 1$, $S_1 = \dfrac{2! - 1}{2!} = \dfrac{1}{2} \Rightarrow P_1$ is true

(2) If P_k is true then

$$\frac{1}{2!} + \frac{2}{3!} + \frac{3}{4!} + ... + \frac{k}{(k+1)!} = \frac{(k+1)! - 1}{(k+1)!}$$

$$\therefore \quad \frac{1}{2!} + \frac{2}{3!} + \frac{3}{4!} + \ldots + \frac{k}{(k+1)!} + \frac{k+1}{(k+2)!}$$

$$= \frac{(k+1)! - 1}{(k+1)!} + \frac{k+1}{(k+2)!}$$

$$= \left(\frac{k+2}{k+2}\right)\left(\frac{(k+1)! - 1}{(k+1)!}\right) + \frac{k+1}{(k+2)!}$$

$$= \frac{(k+2)! - (k+2) + k + 1}{(k+2)!}$$

$$= \frac{(k+2)! - 1}{(k+2)!}$$

Thus P_1 is true and P_{k+1} is true whenever P_k is true

$\Rightarrow P_n$ is true {POMI}

d Since $S_n = 1 - \dfrac{1}{(n+1)!}$, $\lim\limits_{n\to\infty} S_n = 1$

$$\therefore \quad \sum_{n=1}^{\infty} \frac{n}{(n+1)!} = 1$$

4 a $S_{16} = 1 + \frac{1}{2} + \left(\frac{1}{3} + \frac{1}{4}\right) + \left(\frac{1}{5} + \frac{1}{6} + \frac{1}{7} + \frac{1}{8}\right)$

$\quad + \left(\frac{1}{9} + \frac{1}{10} + \frac{1}{11} + \frac{1}{12} + \frac{1}{13} + \frac{1}{14} + \frac{1}{15} + \frac{1}{16}\right)$

$\therefore S_{16} > 1 + \frac{1}{2} + \left(\frac{1}{4} + \frac{1}{4}\right) + \left(\frac{1}{8} + \frac{1}{8} + \frac{1}{8} + \frac{1}{8}\right)$

$\quad + \left(\frac{1}{16} + \frac{1}{16} + \frac{1}{16} + \frac{1}{16} + \frac{1}{16} + \frac{1}{16} + \frac{1}{16} + \frac{1}{16}\right)$

$\therefore S_{16} > 1 + \frac{1}{2} + \frac{1}{2} + \frac{1}{2} + \frac{1}{2}$

$\therefore S_{16} > 1 + \frac{4}{2}$

b $S_{2^0} = 1 + \frac{0}{2}$

$S_{2^1} = 1 + \frac{1}{2}$

$S_{2^2} = 1 + \frac{2}{2}$

$S_{2^3} = 1 + \frac{3}{2}$

$S_{2^4} = 1 + \frac{4}{2}$

So, we conjecture: $S_{2^m} = 1 + \dfrac{m}{2}$, $m \in \mathbb{Z}$, $m \geqslant 0$.

Proof: (by induction on m)

(1) If $m = 0$, $S_{2^0} = S_1 = 1 + \frac{0}{2} = 1$ ✓

$\Rightarrow P_0$ is true

(2) If P_k is true, $S_{2^k} > 1 + \dfrac{k}{2}$

Now

$$S_{2^{k+1}} = S_{2^k} + \left(\frac{1}{2^{k-1}+1} + \ldots + \frac{1}{2^k - 1} + \frac{1}{2^k}\right)$$

$$\therefore \quad S_{2^{k+1}} > 1 + \frac{k}{2} + \underbrace{\left(\frac{1}{2^k} + \frac{1}{2^k} + \ldots + \frac{1}{2^k}\right)}_{2^{k-1} \text{ of these}}$$

$$\therefore \quad S_{2^{k+1}} > 1 + \frac{k}{2} + 2^{k-1}\left(\frac{1}{2^k}\right)$$

$$\therefore \quad S_{2^{k+1}} > 1 + \frac{k}{2} + \frac{1}{2}$$

$$\therefore \quad S_{2^{k+1}} > 1 + \frac{k+1}{2}$$

Thus P_1 is true and P_{k+1} is true whenever P_k is true

$\Rightarrow P_n$ is true {POMI}

c As $m \to \infty$, $1 + \dfrac{m}{2} \to \infty$ $\Rightarrow S_{2^m} \to \infty$

Thus S_n is divergent.

EXERCISE K.3

1 a $\displaystyle\sum_{n=1}^{\infty} \frac{1-n}{n^2} = \sum_{n=1}^{\infty} \frac{1}{n^2} - \sum_{n=1}^{\infty} \frac{1}{n}$ where $\displaystyle\sum_{n=1}^{\infty} \frac{1}{n^2}$ converges

and $\displaystyle\sum_{n=1}^{\infty} \frac{1}{n}$ diverges {p-series test}

$\therefore \displaystyle\sum_{n=1}^{\infty} \frac{1-n}{n^2}$ diverges.

b $\displaystyle\sum_{n=1}^{\infty} \frac{1}{n} - \sum_{n=1}^{\infty} \frac{1-n}{n^2}$

$= \displaystyle\sum_{n=1}^{\infty} \frac{1}{n} - \left[\sum_{n=1}^{\infty} \frac{1}{n^2} - \sum_{n=1}^{\infty} \frac{1}{n}\right]$

$= 2\underbrace{\displaystyle\sum_{n=1}^{\infty} \frac{1}{n}}_{\text{diverges}} - \underbrace{\displaystyle\sum_{n=1}^{\infty} \frac{1}{n^2}}_{\text{converges}}$

$\therefore \displaystyle\sum_{n=1}^{\infty} \frac{1}{n} - \sum_{n=1}^{\infty} \frac{1-n}{n^2}$ diverges.

c $\displaystyle\sum_{n=1}^{\infty} \frac{1}{n} - \sum_{n=1}^{\infty} \frac{n-1}{n^2}$

$= \displaystyle\sum_{n=1}^{\infty} \frac{\cancel{1}}{n} - \left[\sum_{n=1}^{\infty} \frac{\cancel{1}}{n} - \sum_{n=1}^{\infty} \frac{1}{n^2}\right]$

$= \displaystyle\sum_{n=1}^{\infty} \frac{1}{n^2}$ which converges {p-series test}

2 a $\dfrac{1}{\ln 2} - \dfrac{1}{\ln 3} + \dfrac{1}{\ln 4} - \dfrac{1}{\ln 5} + \ldots$

$= \displaystyle\sum_{n=2}^{\infty} \frac{(-1)^n}{\ln n}$

which is an alternating series of the form $\displaystyle\sum_{n=2}^{\infty}(-1)^n b_n$

where $b_n = \dfrac{1}{\ln n}$

Consider $y = \ln x$, $x > 0$, $x \in \mathbb{R}$

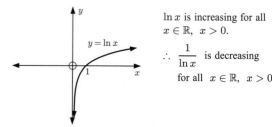

$\ln x$ is increasing for all $x \in \mathbb{R}$, $x > 0$.

$\therefore \dfrac{1}{\ln x}$ is decreasing for all $x \in \mathbb{R}$, $x > 0$

Thus $b_n = \dfrac{1}{\ln n}$ is decreasing for all $n \geqslant 2$, $n \in \mathbb{Z}^+$

Also $\lim\limits_{n\to\infty} b_n = 0$

$\Rightarrow \displaystyle\sum_{n=2}^{\infty} \frac{(-1)^n}{\ln n}$ converges

b For $\displaystyle\sum_{n=1}^{\infty}(-1)^{n-1}\frac{\sqrt{n}}{n+4}$, consider $f(x)=\dfrac{x^{\frac{1}{2}}}{x+4}$

where $f'(x)=\dfrac{\frac{1}{2}x^{-\frac{1}{2}}(x+4)-x^{\frac{1}{2}}(1)}{(x+4)^2}$

$=\dfrac{\frac{1}{2}\sqrt{x}+\frac{2}{\sqrt{x}}-\sqrt{x}}{(x+4)^2}$

$=\dfrac{\frac{2}{\sqrt{x}}-\frac{\sqrt{x}}{2}}{(x+4)^2}$

$=\dfrac{4-x}{2\sqrt{x}(x+4)^2}$

$\therefore$ $f'(x)\leqslant 0$ for all $x\geqslant 4$

$\therefore$ $f(x)$ is decreasing for all $x\geqslant 4$

Thus if $b_n=\dfrac{\sqrt{n}}{n+4}$ then b_n is decreasing for all $n\geqslant 4$

Also, as $n\to\infty$, $b_n=\dfrac{\frac{1}{\sqrt{n}}}{1+\frac{4}{n}}\to 0$

$\therefore$ $\displaystyle\lim_{n\to\infty}b_n=0$

$\therefore$ $\displaystyle\sum_{n=1}^{\infty}\frac{(-1)^{n-1}\sqrt{n}}{n+4}$ is convergent

{Alternating series test}

3 a　Let $a_n=\dfrac{(-1)^n n^n}{n!}$

$\therefore$ $\left|\dfrac{a_{n+1}}{a_n}\right|=\dfrac{(n+1)^{n+1}}{(n+1)!}\times\dfrac{n!}{n^n}$

$=\left(\dfrac{n+1}{n}\right)^n$

$=\left(1+\dfrac{1}{n}\right)^n$

$\therefore$ $\displaystyle\lim_{n\to\infty}\left|\dfrac{a_{n+1}}{a_n}\right|=e$ which is >1

$\therefore$ $\displaystyle\sum_{n=1}^{\infty}a_n$ is divergent　{Ratio Test}

b Consider $f(x)=\sin\left(\dfrac{\pi}{x}\right)$ for all $x\geqslant 1$

$f'(x)=\cos\left(\dfrac{\pi}{x}\right)\times\dfrac{-\pi}{x^2}=\dfrac{-\pi\cos\left(\frac{\pi}{x}\right)}{x^2}$

$\therefore$ $f'(x)\leqslant 0$ for all $x\geqslant 2$, $x\in\mathbb{R}$

$\therefore$ $b_n=\sin\left(\dfrac{\pi}{n}\right)$ is decreasing for all $n\geqslant 2$, $n\in\mathbb{Z}^+$

Also $\displaystyle\lim_{n\to\infty}b_n=0$

Hence, $\displaystyle\sum_{n=2}^{\infty}(-1)^n\sin\left(\dfrac{\pi}{n}\right)$ is convergent

{Alternating Series Test}

$\Rightarrow$ $\displaystyle\sum_{n=1}^{\infty}(-1)^n\sin\left(\dfrac{\pi}{n}\right)$ is convergent.

c Consider $f(x)=\dfrac{1}{\sqrt[3]{\ln x}}=[\ln x]^{-\frac{1}{3}}$

$\therefore$ $f'(x)=-\frac{1}{3}[\ln x]^{-\frac{4}{3}}\left(\dfrac{1}{x}\right)$

$\therefore$ $f'(x)=\dfrac{-1}{3x(\ln x)^{\frac{4}{3}}}$ which is <0 for all $x\geqslant 2$

$\Rightarrow$ $f(x)$ is decreasing for all $x\geqslant 2$

Hence $b_n=\dfrac{1}{\sqrt[3]{\ln n}}$ is decreasing for all $n\geqslant 2$ and since

$\displaystyle\lim_{n\to\infty}b_n=0$, $\displaystyle\sum_{n=2}^{\infty}\frac{(-1)^{n-1}}{\sqrt[3]{\ln n}}$ is convergent.

{Alternating Series Test}

d $\displaystyle\sum_{n=1}^{\infty}\frac{\sin\left(\frac{n\pi}{2}\right)}{n!}=\frac{1}{1!}-\frac{1}{3!}+\frac{1}{5!}-\frac{1}{7!}+\frac{1}{9!}-\dots.$

$=\displaystyle\sum_{n=1}^{\infty}\frac{(-1)^{n-1}}{(2n-1)!}$

Let $a_n=\dfrac{(-1)^{n-1}}{(2n-1)!}$

$\therefore$ $\left|\dfrac{a_{n+1}}{a_n}\right|=\dfrac{1}{(2n+1)!}\times\dfrac{(2n-1)!}{1}$

$\Rightarrow$ $\left|\dfrac{a_{n+1}}{a_n}\right|=\dfrac{1}{(2n+1)(2n)}$

Thus $\displaystyle\lim_{n\to\infty}\left|\dfrac{a_{n+1}}{a_n}\right|=0$ which is <1

Hence, $\displaystyle\sum_{n=1}^{\infty}\frac{\sin\left(\frac{n\pi}{2}\right)}{n!}$ is convergent　{Ratio Test}

{Alternatively the Alternating Series Test can be used}

e　Let $a_n=\dfrac{(-1)^n}{2^n n!}$

$\therefore$ $\left|\dfrac{a_{n+1}}{a_n}\right|=\dfrac{1}{2^{n+1}(n+1)!}\times\dfrac{2^n n!}{1}$

$=\dfrac{1}{2(n+1)}$

$\therefore$ $\displaystyle\lim_{n\to\infty}\left|\dfrac{a_{n+1}}{a_n}\right|=0$ which is <1

Hence $\displaystyle\sum_{n=1}^{\infty}\frac{(-1)^n}{2^n n!}$ is convergent　{Ratio Test}

f Let $f(x)=\dfrac{x^2}{x^3+1}$ $\therefore$ $f'(x)=\dfrac{2x(x^3+1)-x^2(3x^2)}{(x^3+1)^2}$

$=\dfrac{2x^4+2x-3x^4}{(x^3+1)^2}$

$=\dfrac{x(2-x^3)}{(x^3+1)^2}$

and for $n\geqslant 2$, $2-x^3\leqslant 0$

$\therefore$ $f'(x)\leqslant 0$ for all $x\geqslant 2$

$\therefore$ $f(x)$ is decreasing for all $x\geqslant 2$

So, if $\displaystyle\sum_{n=1}^{\infty}(-1)^{n+1}\frac{n^2}{n^3+1} = \sum_{n=1}^{\infty}(-1)^{n+1}b_n$ then b_n

is decreasing for all $n \geqslant 2$ and also

$$\lim_{n\to\infty} b_n = \lim_{n\to\infty} \frac{\dfrac{1}{n}}{1+\dfrac{1}{n^3}} = 0$$

Hence, $\displaystyle\sum_{n=2}^{\infty}(-1)^{n+1}\frac{n^2}{n^3+1}$ is convergent

$\Rightarrow \displaystyle\sum_{n=1}^{\infty}(-1)^{n+1}\frac{n^2}{n^3+1}$ is convergent $\{$as $a_1 = \frac{1}{2}\}$

4 a $\displaystyle\sum_{n=1}^{\infty}\frac{(-1)^{n+1}}{n!}$ is an alternating series with $b_n = \dfrac{1}{n!}$

As $0 < \dfrac{1}{(n+1)!} \leqslant \dfrac{1}{n!}$ for all $n \in \mathbb{Z}^+$, then

$\quad 0 < b_{n+1} \leqslant b_n$ for all $n \in \mathbb{Z}^+$

$\Rightarrow \{b_n\}$ is decreasing for all $n \geqslant 1$

Also $\displaystyle\lim_{n\to\infty} b_n = 0$

Thus $\displaystyle\sum_{n=1}^{\infty}\frac{(-1)^{n+1}}{n!}$ is convergent

{Alternating Series Test}

Now $S = \dfrac{1}{1!} - \dfrac{1}{2!} + \dfrac{1}{3!} - \dfrac{1}{4!} + \dfrac{1}{5!} - \dfrac{1}{6!} + \dfrac{1}{7!} - \dots$

where $b_6 = \dfrac{1}{6!} = \dfrac{1}{720} \approx 0.001\,39$

$\quad \therefore \quad b_6 < 0.005$

and $S_5 = 1 - \dfrac{1}{2} + \dfrac{1}{6} - \dfrac{1}{24} + \dfrac{1}{120} \approx 0.633\,33$

So, by the Estimation Theorem,

$\quad |S - S_5| \leqslant b_6$

$\Rightarrow \quad -0.001\,39 \leqslant S - 0.633\,33 \leqslant 0.001\,39$

$\Rightarrow \quad 0.631\,94 \leqslant S \leqslant 0.634\,72$

Thus $S \approx 0.63$

b $\displaystyle\sum_{n=1}^{\infty}\frac{(-1)^{n-1}}{(2n-1)!}$ is an alternating series with

$b_n = \dfrac{1}{(2n-1)!}$

Now as $0 < \dfrac{1}{(2n+1)!} < \dfrac{1}{(2n-1)!}$,

$\quad 0 < b_{n+1} < b_n$ for all $n \in \mathbb{Z}^+$

$\Rightarrow \{b_n\}$ is a decreasing sequence, $n \in \mathbb{Z}^+$.

Also $\displaystyle\lim_{n\to\infty} b_n = 0$

Thus $\displaystyle\sum_{n=1}^{\infty}\frac{(-1)^{n-1}}{(2n-1)!}$ is convergent

{Alternating Series Test}

Now $S = \dfrac{1}{1!} - \dfrac{1}{3!} + \dfrac{1}{5!} - \dfrac{1}{7!} + \dfrac{1}{9!} - \dots$

and $b_5 \approx \dfrac{1}{9!} \approx 0.000\,002\,76 < 0.000\,05$

and $S_4 \approx 0.841\,468\,25$

So, by the Estimation Theorem,

$\quad |S - S_4| \leqslant b_5$

$\Rightarrow \quad S_4 - b_5 \leqslant S \leqslant S_4 + b_5$

$\Rightarrow \quad 0.841\,465 \leqslant S \leqslant 0.841\,471$

$\quad \therefore \quad S \approx 0.8415$

c $\displaystyle\sum_{n=0}^{\infty}\frac{(-1)^n}{2^n n!}$ is an alternating series with $b_n = \dfrac{1}{2^n n!}$

Now $b_{n+1} - b_n = \dfrac{1}{2^{n+1}(n+1)!} - \dfrac{1}{2^n n!}$

$\quad = \dfrac{1}{2^n n!}\left(\dfrac{1}{2(n+1)} - 1\right)$

$\quad = \dfrac{1}{2^n n!}\left(\dfrac{1 - 2n - 2}{2(n+1)}\right)$

$\quad = \dfrac{-(2n+1)}{2^{n+1}(n+1)!}$

which is < 0 for all $n \in \mathbb{Z}^+$

Thus $b_{n+1} < b_n$ for all $n \in \mathbb{Z}^+$

$\Rightarrow \{b_n\}$ is decreasing for all $n \in \mathbb{Z}^+$

Also $\displaystyle\lim_{n\to\infty} b_n = 0$

Hence, $\displaystyle\sum_{n=0}^{\infty}\frac{(-1)^n}{2^n n!}$ is convergent

{Alternating Series Test}

Now $S = 1 - \frac{1}{2} + \frac{1}{8} - \frac{1}{48} + \frac{1}{384} - \frac{1}{3840} + \frac{1}{46\,084} - \dots$

where $b_7 = \frac{1}{46\,084} \approx 0.000\,021\,70 < 0.000\,05$

and $S_6 \approx 0.606\,510\,42$

But, by the Estimation Theorem

$\quad |S - S_6| \leqslant b_7$

$\Rightarrow \quad S_6 - b_7 \leqslant S \leqslant S_6 + b_7$

$\Rightarrow \quad 0.606\,489 \leqslant S \leqslant 0.606\,532$

$\quad \therefore \quad S \approx 0.6065$

5 $\displaystyle\sum_{n=1}^{\infty}\frac{(-1)^{n-1}}{n^3} = \frac{1}{1} - \frac{1}{8} + \frac{1}{27} - \frac{1}{64} + \frac{1}{125} - \frac{1}{216} + \dots$

$S_1 = 1$ $S_6 \approx 0.899\,782\,4$

$S_2 = 0.875$ $S_7 \approx 0.902\,697\,9$

$S_3 \approx 0.912\,037\,0$ $S_8 \approx 0.900\,744\,7$

$S_4 \approx 0.896\,412\,0$ $S_9 \approx 0.902\,116\,5$

$S_5 \approx 0.904\,412\,0$ $S_{10} \approx 0.902\,111\,6$

An estimate of the error in using S_{10} to approximate S is

$b_{11} = \frac{1}{11^3} \approx 0.000\,751\,3$.

6 We are given $S = \displaystyle\sum_{n=1}^{\infty}(-1)^{n-1}b_n$ where $b_n \geqslant 0$, $\{b_n\}$ is

decreasing and $\displaystyle\lim_{n\to\infty} b_n = 0$.

a $S_2 = (-1)^0 b_1 + (-1)^1 b_2 = b_1 - b_2$

But $b_{n+1} \leqslant b_n$ for all $n \in \mathbb{Z}^+ \Rightarrow b_2 \leqslant b_1$

$\quad \therefore \quad S_2 \geqslant 0$

b $S_4 = (-1)^0 b_1 + (-1)^1 b_2 + (-1)^2 b_3 + (-1)^3 b_4$

$\quad = b_1 - b_2 + b_3 - b_4$

Thus $S_4 - S_2 = b_1 - b_2 + b_3 - b_4 - (b_1 - b_2)$

$$= b_3 - b_4$$

which is $\geqslant 0$ {as $\{b_n\}$ is decreasing}

Likewise $S_6 - S_4 \geqslant 0$, $S_8 - S_6 \geqslant 0$, etc,

and as $S_{2n} - S_{2n-2} = b_{2n-1} - b_{2n} \geqslant 0$

$$S_{2n} - S_{2n-2} \geqslant 0 \text{ for all } n \in \mathbb{Z}^+.$$

Thus $S_{2n} \geqslant S_{2n-2} \geqslant S_{2n-4} \geqslant \ldots \geqslant S_4 \geqslant S_2$

So $0 \leqslant S_2 \leqslant S_4 \leqslant \ldots \leqslant S_{2n-4} \leqslant S_{2n-2} \leqslant S_{2n}$

c $S_{2n} = b_1 - b_2 + b_3 - b_4 + \ldots - b_{2n-2} + b_{2n-1} - b_{2n}$

$\therefore$ $S_{2n} = b_1 - (b_2 - b_3) - (b_4 - b_5) - \ldots$

$$- (b_{2n-2} - b_{2n-1}) - b_{2n}$$

where $b_2 - b_3 \geqslant 0$, $b_4 - b_5 \geqslant 0$, ..., $b_{2n-2} - b_{2n-1} \geqslant 0$, and $b_{2n} \geqslant 0$

$\therefore$ $S_{2n} \leqslant b_1$

d From **b** and **c**, $\{S_{2n}\}$ is increasing and has an upper bound of b_1

$\Rightarrow$ $\{S_{2n}\}$ is convergent to S, say

$\therefore$ $\displaystyle\lim_{n\to\infty} S_{2n} = S$.

e S_{2n+1}

$$= \underbrace{b_1 - b_2 + b_3 - b_4 + \ldots + b_{2n+1} - b_{2n}}_{S_{2n}} + b_{2n+1}$$

$\therefore$ $S_{2n+1} = S_{2n} + b_{2n+1}$

f From **e**, $\displaystyle\lim_{n\to\infty} S_{2n+1} = \lim_{n\to\infty} S_{2n} + \lim_{n\to\infty} b_{2n+1}$

$$= S + 0$$

$$= S$$

Thus $\displaystyle\lim_{n\to\infty} S_{2n} = \lim_{n\to\infty} S_{2n+1} = S$

$\Rightarrow$ $\displaystyle\lim_{n\to\infty} S_n = S$

7 a If $a_n = \dfrac{(-3)^n}{n!}$, $\displaystyle\lim_{n\to\infty} \left| \dfrac{a_{n+1}}{a_n} \right| = \lim_{n\to\infty} \left| \dfrac{3^{n+1}}{(n+1)!} \dfrac{n!}{3^n} \right|$

$$= \lim_{n\to\infty} \dfrac{3}{n+1}$$

$$= 0$$

$\Rightarrow$ $\displaystyle\sum_{n=1}^{\infty} \dfrac{(-3)^n}{n!}$ is absolutely convergent {Ratio test}

b If $a_n = \dfrac{(-1)^n 2^n}{n^2 + 1}$, $\displaystyle\lim_{n\to\infty} \left| \dfrac{a_{n+1}}{a_n} \right|$

$$= \lim_{n\to\infty} \dfrac{2^{n+1}}{(n+1)^2 + 1} \left(\dfrac{n^2 + 1}{2^n} \right)$$

$$= \lim_{n\to\infty} 2 \left(\dfrac{n^2 + 1}{n^2 + 2n + 2} \right)$$

$$= \lim_{n\to\infty} 2 \left(\dfrac{1 + \frac{1}{n^2}}{1 + \frac{2}{n} + \frac{2}{n^2}} \right)$$

$$= 2 \times \dfrac{1}{1}$$

$$= 2$$

$\Rightarrow$ $\displaystyle\sum_{n=1}^{\infty} \dfrac{(-1)^n 2^n}{n^2 + 1}$ is divergent {Ratio test}

c If $a_n = \dfrac{(-1)^n \arctan n}{n^3}$ then

$$|a_n| = \dfrac{|\arctan n|}{n^3} \leqslant \dfrac{\frac{\pi}{2}}{n^3}$$

But $\displaystyle\sum_{n=1}^{\infty} \dfrac{1}{n^3}$ converges {p-series test}

$\Rightarrow$ $\displaystyle\sum_{n=1}^{\infty} \dfrac{\frac{\pi}{2}}{n^3}$ also converges

$\Rightarrow$ $\displaystyle\sum_{n=1}^{\infty} |a_n|$ converges {Comparison test}

$\Rightarrow$ $\displaystyle\sum_{n=1}^{\infty} \dfrac{(-1)^n \arctan n}{n^3}$ is absolutely convergent.

d If $a_n = \left(\dfrac{1 - 3n}{3 + 4n} \right)^n$ then $|a_n| = \left(\dfrac{3n - 1}{4n + 3} \right)^n$

$$\Rightarrow |a_n| < \left(\tfrac{3}{4} \right)^n$$

But $\displaystyle\sum_{n=1}^{\infty} \left(\tfrac{3}{4} \right)^n$ is convergent {a convergent GS}

$\Rightarrow$ $\displaystyle\sum_{n=1}^{\infty} |a_n|$ is convergent {Comparison test}

$\Rightarrow$ $\displaystyle\sum_{n=1}^{\infty} \left(\dfrac{1 - 3n}{3 + 4n} \right)$ is absolutely convergent.

e Consider $f(x) = \dfrac{\ln x}{x}$

Now $f'(x) = \dfrac{\frac{1}{x} x - \ln x}{x^2} = \dfrac{1 - \ln x}{x^2}$

$\therefore$ $f'(x) < 0$ for all x such that $\ln x > 1$, that is, $x > e$

Thus $\left\{ \dfrac{\ln n}{n} \right\}$ is decreasing for all $n \geqslant 3$, $n \in \mathbb{Z}^+$ .... (1)

By l'Hôpital's Rule, $\displaystyle\lim_{x\to\infty} \dfrac{\ln x}{x} = \lim_{n\to\infty} \dfrac{\frac{1}{x}}{1} = 0$

$\therefore$ $\displaystyle\lim_{n\to\infty} \dfrac{\ln n}{n} = 0$, $n \in \mathbb{Z}^+$ .... (2)

$\therefore$ $\displaystyle\sum_{n=1}^{\infty} \dfrac{(-1)^{n+1} \ln n}{n}$ is convergent

{Alternating Series Test}

But $\displaystyle\sum_{n=1}^{\infty} \dfrac{\ln n}{n}$ is divergent {Integral test}

$\therefore$ $\displaystyle\sum_{n=1}^{\infty} \dfrac{(-1)^{n+1} \ln n}{n}$ is conditionally convergent.

f Let $b_n = \dfrac{1}{n \ln n}$, then $\displaystyle\lim_{n\to\infty} b_n = 0$

Now consider $f(x) = \dfrac{1}{x \ln x} = [x \ln x]^{-1}$, $x \geqslant 2$

$\therefore$ $f'(x) = -[x \ln x]^{-2} \left(1 \ln x + x \left(\dfrac{1}{x} \right) \right)$

$$= \dfrac{-(\ln x + 1)}{(x \ln x)^2}$$

So, $f'(x) < 0$ for all $x \geqslant 2$

$\Rightarrow$ $b_n = \dfrac{1}{n \ln n}$ is decreasing for all $n \geqslant 2$, $n \in \mathbb{Z}^+$

Thus $\displaystyle\sum_{n=2}^{\infty} \frac{(-1)^n}{n \ln n}$ is convergent.

But $\displaystyle\sum_{n=2}^{\infty} \frac{1}{n \ln n}$ is divergent $\{$Integral test$\}$

$\therefore \displaystyle\sum_{n=2}^{\infty} \frac{(-1)^n}{n \ln n}$ is conditionally convergent.

g Let $b_r = \sqrt{r+1} - \sqrt{r}$

$\therefore b_r = \left(\sqrt{r+1} - \sqrt{r}\right)\left(\dfrac{\sqrt{r+1} + \sqrt{r}}{\sqrt{r+1} + \sqrt{r}}\right)$

$\therefore b_r = \dfrac{r+1-r}{\sqrt{r+1} + \sqrt{r}}$

$\therefore b_r = \dfrac{1}{\sqrt{r+1} + \sqrt{r}} \geqslant \dfrac{1}{2\sqrt{r+1}}$

$\therefore \displaystyle\sum_{r=1}^{\infty} b_r \geqslant \frac{1}{2}\sum_{r=1}^{\infty} \frac{1}{\sqrt{r+1}}$

$\therefore \displaystyle\sum_{r=1}^{\infty} b_r \geqslant \frac{1}{2}\sum_{n=2}^{\infty} \frac{1}{\sqrt{n}} \quad \{n = r+1\}$

where $\displaystyle\sum_{n=2}^{\infty} \frac{1}{\sqrt{n}}$ is divergent $\{p$-series test$\}$

$\therefore \displaystyle\sum_{r=1}^{\infty} b_r$ is divergent

$\Rightarrow \displaystyle\sum_{r=1}^{\infty} (-1)^{r-1}(\sqrt{r+1} - \sqrt{r})$ is divergent.

8 a Let $a_n = \dfrac{x^n}{n!}$ for $x \in \mathbb{R}$.

Now $\left|\dfrac{a_{n+1}}{a_n}\right| = \left|\dfrac{x^{n+1}}{(n+1)!} \dfrac{n!}{x^n}\right| = \dfrac{|x|}{n+1}$

$\therefore \displaystyle\lim_{n\to\infty}\left|\dfrac{a_{n+1}}{a_n}\right| = 0$

$\Rightarrow \displaystyle\sum_{n=0}^{\infty} \frac{x^n}{n!}$ is absolutely convergent and $\therefore$ convergent.

b By the Converse of the Test for divergence,

$\displaystyle\sum_{n=0}^{\infty} a_n$ is convergent $\Rightarrow \displaystyle\lim_{n\to\infty} a_n = 0$

$\therefore \displaystyle\sum_{n=0}^{\infty} \frac{x^n}{n!}$ is convergent

$\Rightarrow \displaystyle\lim_{n\to\infty} \frac{x^n}{n!} = 0$

9 a $\displaystyle\sum_{n=0}^{\infty} \frac{10^n}{n!}$ is $\displaystyle\sum_{n=0}^{\infty} \frac{x^n}{n!}$ with $x = 10$

$\therefore$ by **8 a**, $\displaystyle\sum_{n=0}^{\infty} \frac{10^n}{n!}$ converges.

b For $n > 1$, $\dfrac{1}{\sqrt{(n+1)(n+1)}} < \dfrac{1}{\sqrt{n(n+1)}}$

$\Rightarrow \dfrac{1}{n+1} < \dfrac{1}{\sqrt{n(n+1)}}$

$\Rightarrow \displaystyle\sum_{n=1}^{\infty} \frac{1}{n+1} < \sum_{n=1}^{\infty} \frac{1}{\sqrt{n(n+1)}}$

Note that $\displaystyle\sum_{n=1}^{\infty} \frac{1}{n+1} = \left(\sum_{n=1}^{\infty} \frac{1}{n}\right) - 1$, which is the Harmonic Series with the first term removed.

Since $\displaystyle\sum_{n=1}^{\infty} \frac{1}{n}$ diverges $\{p$-series test$\}$, it follows that $\displaystyle\sum_{n=1}^{\infty} \frac{1}{n+1}$ diverges.

Hence $\displaystyle\sum_{n=1}^{\infty} \frac{1}{\sqrt{n(n+1)}}$ diverges

$\{$Comparison test for series$\}$

c $\displaystyle\lim_{n\to\infty} \frac{2n}{8n-5} = \lim_{n\to\infty} \frac{2}{8 - \frac{5}{n}} = \frac{1}{4} \neq 0$

$\therefore \displaystyle\sum_{n=1}^{\infty} \frac{2n}{8n-5}$ is divergent.

d Let $a_n = \dfrac{\cos\left(\frac{n}{2}\right)}{n^2 + 4n}$

Now $\left|\cos\left(\dfrac{n}{2}\right)\right| \leqslant 1$ and $n^2 + 4n > n^2$, $n \in \mathbb{Z}^+$

$\therefore |a_n| \leqslant \dfrac{1}{n^2}$

$\therefore 0 \leqslant \displaystyle\sum_{n=1}^{\infty} |a_n| \leqslant \sum_{n=1}^{\infty} \frac{1}{n^2}$

where $\displaystyle\sum_{n=1}^{\infty} \frac{1}{n^2}$ is convergent $\{p$-series test$\}$

$\Rightarrow \displaystyle\sum_{n=1}^{\infty} |a_n|$ is convergent $\quad \{$Comparison test$\}$

$\Rightarrow \displaystyle\sum_{n=1}^{\infty} \frac{\cos\left(\frac{n}{2}\right)}{n^2 + 4n}$ is absolutely convergent and

$\therefore$ convergent.

e $\dfrac{n^3 + 1}{n^4 - 1} > \dfrac{n^3}{n^4}$ for all $n \in \mathbb{Z}^+$, $n \geqslant 2$

$\therefore \displaystyle\sum_{n=2}^{\infty} \frac{n^3 + 1}{n^4 - 1} > \sum_{n=2}^{\infty} \frac{1}{n}$

But $\displaystyle\sum_{n=2}^{\infty} \frac{1}{n}$ diverges $\quad \{p$-series test$\}$

$\Rightarrow \displaystyle\sum_{n=2}^{\infty} \frac{n^3 + 1}{n^4 - 1}$ diverges $\{$Comparison test$\}$

f Let $a_n = \dfrac{n!}{2 \times 5 \times 8 \times .... \times (3n+2)}$

$\therefore \left|\dfrac{a_{n+1}}{a_n}\right| = \dfrac{(n+1)!}{2 \times 5 \times 8 \times .... \times (3n+5)}$

$\times \dfrac{2 \times 5 \times 8 \times .... \times (3n+2)}{n!}$

$= \dfrac{n+1}{3n+5}$

$\therefore \displaystyle\lim_{n\to\infty}\left|\dfrac{a_{n+1}}{a_n}\right| = \lim_{n\to\infty} \frac{1 + \frac{1}{n}}{3 + \frac{5}{n}} = \frac{1}{3} \neq 0$

$\therefore$ by the Ratio test, $\displaystyle\sum_{n=0}^{\infty} a_n$ converges.

10 If $a_n = \dfrac{1}{n^2}$, $\displaystyle\lim_{n\to\infty}\left|\dfrac{a_{n+1}}{a_n}\right| = \lim_{n\to\infty}\dfrac{1}{(n+1)^2}\dfrac{n^2}{1}$

$$= \lim_{n\to\infty}\dfrac{n^2}{n^2+2n+1}$$

$$= \lim_{n\to\infty}\dfrac{1}{1+\dfrac{2}{n}+\dfrac{1}{n^2}}$$

$$= 1$$

$\therefore$ by the Ratio test $\displaystyle\sum_{n=1}^{\infty}\dfrac{1}{n^2}$ could be either convergent or divergent.

But, from the p-series test it is convergent.

Likewise, if $a_n = \dfrac{1}{n}$, $\displaystyle\lim_{n\to\infty}\left|\dfrac{a_{n+1}}{a_n}\right| = \lim_{n\to\infty}\dfrac{1}{n+1}\dfrac{n}{1}$

$$= \lim_{n\to\infty}\dfrac{1}{1+\dfrac{1}{n}}$$

$$= 1$$

So, once again the ratio test is inconclusive.

EXERCISE K.4 ▮▮▮▮▮

1 a $\displaystyle\sum_{n=0}^{\infty}x^{3n} = 1+x^3+x^6+x^9+x^{12}+....$ which is geometric with $u_1 = 1$ and $r = x^3$.

$\therefore$ $\displaystyle\sum_{n=0}^{\infty}x^{3n} = \dfrac{u_1}{1-r} = \dfrac{1}{1-x^3}$ provided $|r| < 1$

$$\Rightarrow \quad |x^3| < 1$$
$$\Rightarrow \quad |x| < 1$$

Thus, the radius of convergence is 1 and the interval of convergence is $]-1,\,1[$.

b $\displaystyle\sum_{n=0}^{\infty}(2-x)^n = 1+(2-x)+(2-x)^2+(2-x)^3+....$
which is geometric with $u_1 = 1$ and $r = 2-x$.

$\therefore$ $\displaystyle\sum_{n=0}^{\infty}(2-x)^n = \dfrac{u_1}{1-r} = \dfrac{1}{1-2+x} = \dfrac{1}{x-1}$

provided $|r| < 1 \Rightarrow \quad |2-x| < 1$
$$\Rightarrow \quad |x-2| < 1$$
$$\Rightarrow \quad -1 < x-2 < 1$$
$$\Rightarrow \quad 1 < x < 3$$

Thus, the radius of convergence is 1 and the interval of convergence is $]1,\,3[$.

c $\displaystyle\sum_{n=0}^{\infty}(-1)^n x^{4n} = 1-x^4+x^8-x^{12}+x^{16}+....$ which is geometric with $u_1 = 1$ and $r = -x^4$.

$\therefore$ $\displaystyle\sum_{n=0}^{\infty}(-1)^n x^{4n} = \dfrac{u_1}{1-r} = \dfrac{1}{1+x^4}$

provided $|r| < 1 \Rightarrow \quad |-x^4| < 1$
$$\Rightarrow \quad |x|^4 < 1$$
$$\Rightarrow \quad |x| < 1$$

Thus, the radius of convergence is 1 and the interval of convergence is $]-1,\,1[$.

2 $\displaystyle\sum_{n=0}^{\infty}\dfrac{1}{x^{2n}} = 1+\dfrac{1}{x^2}+\dfrac{1}{x^4}+\dfrac{1}{x^6}+....$ is geometric with $a_1 = 1$ and $r = \dfrac{1}{x^2}$.

$\therefore$ $\displaystyle\sum_{n=0}^{\infty}\dfrac{1}{x^{2n}} = \dfrac{a_1}{1-r} = \dfrac{1}{1-\dfrac{1}{x^2}}\left(\dfrac{x^2}{x^2}\right) = \dfrac{x^2}{x^2-1}$

provided $|r| < 1 \Rightarrow \quad \left|\dfrac{1}{x^2}\right| < 1$

$$\Rightarrow \quad |x^2| > 1$$
$$\Rightarrow \quad |x| > 1$$
$$\Rightarrow \quad x > 1 \text{ or } x < -1$$

$\therefore$ the interval of convergence is $]-\infty,\,-1[\,\cup\,]1,\,\infty[$.

3 a If $a_n = n5^n x^n$,

$$\lim_{n\to\infty}\left|\dfrac{a_{n+1}}{a_n}\right| = \lim_{n\to\infty}\left|\dfrac{(n+1)5^{n+1}x^{n+1}}{n5^n x^n}\right|$$

$$= \lim_{n\to\infty}\left|\left(1+\dfrac{1}{n}\right)5x\right|$$

$$= |5x|$$

$$= 5|x|$$

So, by the Ratio test $\displaystyle\sum_{n=0}^{\infty}n5^n x^n$ converges if $|x| < \dfrac{1}{5}$ and diverges for $|x| > \dfrac{1}{5}$.

$\therefore$ the radius of convergence is $\dfrac{1}{5}$.

As the Ratio test is inconclusive for $|x| = \dfrac{1}{5}$ we examine each case $(x = \dfrac{1}{5}$ and $x = -\dfrac{1}{5})$ separately.

<u>If $x = \dfrac{1}{5}$</u>, $a_n = n5^n\left(\dfrac{1}{5}\right)^n = n$ and $\displaystyle\sum_{n=1}^{\infty}a_n = \sum_{n=1}^{\infty}n$

diverges $\{$since $\displaystyle\lim_{n\to\infty}n \neq 0\}$

<u>If $x = -\dfrac{1}{5}$</u>, $a_n = n5^n\left(-\dfrac{1}{5}\right)^n = (-1)^n n$ and

$$\sum_{n=1}^{\infty}a_n = \sum_{n=1}^{\infty}(-1)^n n \text{ diverges}$$

$\{$since $\displaystyle\lim_{n\to\infty}(-1)^n n \neq 0\}$

$\therefore$ $\displaystyle\sum_{n=0}^{\infty}n5^n x^n$ is convergent for $-\dfrac{1}{5} < x < \dfrac{1}{5}$ only; its radius of convergence is $\dfrac{1}{5}$ and its interval of convergence is $]-\dfrac{1}{5},\,\dfrac{1}{5}[$.

b If $a_n = \dfrac{3^n x^n}{(n+1)^2}$,

$$\lim_{n\to\infty}\left|\dfrac{a_{n+1}}{a_n}\right| = \lim_{n\to\infty}\left|\dfrac{3^{n+1}x^{n+1}}{(n+2)^2}\dfrac{(n+1)^2}{3^n x^n}\right|$$

$$= \lim_{n\to\infty}\left|3x\left(\dfrac{n+1}{n+2}\right)^2\right|$$

$$= \lim_{n\to\infty}\left|3x\left(\dfrac{1+\dfrac{1}{n}}{1+\dfrac{2}{n}}\right)^2\right|$$

But $\displaystyle\lim_{n\to\infty}\left(\dfrac{1+\frac{1}{n}}{1+\frac{2}{n}}\right)=1,$ so $\displaystyle\lim_{n\to\infty}\left|\dfrac{a_{n+1}}{a_n}\right|=|3x|$

Thus $\displaystyle\sum_{n=1}^{\infty}\dfrac{3^n x^n}{(n+1)^2}$ is convergent if

$|3x|<1$

$\therefore\ |x|<\frac{1}{3}$

$\Rightarrow\ -\frac{1}{3}<x<\frac{1}{3}$ {Ratio test}

As the Ratio test is inconclusive for $|x|=\frac{1}{3}$, we examine the cases $x=\frac{1}{3}$ and $x=-\frac{1}{3}$ separately.

If $x=\frac{1}{3}$, $\displaystyle\sum_{n=0}^{\infty}a_n=\sum_{n=0}^{\infty}\dfrac{3^n\left(\frac{1}{3}\right)^n}{(n+1)^2}=\sum_{n=0}^{\infty}\dfrac{1}{(n+1)^2}$

But $0<\displaystyle\sum_{n=0}^{\infty}\dfrac{1}{(n+1)^2}<\sum_{n=0}^{\infty}\dfrac{1}{n^2}$ where

$\displaystyle\sum_{n=0}^{\infty}\dfrac{1}{n^2}$ converges {p-series test}

$\therefore$ by the Comparison test $\displaystyle\sum_{n=0}^{\infty}\dfrac{1}{(n+1)^2}$ converges.

If $x=-\frac{1}{3}$, $\displaystyle\sum_{n=0}^{\infty}a_n=\sum_{n=0}^{\infty}\dfrac{3^n\left(-\frac{1}{3}\right)^n}{(n+1)^2}=\sum_{n=0}^{\infty}\dfrac{(-1)^n}{(n+1)^2}$

which converges by the Alternating series test.

$\therefore\ \displaystyle\sum_{n=0}^{\infty}\dfrac{3^n x^n}{(n+1)^2}$ is convergent for $-\frac{1}{3}\leqslant x\leqslant\frac{1}{3}$.

It has a radius of convergence of $\frac{1}{3}$ and its interval of convergence is $[-\frac{1}{3},\frac{1}{3}]$.

c If $a_n=\dfrac{(-1)^n x^{2n-1}}{(2n-1)!}$, then

$\displaystyle\lim_{n\to\infty}\left|\dfrac{a_{n+1}}{a_n}\right|=\lim_{n\to\infty}\left|\dfrac{x^{2n+1}}{(2n+1)!}\dfrac{(2n-1)!}{x^{2n-1}}\right|$

$=\displaystyle\lim_{n\to\infty}\left|\dfrac{x^2}{2n(2n+1)}\right|$

$=0$

$\therefore\ \displaystyle\sum_{n=0}^{\infty}a_n$ is convergent for all $x\in\mathbb{R}$.

It has an infinite radius of convergence and its interval of convergence is $\mathbb{R}$.

d If $a_n=\dfrac{(-1)^n(2x+3)^n}{n\ln n}$,

$\displaystyle\lim_{n\to\infty}\left|\dfrac{a_{n+1}}{a_n}\right|$

$=\displaystyle\lim_{n\to\infty}\left|\dfrac{(2x+3)^{n+1}}{(n+1)\ln(n+1)}\times\dfrac{n\ln n}{(2x+3)^n}\right|$

$=\displaystyle\lim_{n\to\infty}\ |2x+3|\times\dfrac{n}{n+1}\times\dfrac{\ln n}{\ln(n+1)}$

$=|2x+3|$

{as $\dfrac{n}{n+1}\to1$ and $\dfrac{\ln n}{\ln(n+1)}\to1$}

$\therefore\ \displaystyle\sum_{n=0}^{\infty}a_n$ is convergent for $|2x+3|<1$

$-1<2x+3<1$

$-4<2x<-2$

$-2<x<-1$

As the Ratio test is inconclusive for $x=-2$ and $x=-1$ we examine each of these cases separately.

If $x=-2$, we have $\displaystyle\sum_{n=2}^{\infty}\dfrac{1}{n\ln n}$

Now $\displaystyle\int_{2}^{\infty}\dfrac{1}{x\ln x}\,dx$

$=\displaystyle\lim_{b\to\infty}\left(\int_{2}^{b}\dfrac{1}{x\ln x}\,dx\right)$

$=\displaystyle\lim_{b\to\infty}\left(\int_{2}^{b}\dfrac{1}{u}\dfrac{du}{dx}\,dx\right)$ $\{u=\ln x,\ \dfrac{du}{dx}=\dfrac{1}{x}\}$

$=\displaystyle\lim_{b\to\infty}\left(\int_{\ln 2}^{\ln b}\dfrac{1}{u}\,du\right)$ $\begin{cases}\text{when }x=2,\ u=\ln 2\\ \text{when }x=b,\ u=\ln b\end{cases}$

$=\displaystyle\lim_{b\to\infty}\left(\Big[\ln|u|\Big]_{\ln 2}^{\ln b}\right)$

$=\displaystyle\lim_{b\to\infty}\left(\ln(\ln b)-\ln(\ln 2)\right)$

which DNE

$\therefore$ by the Integral test, $\displaystyle\sum_{n=2}^{\infty}\dfrac{1}{n\ln n}$ is divergent.

For $x=-1$, we have $\displaystyle\sum_{n=2}^{\infty}\dfrac{(-1)^n}{n\ln n}$ where $b_n=\dfrac{1}{n\ln n}$, $n\geqslant 2$.

Consider $f(x)=\dfrac{1}{x\ln x}=[x\ln x]^{-1}$

$\therefore\ f'(x)=-[x\ln x]^{-2}\left(1\ln x+x\left(\dfrac{1}{x}\right)\right)$

$=-\dfrac{(\ln x+1)}{[x\ln x]^2}$

$\therefore\ f'(x)<0$ for all $x\geqslant 2$

$\{\ln x+1>0,\ [x\ln x]^2>0\}$

$\therefore\ f(x)$ is decreasing for all $x\geqslant 2$

$\Rightarrow\ b_n=\dfrac{1}{n\ln n}$ is decreasing for all $n\geqslant 2,\ n\in\mathbb{Z}^+$

and $\displaystyle\lim_{n\to\infty}b_n=0$

$\Rightarrow\ \displaystyle\sum_{n=2}^{\infty}\dfrac{(-1)^n}{n\ln n}$ is convergent {Alternating Series test}

So, $\displaystyle\sum_{n=2}^{\infty}\dfrac{(-1)^n(2x+3)^n}{n\ln n}$ is convergent for

$-2<x\leqslant-1$.

Hence, the radius of convergence is $\frac{1}{2}$ and the interval of convergence is $]-2,-1]$.

4 Let $a_n = \dfrac{2 \times 4 \times 6 \times 8 \times \dots \times (2n)x^n}{1 \times 3 \times 5 \times 7 \times \dots \times (2n-1)}$

Now $\dfrac{a_{n+1}}{a_n} = \dfrac{2 \times 4 \times 6 \times 8 \times \dots \times (2n+2)x^{n+1}}{1 \times 3 \times 5 \times 7 \times \dots \times (2n+1)}$

$\qquad \times \dfrac{1 \times 3 \times 5 \times 7 \times \dots \times (2n-1)}{2 \times 4 \times 6 \times 8 \times \dots \times (2n)x^n}$

$\qquad = \left(\dfrac{2n+2}{2n+1}\right) x$

$\therefore \displaystyle\lim_{n\to\infty} \left| \dfrac{a_{n+1}}{a_n} \right| = \lim_{n\to\infty} \left(\dfrac{2n+2}{2n+1}\right)|x|$

$\qquad = 1 \times |x|$

$\qquad = |x|$

$\Rightarrow \displaystyle\sum_{n=1}^{\infty} a_n$ is convergent for $|x| < 1$

$\qquad$ that is, for $-1 < x < 1$

As the Ratio test is inconclusive for $x = \pm 1$, we examine each of these cases separately.

If $x = -1$, $a_n = \dfrac{2 \times 4 \times 6 \times 8 \times \dots \times (2n)(-1)^n}{1 \times 3 \times 5 \times 7 \times \dots \times (2n-1)}$

$\qquad = \left(\tfrac{2}{1}\right) \times \left(\tfrac{4}{3}\right) \times \left(\tfrac{6}{5}\right) \times \left(\tfrac{8}{7}\right) \times \dots$

$\qquad \times \left(\dfrac{2n}{2n-1}\right) \times (-1)^n$

$\therefore |a_n| > 1$ {as each fraction is > 1}

$\therefore \displaystyle\lim_{n\to\infty} a_n \neq 0$

$\Rightarrow \displaystyle\sum_{n=1}^{\infty} a_n$ diverges {Test for divergence}

If $x = 1$, $a_n = \left(\tfrac{2}{1}\right)\left(\tfrac{4}{3}\right)\left(\tfrac{6}{5}\right)\left(\tfrac{8}{7}\right) \dots \left(\dfrac{2n}{2n-1}\right)$

$\therefore a_n > 1$ also

$\therefore \displaystyle\lim_{n\to\infty} a_n \neq 0$

$\Rightarrow \displaystyle\sum_{n=1}^{\infty} a_n$ diverges {Test for divergence}

Thus $\displaystyle\sum_{n=1}^{\infty} a_n$ converges for all x in $-1 < x < 1$.

Hence, the radius of convergence is 1 and the interval of convergence is $]-1, 1[$.

5 a $f(x)$

$\qquad = 1 + 2x + x^2 + 2x^3 + x^4 + \dots$

$\qquad = (1 + x^2 + x^4 + x^6 + \dots) + 2x(1 + x^2 + x^4 + \dots)$

$\qquad = (1 + 2x)(1 + x^2 + x^4 + x^6 + \dots)$

$\qquad\qquad\qquad \uparrow$

$\qquad$ GS with $u_1 = 1$, $r = x^2$

$\qquad = (1 + 2x) \times \dfrac{1}{1 - x^2}$ provided $\left| x^2 \right| < 1$

$\qquad = \dfrac{1 + 2x}{1 - x^2}$ provided $|x| < 1$

$\therefore$ the interval of convergence is $]-1, 1[$.

b $f(x) = \dfrac{1 + 2x}{1 - x^2}$

6 If $\displaystyle\sum_{n=0}^{\infty} c_n x^n$ has radius of convergence R, then $|x| < R$.

Now let $x = y^2$

$\therefore \displaystyle\sum_{n=0}^{\infty} c_n y^{2n}$ has radius of convergence R

$\therefore \left| y^2 \right| < R$

$\therefore |y|^2 < R$

$\therefore |y| < \sqrt{R}$

Thus $\displaystyle\sum_{n=0}^{\infty} c_n x^{2n}$ converges when $|x| < \sqrt{R}$

$\therefore$ the radius of convergence is $\sqrt{R}$.

7 $\displaystyle\sum_{n=0}^{\infty} (c_n + d_n)x^n = \sum_{n=0}^{\infty} c_n x^n + \sum_{n=0}^{\infty} d_n x^n$

where $\displaystyle\sum_{n=0}^{\infty} c_n x^n$ is convergent with $|x| < 2$

and $\displaystyle\sum_{n=0}^{\infty} d_n x^n$ is convergent with $|x| < 3$.

Since $|x| < 2$ **and** $|x| < 3$, we demand $|x| < 2$

$\therefore$ the radius of convergence is 2.

8 If $a_n = \dfrac{x^n}{n^2 3^n}$ then $\displaystyle\lim_{n\to\infty} \left| \dfrac{a_{n+1}}{a_n} \right|$

$\qquad = \displaystyle\lim_{n\to\infty} \left| \dfrac{x^{n+1}}{(n+1)^2 3^{n+1}} \dfrac{n^2 3^n}{x^n} \right|$

$\qquad = \displaystyle\lim_{n\to\infty} \left(\dfrac{n}{n+1}\right)^2 \left| \dfrac{x}{3} \right|$

$\qquad = \left| \dfrac{x}{3} \right|$

$\therefore \displaystyle\sum_{n=1}^{\infty} \dfrac{x^n}{n^2 3^n}$ converges for $\left| \dfrac{x}{3} \right| < 1$, that is, for $|x| < 3$.

When $x = 3$, $a_n = \dfrac{1}{n^2}$ where $\displaystyle\sum_{n=0}^{\infty} \dfrac{1}{n^2}$ is convergent.

When $x = -3$, $a_n = \dfrac{(-1)^n}{n^2}$ where $\displaystyle\sum_{n=0}^{\infty} \dfrac{(-1)^n}{n^2}$ converges absolutely.

$\therefore \displaystyle\sum_{n=0}^{\infty} \dfrac{x^n}{n^2 3^n}$ converges for all $x \in [-3, 3]$, and has radius of convergence 3.

If $a_n = \dfrac{n x^{n-1}}{n^2 3^n} = \dfrac{x^{n-1}}{n\, 3^n}$ then

$\displaystyle\lim_{n\to\infty} \left| \dfrac{a_{n+1}}{a_n} \right| = \lim_{n\to\infty} \left| \dfrac{x^n}{(n+1)3^{n+1}} \times \dfrac{n\, 3^n}{x^{n-1}} \right|$

$\qquad = \displaystyle\lim_{n\to\infty} \left(\dfrac{n}{n+1}\right) \left| \dfrac{x}{3} \right|$

$\qquad = \left| \dfrac{x}{3} \right|$

$\therefore \displaystyle\sum_{n=1}^{\infty} \dfrac{n x^{n-1}}{n^2 3^n}$ converges when $\left| \dfrac{x}{3} \right| < 1$, that is, for $|x| < 3$.

When $\underline{x = 3}$, $a_n = \dfrac{1}{3n}$ and $\displaystyle\sum_{n=1}^{\infty} \dfrac{1}{3n} = \dfrac{1}{3}\sum_{n=1}^{\infty}\dfrac{1}{n}$ is

divergent. {p-series test}

When $\underline{x = -3}$, $a_n = \dfrac{(-1)^{n-1}}{3n}$ and

$$\sum_{n=1}^{\infty} a_n = \sum_{n=1}^{\infty} \dfrac{(-1)^{n-1}}{3n} \quad \text{which}$$

converges conditionally.

$\therefore \displaystyle\sum_{n=0}^{\infty} \dfrac{nx^{n-1}}{n^2 3^n}$ converges for all $x \in [-3, 3[$, and has radius

of convergence 3.

9 $\dfrac{d}{dx}\left(\displaystyle\sum_{n=1}^{\infty} \dfrac{x^n}{n!}\right) = \displaystyle\sum_{n=1}^{\infty}\left(\dfrac{d}{dx}\dfrac{x^n}{n!}\right)$

$$= \sum_{n=1}^{\infty} \dfrac{nx^{n-1}}{n!}$$

$$= \sum_{n=1}^{\infty} \dfrac{x^{n-1}}{(n-1)!}$$

where $\displaystyle\lim_{n\to\infty}\left|\dfrac{a_{n+1}}{a_n}\right| = \lim_{n\to\infty}\left|\dfrac{x^n}{n!}\dfrac{(n-1)!}{x^{n-1}}\right|$

$$= \lim_{n\to\infty} \dfrac{|x|}{n}$$

$$= 0$$

$\therefore \displaystyle\sum_{n=1}^{\infty} \dfrac{x^{n-1}}{(n-1)!}$ converges for all $x \in \mathbb{R}$ {Ratio test}

$\displaystyle\int_0^x \left(\sum_{n=0}^{\infty} \dfrac{t^n}{n!}\right) dt = \sum_{n=0}^{\infty}\left(\int_0^x \dfrac{t^n}{n!} dt\right)$

$$= \sum_{n=0}^{\infty} \dfrac{1}{n!}\left(\int_0^x t^n\, dt\right)$$

$$= \sum_{n=0}^{\infty} \dfrac{1}{n!}\left[\dfrac{t^{n+1}}{n+1}\right]_0^x$$

$$= \sum_{n=0}^{\infty} \dfrac{1}{n!}\left(\dfrac{x^{n+1}}{n+1}\right)$$

$$= \sum_{n=0}^{\infty} \dfrac{x^{n+1}}{(n+1)!}$$

where $\displaystyle\lim_{n\to\infty}\left|\dfrac{a_{n+1}}{a_n}\right| = \lim_{n\to\infty}\left|\dfrac{x^{n+2}}{(n+2)!}\dfrac{(n+1)!}{x^{n+1}}\right|$

$$= \lim_{n\to\infty}\dfrac{|x|}{n+2}$$

$$= 0$$

$\therefore \displaystyle\sum_{n=1}^{\infty} \dfrac{x^{n+1}}{(n+1)!}$ converges for all $x \in \mathbb{R}$ {Ratio test}

10 In each case we first need to find the interval of congruence for each series, to check that the given interval is defined.

a $\displaystyle\sum_{n=1}^{\infty} \dfrac{x^{n-1}}{(n-1)!} = \sum_{n=0}^{\infty} \dfrac{x^n}{n!}$ by **Example 38 a** this has an

infinite radius of convergence.

$\therefore \displaystyle\int_0^{0.1} \sum_{n=1}^{\infty} \dfrac{x^{n-1}}{(n-1)!}\, dx$ is defined

$\therefore \displaystyle\int_0^{0.1}\left(\sum_{n=1}^{\infty} \dfrac{x^{n-1}}{(n-1)!}\right) dx$

$$= \sum_{n=1}^{\infty} \dfrac{1}{(n-1)!}\left(\int_0^{0.1} x^{n-1}\, dx\right)$$

$$= \sum_{n=1}^{\infty} \dfrac{1}{(n-1)!}\left(\left[\dfrac{x^n}{n}\right]_0^{0.1}\right)$$

$$= \sum_{n=1}^{\infty} \dfrac{1}{(n-1)!}\left(\dfrac{(0.1)^n}{n} - 0\right)$$

$$= \sum_{n=1}^{\infty} \dfrac{1}{10^n n(n-1)!} \quad or \quad \sum_{n=1}^{\infty} \dfrac{(0.1)^n}{n(n-1)!}$$

b $\displaystyle\sum_{n=0}^{\infty} \dfrac{(-1)^n}{x^{2n}}$

$\left|\dfrac{a_{n+1}}{a_n}\right| = \left|\dfrac{1}{x^{2(n+1)}} \times x^{2n}\right| = \dfrac{1}{x^2}$

$\therefore$ interval of convergence $\left|\dfrac{1}{x^2}\right| < 1$

$$\therefore \quad x^2 > 1$$
$$\therefore \quad x > 1 \text{ or } x < -1$$
$$\therefore \quad x \in {]-\infty, -1[} \cup {]1, \infty[}$$

$\therefore$ $[-2, -1.5]$ is within the interval of convergence
$\therefore$ the interval is defined.

$\displaystyle\int_{-2}^{-1.5}\left(\sum_{n=0}^{\infty} \dfrac{(-1)^n}{x^{2n}}\right) dx$

$$= \sum_{n=0}^{\infty} (-1)^n\left(\int_{-2}^{-1.5} x^{-2n}\, dx\right)$$

$$= \sum_{n=0}^{\infty} (-1)^n\left(\left|\dfrac{x^{-2n+1}}{-2n+1}\right|_{-2}^{-1.5}\right)$$

$$= \sum_{n=0}^{\infty} \dfrac{(-1)^n}{(1-2n)}\left((-1.5)^{1-2n} - (-2)^{1-2n}\right)$$

$or \quad = \displaystyle\sum_{n=0}^{\infty} \dfrac{(-1)^{1-n}}{(1-2n)}\left((1.5)^{1-2n} - 2^{1-2n}\right)$

c $\displaystyle\sum_{n=0}^{\infty} x^{2n}$

$\left|\dfrac{a_{n+1}}{a_n}\right| = \left|\dfrac{x^{2(n+1)}}{x^{2n}}\right| = x^2$

$\displaystyle\lim_{n\to\infty}\left|\dfrac{a_{n+1}}{a_n}\right| = x^2$

$\therefore$ series converges for $\left|x^2\right| < 1$

that is, for $-1 < x < 1$

When $\underline{x = -1}$, $\displaystyle\sum_{n=0}^{\infty}(-1)^{2n} = \sum_{n=0}^{\infty} 1^n = \sum_{n=0}^{\infty} 1$ diverges,

since $\displaystyle\lim_{n\to\infty} 1 \neq 0$.

When $x = 1$, $\displaystyle\sum_{n=0}^{\infty} 1^{2n} = \sum_{n=0}^{\infty} 1$ diverges,

since $\displaystyle\lim_{n\to\infty} 1 \neq 0$.

$\therefore$ the interval of convergence is $]-1, 1[$

$$\int_0^{\frac{1}{2}} \left(\sum_{n=0}^{\infty} x^{2n} \right) dx = \sum_{n=0}^{\infty} \left(\int_0^{\frac{1}{2}} x^{2n}\, dx \right)$$

$$= \sum_{n=0}^{\infty} \left(\left[\frac{x^{2n+1}}{2n+1} \right]_0^{\frac{1}{2}} \right)$$

$$= \sum_{n=0}^{\infty} \frac{1}{2n+1} \left(\left(\tfrac{1}{2}\right)^{2n+1} - 0 \right)$$

$$= \sum_{n=0}^{\infty} \frac{1}{(2n+1) \times 2^{2n+1}}$$

11 From question **10** part **c**, $\displaystyle\sum_{n=0}^{\infty} x^{2n}$ has an interval of convergence

of $]-1, 1[$.

$\therefore$ $\displaystyle\int_0^2 \left(\sum_{n=0}^{\infty} x^{2n} \right) dx$ is not defined as the interval $[0, 2]$

lies partly outside the interval of convergence.

EXERCISE L.1

1 **a** $f(x) = \sin x$ $\therefore$ $f(0) = 0$

     $f'(x) = \cos x$ $f'(0) = 1$

     $f''(x) = -\sin x$ $f''(0) = 0$

     $f'''(x) = -\cos x$ $f'''(0) = -1$

$$T_3(x) = \sum_{k=0}^{3} \frac{f^{(k)}(0) x^k}{k!}$$

$$= f(0) + f'(0)\, x + f''(0) \frac{x^2}{2!} + f'''(0) \frac{x^3}{3!}$$

$$= 0 + x + 0 - \frac{x^3}{3!}$$

$$= x - \frac{x^3}{3!}$$

b $\sin\left(\frac{\pi}{5}\right) = T_3\left(\frac{\pi}{5}\right)$

$$= \tfrac{\pi}{5} - \tfrac{\pi^3}{125} \times \tfrac{1}{6}$$

$$= \tfrac{\pi}{5} - \tfrac{\pi^3}{750}$$

$$\approx 0.5870 \quad \text{(4 d.p.)}$$

c $R_3\left(\frac{\pi}{5} : 0\right) = \dfrac{f^{(4)}(c) \times \left(\frac{\pi}{5}\right)^4}{4!}$, $c \in]0, \frac{\pi}{5}[$

$$= \dfrac{\sin c \times \left(\frac{\pi}{5}\right)^4}{4!}$$

$\therefore$ $\left| R_3\left(\frac{\pi}{5}, 0\right) \right| < \dfrac{\left(\frac{\pi}{5}\right)^4}{4!} \approx 0.006\,49$

$\therefore$ $\left| T_3\left(\frac{\pi}{5}\right) - \sin\left(\frac{\pi}{5}\right) \right| < 0.0065$

$\Rightarrow$ $-0.0065 < T_3\left(\frac{\pi}{5}\right) - \sin\left(\frac{\pi}{5}\right) < 0.0065$

$\Rightarrow$ $-0.0065 < 0.5870 - \sin\left(\frac{\pi}{5}\right) < 0.0065$

$\Rightarrow$ $-0.5935 < -\sin\left(\frac{\pi}{5}\right) < -0.5805$

$\Rightarrow$ $0.5805 < \sin\left(\frac{\pi}{5}\right) < 0.5935$

$\therefore$ the approximation is accurate to 1 decimal place only.

2 $\sin x \approx x - \dfrac{x^3}{3!} + \dfrac{x^5}{5!} + R_5(x : 0)$

where $|R_5(x : 0)| = \left| \dfrac{f^{(6)}(c) x^6}{6!} \right|$

$$= \left| \dfrac{-\sin c \times x^6}{6!} \right|$$

$$= \dfrac{|\sin c|\, |x|^6}{6!}$$

and c lies between 0 and x.

But $|x| \leqslant 0.3$ and $\max |\sin c| = \sin(0.3)$

$\therefore$ $|R_5(x : 0)| < \dfrac{\sin(0.3)(0.3)^6}{6!}$

$\therefore$ upper bound is 2.99×10^{-7}

3 The Maclaurin series for $\sin x$ is

$$\sin x = x - \frac{x^3}{3!} + \frac{x^5}{5!} - \frac{x^7}{7!} + \frac{x^9}{9!} - \dots.$$

The error term is $R_n(x : 0) = \dfrac{f^{(n+1)}(c) x^{n+1}}{(n+1)!}$

But $f^{(n+1)}(c) = \pm \sin x$ or $\pm \cos x$

$\therefore$ $|R_n(x : 0)| \leqslant \dfrac{x^{n+1}}{(n+1)!}$

$\therefore$ $\left| R_n\left(\frac{\pi}{60} : 0\right) \right| \leqslant \dfrac{\left(\frac{\pi}{60}\right)^{n+1}}{(n+1)!}$

So, we require $\dfrac{\left(\frac{\pi}{60}\right)^{n+1}}{(n+1)!} < 0.000\,005$

when $n = 1$,   LHS $= 0.001\,371$

     $n = 2$,   LHS $= 0.000\,024$

     $n = 3$,   LHS $= 0.000\,000\,3$ ✓

Using $n = 3$, $\sin 3^c = \sin\left(\frac{\pi}{60}\right)$

$$\approx \frac{\pi}{60} - \frac{\left(\frac{\pi}{60}\right)^3}{3!}$$

$$\approx 0.052\,34$$

4 $f(x) = \cos x$ $\therefore$ $f\left(\frac{\pi}{6}\right) = \frac{\sqrt{3}}{2}$

    $f'(x) = -\sin x$ $\therefore$ $f'\left(\frac{\pi}{6}\right) = -\frac{1}{2}$

    $f''(x) = -\cos x$ $\therefore$ $f''\left(\frac{\pi}{6}\right) = -\frac{\sqrt{3}}{2}$

    $f'''(x) = \sin x$ $\therefore$ $f'''\left(\frac{\pi}{6}\right) = \frac{1}{2}$

The Taylor series for $f(x) = \cos x$ about $a = \frac{\pi}{6}$ is

$$T_n(x) = f\left(\frac{\pi}{6}\right) + f'\left(\frac{\pi}{6}\right)\left(x - \frac{\pi}{6}\right) + \frac{f''\left(\frac{\pi}{6}\right)\left(x - \frac{\pi}{6}\right)^2}{2!}$$

$$+ \frac{f'''\left(\frac{\pi}{6}\right)\left(x - \frac{\pi}{6}\right)^3}{3!} + \ldots$$

$$+ \frac{f^{(n)}\left(\frac{\pi}{6}\right)\left(x - \frac{\pi}{6}\right)^n}{n!} + R_n\left(x : \frac{\pi}{6}\right)$$

$$\therefore \quad T_n(x) = \frac{\sqrt{3}}{2} - \frac{1}{2}\left(x - \frac{\pi}{6}\right) - \frac{\frac{\sqrt{3}}{2}\left(x - \frac{\pi}{6}\right)^2}{2!}$$

$$+ \frac{\frac{1}{2}\left(x - \frac{\pi}{6}\right)^3}{3!} + \ldots$$

$$+ \frac{f^{(n)}\left(\frac{\pi}{6}\right)\left(x - \frac{\pi}{6}\right)^n}{n!} + R_n\left(x : \frac{\pi}{6}\right)$$

But $R_n\left(x : \frac{\pi}{6}\right) = \dfrac{f^{(n+1)}(c)\left(x - \frac{\pi}{6}\right)^{n+1}}{(n+1)!}$ where c lies between $\frac{\pi}{6}$ and x.

$$\therefore \quad \left|R_n\left(\frac{\pi}{6} + 0.2 : \frac{\pi}{6}\right)\right| = \frac{\left|f^{(n+1)}(c)\right|(0.2)^{n+1}}{(n+1)!}$$

But $\cos f^{(n+1)}(c) = \pm \sin c$ or $\pm \cos c$

$$\therefore \quad \left|R_n\left(\frac{\pi}{6} + 0.2 : \frac{\pi}{6}\right)\right| \leqslant \frac{(0.2)^{n+1}}{(n+1)!}$$

So, we require $\dfrac{(0.2)^{n+1}}{(n+1)!} < 0.001$

If $n = 2$, LHS $= \dfrac{(0.2)^3}{3!} \approx 0.0013$

$\therefore$ we require $n = 3$ and

$$T_3\left(\frac{\pi}{6} + 0.2\right) \approx \frac{\sqrt{3}}{2} - \frac{1}{2}(0.2) - \frac{\sqrt{3}}{4}(0.2)^2 + \frac{1}{12}(0.2)^3$$

$$\approx 0.7494$$

5 $e^x = \displaystyle\sum_{k=0}^{\infty} \frac{x^k}{k!} \qquad \therefore \quad e^{-x^2} = \sum_{k=0}^{\infty} \frac{(-x^2)^k}{k!}$

$$\therefore \quad \int_0^1 e^{-x^2}\, dx = \int_0^1 \left(\sum_{k=0}^{\infty} \frac{(-1)^k x^{2k}}{k!}\right) dx$$

$$= \sum_{k=0}^{\infty} \frac{(-1)^k}{k!} \int_0^1 x^{2k}\, dx$$

$$= \sum_{k=0}^{\infty} \frac{(-1)^k}{k!}\left[\frac{x^{2k+1}}{2k+1}\right]_0^1$$

$$= \sum_{k=0}^{\infty} \frac{(-1)^k}{k!(2k+1)}$$

$$= 1 - \frac{1}{3} + \frac{1}{10} - \frac{1}{42} + \frac{1}{216} - \frac{1}{1320}$$

$$+ \frac{1}{9360} - \ldots.$$

where $\frac{1}{9360} \approx 0.000\,107$

$$\therefore \quad \int_0^1 e^{-x^2}\, dx \approx 0.747 \quad \{\text{using first 6 terms}\}$$

6 $e^x = \displaystyle\sum_{k=0}^{\infty} \frac{x^k}{k!} \qquad \therefore \quad e^{x^2} = \sum_{k=0}^{\infty} \frac{x^{2k}}{k!}$

$$\therefore \quad \int_0^1 e^{x^2}\, dx = \int_0^1 \left(\sum_{k=0}^{\infty} \frac{x^{2k}}{k!}\right) dx$$

$$= \sum_{k=0}^{\infty} \frac{1}{k!} \int_0^1 x^{2k}\, dx$$

$$= \sum_{k=0}^{\infty} \frac{1}{k!}\left[\frac{x^{2k+1}}{2k+1}\right]_0^1$$

$$= \sum_{k=0}^{\infty} \frac{1}{k!(2k+1)}$$

$$= 1 + \frac{1}{3} + \frac{1}{10} + \frac{1}{42} + \frac{1}{216} + \frac{1}{1320}$$

$$+ \frac{1}{9360} + \ldots.$$

where $\frac{1}{9360} \approx 0.000\,107$

$$\therefore \quad \int_0^1 e^{x^2}\, dx \approx 1.463 \quad \{\text{using first 6 terms}\}$$

7 $e^x = \displaystyle\sum_{k=0}^{\infty} \frac{x^k}{k!} \qquad \therefore \quad e^{-x} = \sum_{k=0}^{\infty} \frac{(-x)^k}{k!}$

Thus, $e^{-1} = \displaystyle\sum_{k=0}^{\infty} \frac{(-1)^k}{k!}$ where $b_k = \frac{1}{k!}$

We want $|R_k(x : 0)| \leqslant b_{k+1}$

{Alternating Series Estimation Theorem}

$\therefore$ we require $\dfrac{1}{(k+1)!} < 0.000\,000\,5$

$k = 8$, $\dfrac{1}{9!} \approx 0.000\,002\,76$

$k = 9$, $\dfrac{1}{10!} \approx 0.000\,000\,276$ ✓

So, we use the first 10 terms

$$\therefore \quad e^{-1} \approx 1 - 1 + \frac{1}{2!} - \frac{1}{3!} + \frac{1}{4!} - \frac{1}{5!} + \frac{1}{6!} - \frac{1}{7!} + \frac{1}{8!} - \frac{1}{9!}$$

$$\therefore \quad e^{-1} \approx 0.367\,879 \quad \text{(to 6 d.p.)}$$

8 a $f(x) = e^x \qquad \therefore \quad f^{(n)}(x) = e^x$

$$T_n(x) = \sum_{k=0}^{n} \frac{x^k}{k!} \quad \text{for all } n \in \mathbb{Z}^+$$

and $R_n(x : 0) = \dfrac{f^{(n+1)}(c)x^{n+1}}{(n+1)!}$ where $0 < c < x$

We require $R_n(3 : 0) < 0.0001$

$$\Rightarrow \quad \frac{e^c 3^{n+1}}{(n+1)!} < 0.0001 \quad \text{where } 0 < c < 3$$

Now $\dfrac{e^c 3^{n+1}}{(n+1)!}$ is greatest when c is just < 3 and

$e^3 < 2.72^3 \approx 20$

So we need to find n when $\dfrac{20 \times 3^{n+1}}{(n+1)!} < 0.0001$

$$\therefore \quad \frac{3^n}{(n+1)!} < 1.7 \times 10^{-6}$$

If $n = 10$, $\dfrac{3^{10}}{11!} \approx 0.0015$

$n = 14$, $\dfrac{3^{14}}{15!} \approx 3.7 \times 10^{-6}$

$n = 15$, $\dfrac{3^{15}}{16!} \approx 6.9 \times 10^{-7}$

and $T_{15}(3) = \displaystyle\sum_{k=0}^{15} \dfrac{3^k}{k!} \approx 20.0855$

b The Taylor series of $f(x) = \sin x$ about $a = \frac{\pi}{2}$ is

$T_n(x) = f\left(\frac{\pi}{2}\right) + f'\left(\frac{\pi}{2}\right)\left(x - \frac{\pi}{2}\right) + \dfrac{f''\left(\frac{\pi}{2}\right)\left(x - \frac{\pi}{2}\right)^2}{2!} + \ldots.$

Now $f\left(\frac{\pi}{2}\right) = \sin\left(\frac{\pi}{2}\right) = 1$

$f'\left(\frac{\pi}{2}\right) = \cos\left(\frac{\pi}{2}\right) = 0$

$f''\left(\frac{\pi}{2}\right) = -\sin\left(\frac{\pi}{2}\right) = -1$

$f'''\left(\frac{\pi}{2}\right) = -\cos\left(\frac{\pi}{2}\right) = 0$

$f^{(4)}\left(\frac{\pi}{2}\right) = \sin\left(\frac{\pi}{2}\right) = 1$

$\therefore\ T_n(x) = 1 - \dfrac{\left(x - \frac{\pi}{2}\right)^2}{2!} + \dfrac{\left(x - \frac{\pi}{2}\right)^4}{4!} - \ldots.$

$\qquad + \dfrac{f^{(n)}\left(\frac{\pi}{2}\right)\left(x - \frac{\pi}{2}\right)^n}{n!}$

where $R_n\left(x : \frac{\pi}{2}\right) = \dfrac{f^{(n+1)}(c)\left(x - \frac{\pi}{2}\right)^{n+1}}{(n+1)!}$

and $\frac{\pi}{2} < c < \frac{\pi}{2} + 0.1$

Since $f^{(n+1)}(c) = \pm\sin c$ or $\pm\cos c$, $\left|f^{(n+1)}(c)\right| \leqslant 1$

Thus $\left|R_n\left(\frac{\pi}{2} + 0.1 : \frac{\pi}{2}\right)\right| \leqslant \dfrac{(0.1)^{n+1}}{(n+1)!}$

$\therefore$ we need to find n such that $\dfrac{(0.1)^{n+1}}{(n+1)!} < 0.0001$

If $n = 2$, $\dfrac{(0.1)^3}{3!} \approx 0.000\,17$

$\therefore$ we use $n = 3$

and $T_3\left(\frac{\pi}{2} + 0.1\right) = 1 - \dfrac{(0.1)^2}{2!} \approx 0.9950$

EXERCISE L.2

1 **a** $f(x) = \sin x$, $\qquad \therefore\ f(0) = 0$

$f'(x) = \cos x$, $\qquad \therefore\ f'(0) = 1$

$f''(x) = -\sin x$, $\qquad \therefore\ f''(0) = 0$

$f'''(x) = -\cos x$, $\qquad \therefore\ f'''(0) = -1$

$f^{(4)}(x) = \sin x$, $\qquad \therefore\ f^{(4)}(0) = 0$

By Maclaurin's theorem,

$f(x) = f(0) + f'(0)\,x + f''(0)\dfrac{x^2}{2!} + f'''(0)\dfrac{x^3}{3!} + \ldots.$

$\qquad + f^{(n)}(0)\dfrac{x^n}{n!} + R_n(x : 0)$

$= x - \dfrac{x^3}{3!} + \dfrac{x^5}{5!} - \dfrac{x^7}{7!} + \ldots. + f^n(0)\dfrac{x^n}{n!}$

$\qquad + R_n(x : 0)$

where $|R_n(x : 0)| = \left|\dfrac{f^{(n+1)}(c)x^{n+1}}{(n+1)!}\right|$ and c lies between x and 0.

But $f^{(n+1)}(c) = \pm\sin c$ or $\pm\cos c$

$\therefore\ \left|f^{(n+1)}(c)\right| \leqslant 1$

Thus $|R_n(x : 0)| \leqslant \dfrac{|x|^{n+1}}{(n+1)!}$

$\therefore\ \displaystyle\lim_{n \to \infty} |R_n(x : 0)| \leqslant \lim_{n \to \infty} \dfrac{|x|^{n+1}}{(n+1)!}$

$\therefore\ \displaystyle\lim_{n \to \infty} |R_n(x : 0)| = 0 \qquad \left\{ \displaystyle\lim_{n \to \infty} \dfrac{a^n}{n!} = 0,\ a \in \mathbb{R} \right\}$

$\therefore\ f(x) = \sin x = \displaystyle\sum_{n=0}^{\infty} \dfrac{(-1)^n x^{2n+1}}{(2n+1)!}$ for all $x \in \mathbb{R}$

The radius of convergence is infinite.

b **i** $x \sin x = x^2 - \dfrac{x^4}{3!} + \dfrac{x^6}{5!} - \dfrac{x^8}{7!} + \ldots.$

$\qquad = \displaystyle\sum_{n=0}^{\infty} \dfrac{(-1)^n x^{2n+2}}{(2n+1)!}$

The radius of convergence is infinite.

ii $\sin(3x) = 3x - \dfrac{(3x)^3}{3!} + \dfrac{(3x)^5}{5!} - \dfrac{(3x)^7}{7!} + \ldots.$

$\qquad = \displaystyle\sum_{n=0}^{\infty} \dfrac{(-1)^n (3x)^{2n+1}}{(2n+1)!}$

The radius of convergence is infinite.

iii $\cos x = \dfrac{d}{dx}(\sin x)$

$\qquad = \dfrac{d}{dx}\left(\displaystyle\sum_{n=0}^{\infty} \dfrac{(-1)^n x^{2n+1}}{(2n+1)!} \right)$

$\qquad = \displaystyle\sum_{n=0}^{\infty} \dfrac{(-1)^n}{(2n+1)!} \dfrac{d}{dx}(x^{2n+1})$

$\qquad = \displaystyle\sum_{n=0}^{\infty} \dfrac{(-1)^n}{(2n+1)!}(2n+1)x^{2n}$

$\qquad = \displaystyle\sum_{n=0}^{\infty} \dfrac{(-1)^n x^{2n}}{(2n)!}$

$\qquad = 1 - \dfrac{x^2}{2!} + \dfrac{x^4}{4!} - \dfrac{x^6}{6!} + \ldots.$

The radius of convergence is infinite.

2 **a** $f(x) = e^{-x}$, $\qquad \therefore\ f(0) = 1$

$f'(x) = -e^{-x}$, $\qquad \therefore\ f'(0) = -1$

$f''(x) = e^{-x}$, $\qquad \therefore\ f''(0) = 1$

$f'''(x) = -e^{-x}$, $\qquad \therefore\ f'''(0) = -1$

By Maclaurin's theorem,

$f(x) = e^{-x} = f(0) + f'(0)x + \dfrac{f''(0)x^2}{2!} + \dfrac{f'''(0)x^3}{3!} +$

$\qquad \ldots. + \dfrac{f^{(n)}(0)x^n}{n!} + R_n(x : 0)$

$$\therefore \quad f(x) = 1 - x + \frac{x^2}{2!} - \frac{x^3}{3!} + \frac{x^4}{4!} + ... + \frac{f^n(0)x^n}{n!}$$
$$+ R_n(x:0)$$

where $R_n(x:0) = \dfrac{f^{(n+1)}(c)x^{n+1}}{(n+1)!}$ and c lies between x and 0.

Now $f^{(n+1)}(c) = \pm e^{-c}$, so $\left| f^{(n+1)}(c) \right| = e^{-c}$

Thus $|R_n(x:0)| = \dfrac{e^c |x|^{n+1}}{(n+1)!}$ {e^c a constant}

But $\displaystyle\lim_{n\to\infty} \frac{a_n}{n!} = 0$, so $\displaystyle\lim_{n\to\infty} |R_n(x:0)| = 0$

$$\therefore \quad f(x) = e^{-x} = \sum_{n=0}^{\infty} \frac{(-1)^n x^n}{n!}$$

The radius of convergence is infinite.

b $e^{-x^2} = \displaystyle\sum_{n=0}^{\infty} \frac{(-1)^n (x^2)^n}{n!}$ or $\displaystyle\sum_{n=0}^{\infty} \frac{(-1)^n x^{2n}}{n!}$

with infinite radius of convergence.

3 $\qquad f(x) = \ln x$

$\qquad f'(x) = \dfrac{1}{x} = x^{-1}$

$\qquad f''(x) = -1x^{-2} = \dfrac{-1}{x^2}$

$\qquad f'''(x) = 2x^{-3} = \dfrac{2}{x^3} = \dfrac{2!}{x^3}$

$\qquad f^{(4)}(x) = -6x^{-4} = \dfrac{-6}{x^4} = \dfrac{-3!}{x^4}$

$\qquad f^{(5)}(x) = 24x^{-5} = \dfrac{24}{x^5} = \dfrac{4!}{x^5}$

$\qquad f^{(6)}(x) = -120x^{-6} = \dfrac{-120}{x^6} = \dfrac{-5!}{x^6}$

$\qquad \vdots$

$\qquad f^{(n)}(x) = \dfrac{(-1)^{n+1}(n-1)!}{x^n}$ for all $n \in \mathbb{Z}^+$

$\qquad\qquad\qquad\qquad\qquad$ {by induction}

$\therefore \quad f^{(n)}(2) = \dfrac{(-1)^{n+1}(n-1)!}{2^n}$ for all $n \in \mathbb{Z}^+$

Thus, the Taylor series for $\ln x$ about $x = 2$ is

$$\ln x = \ln 2 + \sum_{n=1}^{\infty} \frac{(-1)^{n+1}(n-1)!(x-2)^n}{2^n \, n!}$$

$$= \ln 2 + \sum_{n=1}^{\infty} \frac{(-1)^{n+1}(x-2)^n}{n \, 2^n}$$

If $a_n = \dfrac{(-1)^{n+1}(x-2)^n}{n2^n}$, then

$$\lim_{n\to\infty} \left| \frac{a_{n+1}}{a_n} \right| = \lim_{n\to\infty} \left| \frac{(x-2)^{n+1}}{(n+1)2^{n+1}} \times \frac{n2^n}{(x-2)^n} \right|$$

$$= \lim_{n\to\infty} \frac{|x-2|}{2} \times \frac{n}{n+1}$$

$$= \frac{|x-2|}{2}$$

$\therefore$ convergence occurs for $\qquad \dfrac{|x-2|}{2} < 1$

$$\Rightarrow \qquad |x-2| < 2$$
$$\Rightarrow \quad -2 < x - 2 < 2$$
$$\Rightarrow \qquad 0 < x < 4$$

and the associated radius of convergence is 2.

4 a $f(x) = 2^x = (e^{\ln 2})^x = e^{x \ln 2}$

But $e^x = 1 + x + \dfrac{x^2}{2!} + \dfrac{x^3}{3!} + \dfrac{x^4}{4!} + ...$

$\therefore \quad 2^x = 1 + x \ln 2 + \dfrac{(x \ln 2)^2}{2!} + \dfrac{(x \ln 2)^3}{3!}$

$$+ \frac{(x \ln 2)^4}{4!} + ...$$

$$\Rightarrow \quad 2^x = \sum_{n=0}^{\infty} \left[\frac{(\ln 2)^n}{n!} \right] x^n$$

and $\displaystyle\lim_{n\to\infty} \left| \frac{a_{n+1}}{a_n} \right| = \lim_{n\to\infty} \left| \frac{(\ln 2)^{n+1}x^{n+1}}{(n+1)!} \times \frac{n!}{(\ln 2)^n x^n} \right|$

$$= \lim_{n\to\infty} \left| \frac{\ln 2 \times x}{n+1} \right|$$

$$= \lim_{n\to\infty} \frac{\ln 2}{n+1} |x|$$

$$= 0$$

$\therefore$ converges for all $x \in \mathbb{R}$.

b Likewise $7^x = \displaystyle\sum_{n=0}^{\infty} \left[\frac{(\ln 7)^n}{n!} \right] x^n$

Letting $x = 1$, $\displaystyle\sum_{n=0}^{\infty} \left[\frac{(\ln 7)^n}{n!} \right] = 7$

$\therefore \quad a_n = \dfrac{(\ln 7)^n}{n!}$

5 a i $\displaystyle\sum_{n=0}^{\infty} x^n = \frac{1}{1-x}$ for all $|x| < 1$

$$\therefore \quad \sum_{n=0}^{\infty} (-x^2)^n = \frac{1}{1-(-x^2)} = \frac{1}{1+x^2}$$

$$\therefore \quad \frac{1}{1+x^2} = \sum_{n=0}^{\infty} (-1)^n x^{2n} \text{ for } \left| -x^2 \right| < 1$$

$$\Rightarrow \qquad \left| x^2 \right| < 1$$
$$\Rightarrow \qquad |x| < 1$$

The radius of convergence is 1.

ii $\dfrac{1}{1+x^3} = \displaystyle\sum_{n=0}^{\infty} (-1)^n x^{3n}$ for $|x| < 1$.

The radius of convergence is 1.

iii $\dfrac{1}{1-x^3} = \displaystyle\sum_{n=0}^{\infty} x^{3n}$ for $|x| < 1$.

The radius of convergence is 1.

b $\displaystyle\int_0^{\frac{1}{3}} \frac{1}{1+x^3} \, dx = \int_0^{\frac{1}{3}} (1 - x^3 + x^6 - x^9 + ...) \, dx$

$$= \left[x - \frac{x^4}{4} + \frac{x^7}{7} - \frac{x^{10}}{10} + ... \right]_0^{\frac{1}{3}}$$

$$\therefore \int_0^{\frac{1}{3}} \frac{1}{1+x^3}\, dx \approx \frac{1}{3} - \frac{1}{4 \times 3^4} + \frac{1}{7 \times 3^7} - \frac{1}{10 \times 3^{10}}$$

$$\text{where } \frac{1}{10 \times 3^{10}} \approx 0.000\,001\,7$$

$$\therefore \int_0^{\frac{1}{3}} \frac{1}{1+x^3}\, dx \approx 0.3303 \quad \text{(to 4 d.p.)}$$

6 From **Example 43**, the Maclaurin series for $\ln(1+x)$ is defined for $|x| < 1$ and

$$\ln(1+x) = x - \frac{x^2}{2} + \frac{x^3}{3} - \frac{x^4}{4} + \frac{x^5}{5} - \dots$$

$$\therefore \ln(1-x) = (-x) - \frac{(-x)^2}{2} + \frac{(-x)^3}{3} - \frac{(-x)^4}{4}$$

$$+ \frac{(-x)^5}{5} - \dots$$

$$= -x - \frac{x^2}{2} - \frac{x^3}{3} - \frac{x^4}{4} - \frac{x^5}{5} + \dots$$

$$\text{for } |x| < 1$$

So, for $|x| < 1$,

$$\ln\left(\frac{1+x}{1-x}\right) = \ln(1+x) - \ln(1-x)$$

$$= 2x + \tfrac{2}{3}x^3 + \tfrac{2}{5}x^5 + \tfrac{2}{7}x^7 + \dots$$

$$= 2 \sum_{n=0}^{\infty} \left(\frac{x^{2n+1}}{2n+1}\right)$$

Letting $x = \frac{1}{3}$,

$$\ln 2 \approx 2 \left(\frac{\frac{1}{3}}{1} + \frac{\left(\frac{1}{3}\right)^3}{3} + \frac{\left(\frac{1}{3}\right)^5}{5} \right)$$

$$\therefore \ \ln 2 \approx 0.693$$

7 a The Maclaurin expansion for e^x is

$$e^x = \sum_{n=0}^{\infty} \frac{x^n}{n!} = 1 + x + \frac{x^2}{2!} + \frac{x^3}{3!} + \frac{x^4}{4!} + \dots$$

i $e^{-x} = \sum_{n=0}^{\infty} \frac{(-x)^n}{n!} = 1 - x + \frac{x^2}{2!} - \frac{x^3}{3!} + \frac{x^4}{4!} - \dots$

ii $e^{-3x} = \sum_{n=0}^{\infty} \frac{(-3x)^n}{n!} = 1 - 3x + \frac{9x^2}{2!} - \frac{27x^3}{3!}$

$$+ \frac{81x^4}{4!} - \dots$$

iii $e^{-(2k-1)x} = \sum_{n=0}^{\infty} \frac{[-(2k-1)x]^n}{n!}$

b Now $\sin x = x - \frac{x^3}{3!} + \frac{x^5}{5!} - \frac{x^7}{7!} + \dots$

$$\therefore \ \sin(e^{-x})$$

$$= e^{-x} - \tfrac{1}{6}e^{-3x} + \tfrac{1}{120}e^{-5x} - \tfrac{1}{5040}e^{-7x} + \dots$$

$$\approx 1 - x - \tfrac{1}{6}(1 - 3x) + \tfrac{1}{120}(1 - 5x) - \tfrac{1}{5040}(1 - 7x)$$

$$\approx \left[1 - \tfrac{1}{6} + \tfrac{1}{120} - \tfrac{1}{5040}\right] + \left[-1 + \tfrac{3}{6} - \tfrac{5}{120} + \tfrac{7}{5040}\right]x$$

$$\approx 0.8415 - 0.5403x$$

c When x is very close to 0, $\sin(e^{-x}) \approx 0.8415$.

d If $f(x) = \sin(e^{-x})$

$$f'(x) = \cos(e^{-x}) \times -e^{-x}$$

$$= -e^{-x} \cos(e^{-x})$$

$$f''(x) = e^{-x}\cos(e^{-x}) - e^{-x}(-\sin(e^{-x})) \times -e^{-x}$$

$$= e^{-x}\cos(e^{-x}) - e^{-2x}\sin(e^{-x})$$

$$\therefore \ f(0) = \sin 1, \ f'(0) = -\cos 1, \ f''(0) = \cos 1 - \sin 1$$

Now $\sin(e^{-x}) \approx f(0) + \dfrac{f'(0)x}{1!} + \dfrac{f''(0)x^2}{2!}$

$$\approx \sin 1 - [\cos 1]x + [\cos 1 - \sin 1]\frac{x^2}{2!}$$

$$\approx 0.8415 - 0.5403x - 0.1506x^2$$

8 a If $f(x) = (1+x)^p$, then

$$f'(x) = p(1+x)^{p-1},$$

$$f''(x) = p(p-1)(1+x)^{p-2},$$

$$\vdots$$

$$f^{(k)}(x) = p(p-1) \dots (p-k+1)(1+x)^{p-k}$$

$$\therefore \ f(0) = 1$$

$$f'(0) = p$$

$$f''(0) = p(p-1) = \frac{p!}{(p-2)!}$$

$$\vdots$$

$$f^{(k)}(0) = \frac{p!}{(p-k)!}$$

$$\therefore \quad (1+x)^p$$

$$= 1 + px + \frac{p(p-1)}{2!}x^2 + \frac{p(p-1)(p-2)}{3!}x^3 + \dots$$

$$+ \frac{p(p-1) \dots (p-n+1)}{n!}x^n + R_n(x:0)$$

where $R_n(x:0)$

$$= \frac{p(p-1) \dots (p - (n+1) + 1)x^{n+1}(1+c)^{p-n-1}}{(n+1)!}$$

for some c between 0 and x.

Now consider

$$\sum_{n=0}^{\infty} \frac{p(p-1) \dots (p-n+1)x^n}{n!} = \sum_{n=0}^{\infty} a_n x^n.$$

When convergent, this is the Maclaurin series of $(1+x)^p$.

b By the Ratio test:

$$\lim_{n\to\infty} \left| \frac{a_{n+1}}{a_n} \right|$$

$$= \lim_{n\to\infty} \left| \frac{\dfrac{p(p-1) \dots (p-(n+1)+1)x^{n+1}}{(n+1)!}}{\dfrac{p(p-1) \dots (p-n+1)x^n}{n!}} \right|$$

$$= \lim_{n\to\infty} \left| \frac{x(p-n)}{(n+1)} \right|$$

$$= |x| \lim_{n\to\infty} \left| \frac{-1 + \frac{p}{n}}{1 + \frac{1}{n}} \right| = |x|$$

$\therefore$ this series converges for $|x| < 1$ $\therefore$ $R = 1$.

c From **b**, for $|x| < 1$, since $\displaystyle\sum_{n=0}^{\infty} a_n x^n$ converges we have

$\displaystyle\lim_{n\to\infty} a_n x^n = 0$,

$\therefore$ $\displaystyle\lim_{n\to\infty} \frac{p(p-1)\,....\,(p-n+1)x^n}{n!} = 0$, for $|x| < 1$.

Now for $0 \leqslant c \leqslant x < 1$, consider

$R_n(x:0)$

$= \dfrac{p(p-1)\,....\,(p-(n+1)+1)x^{n+1}}{(n+1)!}(1+c)^{p-n-1}$

$= \left[\dfrac{p(p-1)\,....\,(p-n)x^{n+1}}{(n+1)!}\right]\dfrac{(1+c)^{p-1}}{(1+c)^n}$

For a given x, x and c are constants

$\therefore$ $(1+c)^{p-1}$ is a constant.

$\therefore$ $\displaystyle\lim_{n\to\infty} R_n(x:0)$

$= \displaystyle\lim_{n\to\infty}\left[\dfrac{p(p-1)\,....\,(p-n)x^{n+1}}{(n+1)!}\right]\dfrac{(1+c)^{p-1}}{(1+c)^n}$

$= (1+c)^{p-1}\displaystyle\lim_{n\to\infty}\left[\dfrac{p(p-1)\,....\,(p-n)x^{n+1}}{(n+1)!}\right]$

$\quad\times\displaystyle\lim_{n\to\infty}\dfrac{1}{(1+c)^n}$

$= (1+c)^{p-1}\times 0 \times 0 = 0$

Thus $(1+x)^p$ equals its Maclaurin series for $0 \leqslant x < 1$.

EXERCISE L.3

1 a $f(x) = \dfrac{1}{1-x^2} = (1-x^2)^{-1}$ where $p = -1$

But $(1+x)^p = \displaystyle\sum_{n=0}^{\infty}\dfrac{p(p-1)(p-2)\,....\,(p-n+1)x^n}{n!}$,

$\qquad\qquad\qquad\qquad\qquad\qquad |x| < 1$

$\therefore$ $f(x) = \displaystyle\sum_{n=0}^{\infty}\dfrac{(-1)(-2)\,....\,(-n)(-x^2)^n}{n!}$, $\left|-x^2\right| < 1$

$= \displaystyle\sum_{n=0}^{\infty}\dfrac{(-1)^n n!(-1)^n x^{2n}}{n!}$, $|x|^2 < 1$

$= \displaystyle\sum_{n=0}^{\infty} x^{2n}$, $|x| < 1$

$= 1 + x^2 + x^4 + x^6 + x^8 + ...$, $|x| < 1$

The radius of convergence is 1.

b If $f(x) = \dfrac{1}{1+x^3}$, $f(x) = (1+x^3)^{-1}$

$\therefore$ $f(x) = \displaystyle\sum_{n=0}^{\infty}\dfrac{(-1)(-2)(-3)\,....\,(-n)(x^3)^n}{n!}$, $\left|x^3\right| < 1$

$= \displaystyle\sum_{n=0}^{\infty}\dfrac{(-1)^n n! x^{3n}}{n!}$, $|x|^3 < 1$

$= \displaystyle\sum_{n=0}^{\infty}(-1)^n x^{3n}$, $|x| < 1$

$= 1 - x^3 + x^6 - x^9 + x^{12} - ....$, $|x| < 1$

The radius of convergence is 1.

c $f(x) = \dfrac{1}{1-x^3} = (1-x^3)^{-1}$

$\therefore$ $f(x) = \displaystyle\sum_{n=0}^{\infty}\dfrac{(-1)(-2)(-3)\,....\,(-n)(-x^3)^n}{n!}$, $\left|-x^3\right| <$

$= \displaystyle\sum_{n=0}^{\infty}\dfrac{(-1)^n n!(-1)^n x^{3n}}{n!}$, $|x|^3 < 1$

$= \displaystyle\sum_{n=0}^{\infty} x^{3n}$, $|x| < 1$

$= 1 + x^3 + x^6 + x^9 + x^{12} + ...$, $|x| < 1$

The radius of convergence is 1.

2 a $f(x) = (1+x^2)^{-1}$

$\therefore$ $f(x) = \displaystyle\sum_{n=0}^{\infty}\dfrac{(-1)(-2)(-3)\,....\,(-n)(x^2)^n}{n!}$, $\left|x^2\right| < 1$

$= \displaystyle\sum_{n=0}^{\infty}\dfrac{(-1)^n n! x^{2n}}{n!}$, $|x| < 1$

$= \displaystyle\sum_{n=0}^{\infty}(-1)^n x^{2n}$, $|x| < 1$

$= 1 - x^2 + x^4 - x^6 + x^8 - ....$, $|x| < 1$

with radius of convergence 1.

b $\arctan x - \arctan(0) = \displaystyle\int_0^x \dfrac{1}{1+x^2}\,dx$, $|x| < 1$

$\Rightarrow$ $\arctan x - 0 = \displaystyle\int_0^x \left(\sum_{n=0}^{\infty}(-1)^n x^{2n}\right)dx$, $|x| < 1$

$\Rightarrow$ $\arctan x = \displaystyle\sum_{n=0}^{\infty}(-1)^n\int_0^x x^{2n}\,dx$, $|x| < 1$

$= \displaystyle\sum_{n=0}^{\infty}(-1)^n\left[\dfrac{x^{2n+1}}{2n+1}\right]_0^x$, $|x| < 1$

$= \displaystyle\sum_{n=0}^{\infty}\dfrac{(-1)^n x^{2n+1}}{2n+1}$, $|x| < 1$

$\therefore$ $\arctan x = x - \dfrac{x^3}{3} + \dfrac{x^5}{5} - \dfrac{x^7}{7} + \dfrac{x^9}{9} - ....$

valid for $x \in\,]-1, 1[$.

c i $\arctan(x^2) \approx x^2 - \dfrac{x^6}{3} + \dfrac{x^{10}}{5} - \dfrac{x^{14}}{7}$

ii $\displaystyle\int_0^1 \arctan(x^2)\,dx$

$\approx \displaystyle\int_0^1\left(x^2 - \dfrac{x^6}{3} + \dfrac{x^{10}}{5} - \dfrac{x^{14}}{7}\right)dx$

$\approx \left[\dfrac{x^3}{3} - \dfrac{x^7}{21} + \dfrac{x^{11}}{55} - \dfrac{x^{15}}{105}\right]_0^1$

$\approx \frac{1}{3} - \frac{1}{21} + \frac{1}{55} - \frac{1}{105} - 0$

≈ 0.294

Check: Calculator gives ≈ 0.298

3 **a** Suppose $f(x) = (1-x^2)^{-\frac{1}{2}}$, $p = -\frac{1}{2}$

$\therefore$ $f(x)$

$$= \sum_{n=0}^{\infty} \frac{\left(-\frac{1}{2}\right)\left(-\frac{3}{2}\right)\left(-\frac{5}{2}\right) \cdots \left(\frac{-[2n-1]}{2}\right)(-x^2)^n}{n!},$$

$$\left|-x^2\right| < 1$$

$$= \sum_{n=0}^{\infty} \frac{(-1)^n[1 \times 3 \times 5 \times \cdots \times (2n-1)](-1)^n x^{2n}}{2^n\, n!},$$

$$|x|^2 < 1$$

$$= \sum_{n=0}^{\infty} \frac{[1 \times 3 \times 5 \times \cdots \times (2n-1)]x^{2n}}{2^n\, n!}, \quad |x| < 1$$

where

$$[1 \times 3 \times 5 \times \cdots \times (2n-1)]$$

$$= [1 \times 3 \times 5 \times \cdots \times (2n-1)] \times \frac{2 \times 4 \times 6 \times \cdots \times 2n}{2 \times 4 \times 6 \times \cdots \times 2n}$$

$$= \frac{(2n)!}{2^n\, n!}$$

Thus $f(x) = \sum_{n=0}^{\infty} \dfrac{(2n)!}{2^n\, n!} \dfrac{x^{2n}}{2^n\, n!}, \quad |x| < 1$

$$= \sum_{n=0}^{\infty} \frac{(2n)!}{4^n\,(n!)^2} x^{2n}, \quad |x| < 1$$

and the radius of convergence is 1.

b $\arcsin x - \arcsin(0) = \displaystyle\int_0^x \frac{1}{\sqrt{1-x^2}}\, dx$

$\Rightarrow$ $\arcsin x - 0 = \displaystyle\int_0^x \sum_{n=0}^{\infty} \frac{(2n)!}{2^{2n}(n!)^2} x^{2n}\, dx, \quad |x| < 1$

$\Rightarrow$ $\arcsin x = \displaystyle\sum_{n=0}^{\infty} \frac{(2n)!}{2^{2n}(n!)^2} \int_0^x x^{2n}\, dx, \quad |x| < 1$

$\Rightarrow$ $\arcsin x = \displaystyle\sum_{n=0}^{\infty} \frac{(2n)!}{2^{2n}(n!)^2} \times \frac{x^{2n+1}}{2n+1}, \quad |x| < 1$

with $R = 1$

c If $x = \frac{1}{2}$,

$$\arcsin\left(\tfrac{1}{2}\right) = \frac{0!}{2^0(1!)^2}\left(\tfrac{1}{2}\right) + \sum_{n=1}^{\infty} \frac{(2n)!\left(\tfrac{1}{2}\right)^{2n+1}}{2^{2n}(n!)^2(2n+1)}$$

$\therefore$ $\dfrac{\pi}{6} = \dfrac{1}{2} + \displaystyle\sum_{n=1}^{\infty} \frac{(2n)!}{2^{4n+1}(n!)^2(2n+1)}$

$$= \frac{1}{2} + \sum_{k=1}^{\infty} \frac{(2k)!}{2^{4k+1}(k!)^2(2k+1)}$$

$\therefore$ $a_k = \dfrac{(2k)!}{2^{4k+1}(k!)^2(2k+1)}$

EXERCISE L.4

1 **a** Let $\sqrt{x+1} = \displaystyle\sum_{n=0}^{\infty} a_n x^n$ for $|x| < 1$

$\therefore$ $x + 1 = \left(\displaystyle\sum_{n=0}^{\infty} a_n x^n\right)^2, \quad |x| < 1$

$\therefore$ $x + 1 \approx (a_0 + a_1 x + a_2 x^2 + a_3 x^3)^2, \quad |x| < 1$

$$\approx a_0^2 + [2a_0 a_1]x + [2a_0 a_2 + a_1^2]x^2$$
$$+ [2a_0 a_3 + 2a_1 a_2]x^3$$

{using the first 4 terms only}

By equating coefficients we get $a_0^2 = 1$, $2a_0 a_1 = 1$,

$2a_0 a_2 + a_1^2 = 0$, $2a_0 a_3 + 2a_1 a_2 = 0$

Thus $a_0 = \pm 1$, but $a_0 > 0$, $\therefore$ $a_0 = 1$

Consequently, $2a_1 = 1 \Rightarrow a_1 = \frac{1}{2}$

and $2(1)a_2 + \frac{1}{4} = 0 \Rightarrow a_2 = -\frac{1}{8}$

and $2(1)a_3 + 2\left(\frac{1}{2}\right)\left(-\frac{1}{8}\right) = 0 \Rightarrow a_3 = \frac{1}{16}$

Thus $\sqrt{x+1} \approx 1 + \frac{1}{2}x - \frac{1}{8}x^2 + \frac{1}{16}x^3, \quad |x| < 1$

b Using the binomial series with $p = \frac{1}{2}$,

$$\sqrt{x+1} = (1+x)^{\frac{1}{2}}$$

$$\Rightarrow \sqrt{x+1} = a_0 + \sum_{n=1}^{\infty} \frac{\left(\frac{1}{2}\right)\left(-\frac{1}{2}\right)\left(-\frac{3}{2}\right) \cdots \left(\frac{3-2n}{2}\right) x^n}{n!}$$

If we let $x = 0$, $1 = a_0 + 0 \Rightarrow a_0 = 1$

Thus $\sqrt{x+1}$

$$\approx 1 + \frac{\frac{1}{2}x}{1!} + \frac{\left(\frac{1}{2}\right)\left(-\frac{1}{2}\right)x^2}{2!} + \frac{\left(\frac{1}{2}\right)\left(-\frac{1}{2}\right)\left(-\frac{3}{2}\right)x^3}{3!}$$

{using the first 4 terms only}

$$\Rightarrow \sqrt{x+1} \approx 1 + \frac{1}{2}x - \frac{1}{8}x^2 + \frac{1}{16}x^3$$

2 **a** From **Example 45**,

$$\arccos x = \frac{\pi}{2} - x - \sum_{k=1}^{\infty} \frac{(2k)!\, x^{2k+1}}{4^k(k!)^2(2k+1)}, \quad |x| < 1$$

$$\approx \frac{\pi}{2} - x - \frac{1}{6}x^3 - \frac{3}{40}x^5, \quad |x| < 1$$

and $e^x \approx 1 + x + \dfrac{x^2}{2} + \dfrac{x^3}{6}$ with infinite R

$\therefore$ $e^x \arccos x$

$$\approx \left(1 + x + \frac{x^2}{2} + \frac{x^3}{6}\right)\left(\frac{\pi}{2} - x - \frac{1}{6}x^3 - \frac{3}{40}x^5\right)$$

$$\approx \frac{\pi}{2} + \left(\frac{\pi}{2} - 1\right)x + \left(\frac{\pi}{4} - 1\right)x^2 + \left(\frac{\pi}{12} - \frac{2}{3}\right)x^3$$

b Now $\arccos x$ has $R = 1$ and is defined for $|x| < 1$. e^x has infinite R.

$\Rightarrow$ $e^x \arccos x$ has $R = 1$ and is defined for $|x| < 1$.

3 **a** $\cos x \approx 1 - \dfrac{x^2}{2!} + \dfrac{x^4}{4!} - \dfrac{x^6}{6!}$

Let $\dfrac{x}{\cos x} = a_0 + a_1 x + a_2 x^2 + a_3 x^3 + a_4 x^4 + \cdots$

then $x \approx \left(1 - \dfrac{x^2}{2!} + \dfrac{x^4}{4!} - \dfrac{x^6}{6!}\right)$

$$\times (a_0 + a_1 x + a_2 x^2 + a_3 x^3 + \cdots)$$

$\Rightarrow$ $x \approx a_0 + a_1 x + [a_2 - \frac{1}{2}a_0]x^2 + [a_3 - \frac{1}{2}a_1]x^3$

$$+ [a_4 - \frac{1}{2}a_2 + \frac{1}{24}a_0]x^4 + [a_5 - \frac{1}{2}a_3 + \frac{1}{24}a_1]x^5$$

Equating coefficients gives

$a_0 = 0$, $a_1 = 1$, $a_2 - \frac{1}{2}a_0 = 0$, $a_3 - \frac{1}{2}a_1 = 0$,

$a_4 - \frac{1}{2}a_2 + \frac{1}{24}a_0 = 0$, and $a_5 - \frac{1}{2}a_3 + \frac{1}{24}a_1 = 0$

$\Rightarrow a_0 = 0, \ a_1 = 1, \ a_2 = 0, \ a_3 = \frac{1}{2}, \ a_4 = 0, \ a_5 = \frac{5}{24}$

Thus $\dfrac{x}{\cos x} \approx x + \frac{1}{2}x^3 + \frac{5}{24}x^5$

b $\cos x$ has $R = \infty$ and is defined for all $x \in \mathbb{R}$.

$\therefore \quad \dfrac{x}{\cos x}$ equals its full Maclaurin series expansion for all

$x \in \mathbb{R}$ such that $\dfrac{x}{\cos x}$ is defined.

That is, for $x \in \mathbb{R}, \ x \neq (2k+1)\dfrac{\pi}{2}, \ k \in \mathbb{Z}$.

4 $\sin x = x - \dfrac{x^3}{3!} + \dfrac{x^5}{5!} - \dots$ and

$\cos x = 1 - \dfrac{x^2}{2!} + \dfrac{x^4}{4!} - \dots$

Let $\tan x = a_0 + a_1 x + a_2 x^2 + a_3 x^3 + a_4 x^4 + \dots$

$\therefore$ as $\tan x = \dfrac{\sin x}{\cos x}, \quad \sin x = \cos x \tan x$

$\Rightarrow \quad x - \dfrac{x^3}{3!} + \dfrac{x^5}{5!} - \dots$

$= \left(1 - \dfrac{x^2}{2!} + \dfrac{x^4}{4!} - \dots\right)(a_0 + a_1 x + a_2 x^2 + \dots)$

$= a_0 + a_1 x + (a_2 - \frac{1}{2}a_0)x^2 + (a_3 - \frac{1}{2}a_1)x^3$

$\quad + (a_4 - \frac{1}{2}a_2 + \frac{1}{24}a_0)x^4 + (a_5 - \frac{1}{2}a_3 + \frac{1}{24}a_1)x^5 + \dots$

By equating coefficients we get

$a_0 = 0, \ a_1 = 1, \ a_2 = 0, \ a_3 = \dfrac{1}{3}, \ a_4 = 0, \ a_5 = \dfrac{5}{24}$

$\therefore \quad \tan x \approx x + \dfrac{1}{3}x^3 + \dfrac{5}{24}x^5$

5 $e^z = \displaystyle\sum_{k=0}^{\infty} \dfrac{z^k}{k!}$ for all z

a $e^{i\theta} = \displaystyle\sum_{k=0}^{\infty} \dfrac{(i\theta)^k}{k!}$

$= 1 + \dfrac{i\theta}{1!} + \dfrac{i^2\theta^2}{2!} + \dfrac{i^3\theta^3}{3!} + \dfrac{i^4\theta^4}{4!} + \dfrac{i^5\theta^5}{5!} + \dots$

$= \left[1 - \dfrac{\theta^2}{2!} + \dfrac{\theta^4}{4!} - \dfrac{\theta^6}{6!} + \dots\right]$

$\quad + i\left[\theta - \dfrac{\theta^3}{3!} + \dfrac{\theta^5}{5!} - \dfrac{\theta^7}{7!} + \dots\right]$

b $e^{i\theta} = \cos\theta + i\sin\theta$

6 a $e^x = 1 + x + \dfrac{x^2}{2!} + \dfrac{x^3}{3!} + \dfrac{x^4}{4!} + \dots$

Now for $x \geqslant 0, \ \dfrac{x^2}{2!} + \dfrac{x^3}{3!} + \dfrac{x^4}{4!} + \dots$ is $\geqslant 0$

$\therefore \quad e^x - (1+x) \geqslant 0$ for all $x \geqslant 0$

$\Rightarrow \quad e^x \geqslant 1 + x$ for all $x \geqslant 0$

b For $u_k \geqslant 0$ for all k,

$1 + u_k \leqslant e^{u_k}$

$\therefore \quad (1+u_1)(1+u_2)(1+u_3)\dots(1+u_n)$

$\quad \leqslant e^{u_1}e^{u_2}e^{u_3}\dots e^{u_n}$

$\quad = e^{u_1+u_2+u_3+\dots+u_n}$

$\Rightarrow \displaystyle\prod_{k=1}^{n}(1+u_k) \leqslant e^{u_1+u_2+u_3+\dots+u_n}$

c As $u_k \geqslant 0$ for all k,

$1 + u_k \geqslant 1$ for all k.

$\therefore \quad \displaystyle\prod_{k=1}^{n}(1+u_k)$ is increasing and as $\displaystyle\sum_{n=1}^{\infty} u_n$ converges

to L, say, then $\displaystyle\prod_{k=1}^{n}(1+u_k) \leqslant e^L$

Thus $\displaystyle\prod_{k=1}^{n}(1+u_k)$ has an upper bound of e^L

As $\displaystyle\prod_{k=1}^{n}(1+u_k)$ is increasing and has an upper bound, it

converges   {Monotonic convergence theorem}

7 a $\sin x = 0$

$\Leftrightarrow \quad x = 0 + k\pi, \ k \in \mathbb{Z}$

$\Leftrightarrow \quad x = k\pi, \ k \in \mathbb{Z}$

$\dfrac{\sin x}{x} = 0 \ \Leftrightarrow \ x = k\pi, \ k \in \mathbb{Z}, \ x \neq 0$

$\therefore \quad \dfrac{\sin x}{x} = 0 \ \Leftrightarrow \ x = \pm\pi, \ \pm 2\pi, \ \pm 3\pi, \ \dots$

b $\sin x = x - \dfrac{x^3}{3!} + \dfrac{x^5}{5!} - \dfrac{x^7}{7!} + \dots$

$\therefore \quad \dfrac{\sin x}{x} = 1 - \dfrac{x^2}{3!} + \dfrac{x^4}{5!} - \dfrac{x^6}{7!} + \dots$

$= \displaystyle\sum_{n=0}^{\infty} \dfrac{(-1)^n x^{2n}}{(2n+1)!}$

If $a_n = \dfrac{(-1)^n x^{2n}}{(2n+1)!}, \quad \lim_{n\to\infty}\left|\dfrac{a_{n+1}}{a_n}\right|$

$= \lim_{n\to\infty}\left|\dfrac{x^{2n+2}}{(2n+3)!} \dfrac{(2n+1)!}{x^{2n}}\right|$

$= \lim_{n\to\infty}\dfrac{x^2}{(2n+3)(2n+2)}$

$= 0$ for all $x \in \mathbb{R}$

$\therefore$ the $\dfrac{\sin x}{x}$ power series converges for all $x \in \mathbb{R}$

{Ratio test}

and the interval of convergence is $\mathbb{R}$.

c The zeros of

$\left(1 - \dfrac{x}{\pi}\right)\left(1 + \dfrac{x}{\pi}\right)\left(1 - \dfrac{x}{2\pi}\right)\left(1 + \dfrac{x}{2\pi}\right)\left(1 - \dfrac{x}{3\pi}\right)\dots$

are $\pm\pi, \pm 2\pi, \pm 3\pi, \pm 4\pi, \dots$

d Now $\left(1 - \dfrac{x}{\pi}\right)\left(1 + \dfrac{x}{\pi}\right) = 1 - \dfrac{x^2}{\pi^2}$

$\left(1 - \dfrac{x}{2\pi}\right)\left(1 + \dfrac{x}{2\pi}\right) = 1 - \dfrac{x^2}{4\pi^2}$

$\left(1 - \dfrac{x}{3\pi}\right)\left(1 + \dfrac{x}{3\pi}\right) = 1 - \dfrac{x^2}{9\pi^2}$, and so on.

$$\therefore \left(1-\frac{x}{\pi}\right)\left(1+\frac{x}{\pi}\right)\left(1-\frac{x}{2\pi}\right)\left(1+\frac{x}{2\pi}\right)\left(1-\frac{x}{3\pi}\right)....$$

$$= \left(1-\frac{x^2}{\pi^2}\right)\left(1-\frac{x^2}{4\pi^2}\right)\left(1-\frac{x^2}{9\pi^2}\right)....$$

From **a**, $\dfrac{\sin x}{x}$ has zeros of $\pm\pi, \pm 2\pi, \pm 3\pi, ...$

From **c**, $\left(1-\dfrac{x}{\pi}\right)\left(1+\dfrac{x}{\pi}\right)\left(1-\dfrac{x}{2\pi}\right)\left(1+\dfrac{x}{2\pi}\right) ....$ has

the same zeros.

This evidence supports Euler's claim that

$\dfrac{\sin x}{x} = 1 - \dfrac{x^2}{3!} + \dfrac{x^4}{5!} - \dfrac{x^6}{7!} + ...$ is equal to

$$\left(1-\frac{x^2}{\pi^2}\right)\left(1-\frac{x^2}{4\pi^2}\right)\left(1-\frac{x^2}{9\pi^2}\right)....\quad (1)$$

e Now,

$$\left(1-\frac{x^2}{\pi^2}\right)\left(1-\frac{x^2}{4\pi^2}\right) = 1 - x^2\left(\frac{1}{\pi^2}+\frac{1}{4\pi^2}\right)+....$$

and $\left(1-\dfrac{x^2}{\pi^2}\right)\left(1-\dfrac{x^2}{4\pi^2}\right)\left(1-\dfrac{x^2}{9\pi^2}\right)$

$$= \left[1 - x^2\left(\frac{1}{\pi^2}+\frac{1}{4\pi^2}\right)+....\right]\left(1-\frac{x^2}{9\pi^2}\right)$$

$$= 1 - x^2\left(\frac{1}{\pi^2}+\frac{1}{4\pi^2}+\frac{1}{9\pi^2}\right)+....$$

By equating the coefficients of x^2 in (1) we get

$$-\frac{1}{3!} = -\left(\frac{1}{\pi^2}+\frac{1}{4\pi^2}+\frac{1}{9\pi^2}+....\right)$$

$$\therefore \frac{\pi^2}{6} = 1 + \frac14 + \frac19 + \frac{1}{16} + ...$$

$$\Rightarrow \sum_{n=1}^{\infty}\frac{1}{n^2} = \frac{\pi^2}{6}$$

f

$$\sum_{n=1}^{\infty}\frac{1}{(2n)^2} = \sum_{n=1}^{\infty}\frac{1}{4n^2} = \frac14\sum_{n=1}^{\infty}\frac{1}{n^2}$$

$$\Rightarrow \sum_{n=1}^{\infty}\frac{1}{(2n)^2} = \frac14\left(\frac{\pi^2}{6}\right) = \frac{\pi^2}{24}$$

and as $\displaystyle\sum_{n=1}^{\infty}\frac{1}{n^2} = \sum_{r=1}^{\infty}\left(\frac{1}{2r}\right)^2 + \sum_{r=1}^{\infty}\frac{1}{(2r-1)^2},$

$$\frac{\pi^2}{6} = \frac{\pi^2}{24} + \sum_{n=1}^{\infty}\frac{1}{(2n-1)^2}$$

$$\therefore \sum_{n=1}^{\infty}\frac{1}{(2n-1)^2} = \frac{\pi^2}{6} - \frac{\pi^2}{24} = \frac{\pi^2}{8}$$

EXERCISE M

1 a If $y = 2x - 2 + ce^{-x}$ then

$$\frac{dy}{dx} = 2 + ce^{-x}(-1)$$

$$= 2 - ce^{-x}$$

$$= 2 - [y - 2x + 2]$$

$$= 2 - y + 2x - 2$$

$$= 2x - y$$

$\therefore \; y = 2x - 2 + ce^{-x}$ is a solution of $\dfrac{dy}{dx} = 2x - y$

b We need graphs of
$$\begin{aligned}
y &= 2x - 2 & (c = 0)\\
y &= 2x - 2 + e^{-x} & (c = 1)\\
y &= 2x - 2 - e^{-x} & (c = -1)\\
y &= 2x - 2 + 2e^{-x} & (c = 2)\\
y &= 2x - 2 - 2e^{-x} & (c = -2)
\end{aligned}$$

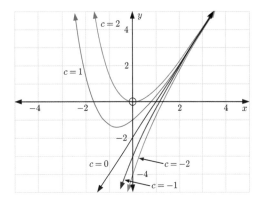

c If $(0, 1)$ lies on $y = 2x - 2 + ce^{-x}$ then

$$1 = -2 + c \Rightarrow c = 3$$

$$\therefore \; y = 2x - 2 + 3e^{-x}$$

d At $(0, 1)$, $\dfrac{dy}{dx} = 2(0) - (1) = -1$

$\therefore$ the equation is $\dfrac{y-1}{x-0} = -1$

That is, $y = -x + 1$

2 a If $y = \sqrt{x^2 + c}$ then $y^2 = x^2 + c$

$$\therefore \; 2y\frac{dy}{dx} = 2x$$

$$\therefore \; \frac{dy}{dx} = \frac{x}{y}$$

Thus $y = \sqrt{x^2 + c}$ is a general solution of $\dfrac{dy}{dx} = \dfrac{x}{y}$.

b As $y(3) = 4$, $\quad 4 = \sqrt{9 + c}$

$$\therefore \; 16 = 9 + c$$

$$\therefore \; c = 7$$

Thus $y = \sqrt{x^2 + 7}$

3 a

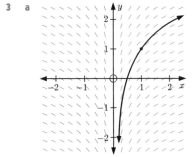

b

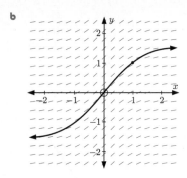

4 $\dfrac{dy}{dx} = 10y\tan x$, x in degrees

	x				
	-2	-1	0	1	2
-2	0.70	0.35	0	-0.35	-0.70
-1	0.35	0.17	0	-0.17	-0.35
y 0	0	0	0	0	0
1	-0.35	-0.17	0	0.17	0.35
2	-0.70	-0.35	0	0.35	0.70

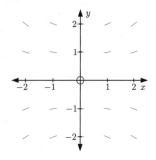

5 If $k = 0$, $x^2 + y - 1 = 0 \Rightarrow y = -x^2 + 1$

If $k = 2$, $x^2 + y - 1 = 2 \Rightarrow y = -x^2 + 3$

If $k = 4$, $x^2 + y - 1 = 4 \Rightarrow y = -x^2 + 5$

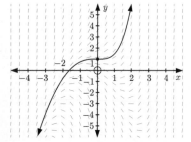

6 a

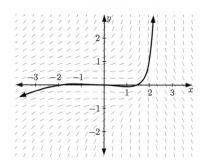

b i $\dfrac{dy}{dx}$ is undefined when $y = 5x - 10$

ii $\dfrac{dy}{dx} = 0$ when $x^2 + 4y^2 = 1$

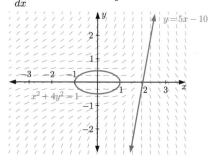

7 $\begin{cases} x_{n+1} = x_n + h \\ y_{n+1} = y_n + hf(x_n, y_n) \end{cases}$ where $h = 0.2$

and $f(x_n, y_n) = 1 + 2x_n - 3y_n$

$\Rightarrow y_{n+1} = y_n + 0.2(1 + 2x_n - 3y_n)$

$\qquad\qquad = 0.2 + 0.4x_n + 0.4y_n$

$\quad x_0 = 0 \qquad\qquad y_0 = 1$

$\quad x_1 = 0.2 \qquad\qquad y_1 = 0.6$

$\quad x_2 = 0.4 \qquad\qquad y_2 = 0.52$

$\quad x_3 = 0.6 \qquad\qquad y_3 = 0.568$

$\quad x_4 = 0.8 \qquad\qquad y_4 = 0.6672$

$\quad x_5 = 1 \qquad\qquad y_5 = 0.78688$

So, $y(1) \approx y_5 \approx 0.787$

8 $\begin{cases} x_{n+1} = x_n + 0.1 \\ y_{n+1} = y_n + 0.1(\sin(x_n + y_n)) \end{cases}$

$\quad x_0 = 0 \qquad\qquad y_0 \approx 0.5$

$\quad x_1 = 0.1 \qquad\qquad y_1 \approx 0.54794$

$\quad x_2 = 0.2 \qquad\qquad y_2 \approx 0.60830$

$\quad x_3 = 0.3 \qquad\qquad y_3 \approx 0.68061$

$\quad x_4 = 0.4 \qquad\qquad y_4 \approx 0.76369$

$\quad x_5 = 0.5 \qquad\qquad y_5 \approx 0.85552$

So, $y(0.5) \approx y_5 \approx 0.856$

EXERCISE N

1 a $(2 - x)\dfrac{dy}{dx} = 1$, $y(4) = 3$

$\qquad \therefore \dfrac{dy}{dx} = \dfrac{1}{2 - x}$

$\qquad \therefore y = -\displaystyle\int \dfrac{1}{x - 2}\, dx$

$\qquad \therefore y = -\ln|x - 2| + c$

But when $x = 4$, $y = 3$

$\therefore \quad 3 = -\ln 2 + c \;\Rightarrow\; c = 3 + \ln 2$

Hence, $y = 3 + \ln 2 - \ln |x - 2|$

$$y = \ln \left| \frac{2}{x - 2} \right| + 3$$

b $\dfrac{dy}{dx} - 3x \sec y = 0, \; y(1) = 0$

$\therefore \quad \dfrac{dy}{dx} = 3x \sec y$

$\cos y \dfrac{dy}{dx} = 3x$

$\therefore \quad \displaystyle\int \cos y \dfrac{dy}{dx} \, dx = \int 3x \, dx$

$\therefore \quad \displaystyle\int \cos y \, dy = \int 3x \, dx$

$\therefore \quad \sin y = \dfrac{3x^2}{2} + c$

But when $x = 1$, $y = 0 \;\Rightarrow\; 0 = \frac{3}{2} + c$

$\Rightarrow\; c = -\frac{3}{2}$

Hence, $\sin y = \dfrac{3x^2}{2} - \dfrac{3}{2} = \dfrac{3}{2}(x^2 - 1)$

$\therefore \quad y = \arcsin \left[\frac{3}{2}(x^2 - 1) \right]$

c $e^y(2x^2 + 4x + 1) \dfrac{dy}{dx} = (x + 1)(e^y + 3), \quad y(0) = 2$

$\therefore \quad \left(\dfrac{e^y}{e^y + 3} \right) \dfrac{dy}{dx} = \dfrac{x + 1}{2x^2 + 4x + 1}$

$\therefore \quad \displaystyle\int \dfrac{e^y}{e^y + 3} \dfrac{dy}{dx} \, dx = \frac{1}{4} \int \dfrac{4x + 4}{2x^2 + 4x + 1} \, dx$

$\therefore \quad \displaystyle\int \dfrac{e^y}{e^y + 3} \, dy = \frac{1}{4} \int \dfrac{4x + 4}{2x^2 + 4x + 1} \, dx$

$\therefore \quad \ln |e^y + 3| = \frac{1}{4} \ln \left| 2x^2 + 4x + 1 \right| + c$

But $e^y + 3 > 0$ for all $y \in \mathbb{R}$

$\therefore \quad \ln(e^y + 3) = \ln \left| 2x^2 + 4x + 1 \right|^{\frac{1}{4}} + c$

But when $x = 0$, $y = 2$

$\Rightarrow\; \ln(e^2 + 3) = \ln 1 + c$

$\Rightarrow\; c = \ln(e^2 + 3)$

Thus, $\ln(e^y + 3) = \ln \left(\left| 2x^2 + 4x + 1 \right|^{\frac{1}{4}} (e^2 + 3) \right)$

$\Rightarrow\; e^y = \sqrt[4]{|2x^2 + 4x + 1|}\,(e^2 + 3) - 3$

$\Rightarrow\; y = \ln \left[\sqrt[4]{|2x^2 + 4x + 1|}\,(e^2 + 3) - 3 \right]$

d $x \dfrac{dy}{dx} = \cos^2 y, \; y(e) = \dfrac{\pi}{4}$

$\therefore \quad \sec^2 y \dfrac{dy}{dx} = \dfrac{1}{x}$

$\therefore \quad \displaystyle\int \sec^2 y \dfrac{dy}{dx} \, dx = \int \dfrac{1}{x} \, dx$

$\therefore \quad \displaystyle\int \sec^2 y \, dy = \int \dfrac{1}{x} \, dx$

$\therefore \quad \tan y = \ln |x| + c$

But, when $x = e$, $y = \frac{\pi}{4} \;\Rightarrow\; 1 = 1 + c$

$\Rightarrow\; c = 0$

$\therefore \quad \tan y = \ln |x|$

$\therefore \quad y = \arctan(\ln |x|)$

2 a $\dfrac{1}{x - 1} - \dfrac{2}{x + 1} = \dfrac{(x + 1) - 2(x - 1)}{(x - 1)(x + 1)}$

$= \dfrac{x + 1 - 2x + 2}{(x - 1)(x + 1)}$

$= \dfrac{3 - x}{x^2 - 1}$

b $\dfrac{dy}{dx} = \dfrac{3y - xy}{x^2 - 1} = y \left(\dfrac{3 - x}{x^2 - 1} \right)$

$\therefore \quad \dfrac{1}{y} \dfrac{dy}{dx} = \dfrac{1}{x - 1} - \dfrac{2}{x + 1} \quad$ {from **a**}

$\therefore \quad \displaystyle\int \dfrac{1}{y} \dfrac{dy}{dx} \, dx = \int \left(\dfrac{1}{x - 1} - \dfrac{2}{x + 1} \right) dx$

$\therefore \quad \ln |y| = \ln |x - 1| - 2 \ln |x + 1| + c$

But when $x = 0$, $y = 1 \;\Rightarrow\; 0 = 0 - 2(0) + c$

$\Rightarrow\; c = 0$

Thus, $\ln |y| = \ln \left| \dfrac{x - 1}{(x + 1)^2} \right|$

$\therefore \quad |y| = \dfrac{|x - 1|}{(x + 1)^2}$

$\therefore \quad y = \pm \dfrac{(x - 1)}{(x + 1)^2}$

Check: When $x = 0$ and $y = \dfrac{(x - 1)}{(x + 1)^2}$ then $y = -1$ which is false.

When $x = 0$ and $y = \dfrac{-(x - 1)}{(x + 1)^2}$ then $y = 1$ which is true.

Hence $y = \dfrac{1 - x}{(x + 1)^2}$

3 a $\dfrac{dT}{dt} \propto T - R, \; t \geqslant 0$

From **a**, $\dfrac{dT}{dt} = k(T - R)$

$\therefore \quad \dfrac{1}{T - R} \dfrac{dT}{dt} = k$

$\therefore \quad \displaystyle\int \dfrac{1}{T - R} \dfrac{dT}{dt} \, dt = \int k \, dt$

$\therefore \quad \displaystyle\int \dfrac{1}{T - R} \, dT = \int k \, dt$

$\therefore \quad \ln |T - R| = kt + c$

$\therefore \quad T - R = \pm e^{kt + c}$

$\therefore \quad T = \pm e^c e^{kt} + R$

$\therefore \quad T = A e^{kt} + R \quad .... \; (1)$

b But when $t = 0$, $R = 18$, and $T = 82$

$$\therefore \quad 82 - 18 = Ae^0$$

$$\Rightarrow \quad A = 64$$

Thus (1) becomes $T = 64e^{kt} + 18$ .... (2)

But when $t = 6$, $T = 50$

$$\therefore \quad 50 = 64e^{6k} + 18$$

$$\therefore \quad 64e^{6k} = 32$$

$$\therefore \quad e^{6k} = \tfrac{1}{2}$$

$$\therefore \quad e^k = \left(\tfrac{1}{2}\right)^{\frac{1}{6}}$$

Thus (2) becomes, $T = 64\left(\tfrac{1}{2}\right)^{\frac{t}{6}} + 18$

$$\text{or } T = 64 \times 2^{-\frac{t}{6}} + 18$$

Now when $T = 26$, $26 = 64 \times 2^{-\frac{t}{6}} + 18$

$$\therefore \quad 64 \times 2^{-\frac{t}{6}} = 8$$

$$\therefore \quad 2^{-\frac{t}{6}} = \tfrac{1}{8} = 2^{-3}$$

$$\therefore \quad t = 18$$

and when $T = 20$, $20 = 64 \times 2^{-\frac{t}{6}} + 18$

$$\therefore \quad 64 \times 2^{-\frac{t}{6}} = 2$$

$$\therefore \quad 2^{-\frac{t}{6}} = \tfrac{1}{32} = 2^{-5}$$

$$\therefore \quad t = 30$$

So, from $t = 18$ to $t = 30$, T decreases from $26°$ to $20°$.
This takes place over a 12 minute time interval.

4

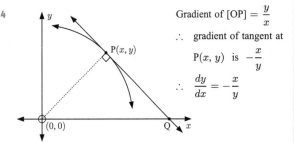

Gradient of [OP] $= \dfrac{y}{x}$

$\therefore$ gradient of tangent at

$P(x, y)$ is $-\dfrac{x}{y}$

$$\therefore \quad \frac{dy}{dx} = -\frac{x}{y}$$

Hence, $y\dfrac{dy}{dx} = -x$

$$\therefore \quad \int y\frac{dy}{dx}\,dx = -\int x\,dx$$

$$\therefore \quad \int y\,dy = -\int x\,dx$$

$$\therefore \quad \frac{y^2}{2} = -\frac{x^2}{2} + c$$

$$\therefore \quad x^2 + y^2 = 2c$$

But when $x = 1$, $y = 2$ $\Rightarrow$ $1 + 4 = 2c$

$$\Rightarrow \quad 2c = 5$$

$$\therefore \quad x^2 + y^2 = 5$$

5

AP : PB $= 2 : 1$

$\therefore$ A is $(3x, 0)$ and
B is $(0, \tfrac{3}{2}y)$

$$\therefore \quad \frac{dy}{dx} = -\frac{\text{OB}}{\text{OA}} = \frac{-\frac{3}{2}y}{3x} = \frac{-y}{2x}$$

$$\therefore \quad \frac{1}{y}\frac{dy}{dx} = \frac{-1}{2x}$$

$$\therefore \quad \int \frac{1}{y}\frac{dy}{dx}\,dx = -\frac{1}{2}\int \frac{1}{x}\,dx$$

$$\therefore \quad \ln|y| = -\tfrac{1}{2}\ln|x| + c$$

But when $x = 1$, $y = 1$

$$\Rightarrow \quad 0 = 0 + c$$

$$\Rightarrow \quad c = 0$$

Thus, $\ln|y| = -\tfrac{1}{2}\ln|x| = \ln|x|^{-\frac{1}{2}}$

$$\therefore \quad y = \pm\frac{1}{\sqrt{x}} \qquad \{\text{as } x \text{ must be } > 0\}$$

Check: When $x = 1$ and $y = \dfrac{1}{\sqrt{x}}$, $y = 1$ ✓

When $x = 1$ and $y = -\dfrac{1}{\sqrt{x}}$, $y = -1$ ✗

$$\therefore \quad y = \frac{1}{\sqrt{x}}$$

6 a

$$\frac{dm}{dt} \propto m$$

$$\therefore \quad \frac{dm}{dt} = km$$

$$\therefore \quad \frac{1}{m}\frac{dm}{dt} = k$$

$$\therefore \quad \int \frac{1}{m}\frac{dm}{dt}\,dt = \int k\,dt$$

$$\therefore \quad \ln|m| = kt + c$$

$$\therefore \quad |m| = e^{kt+c}$$

$$\therefore \quad m = \pm e^c e^{kt}$$

$$\therefore \quad m = Ae^{kt} \quad \text{.... (1)}$$

But at $t = 0$, $m = m_0$ $\Rightarrow$ $m_0 = A$

$\therefore$ (1) becomes $m = m_0 e^{kt}$

That is, $m(t) = m_0 e^{kt}$ .... (2)

b At $t = 30$, $m(t) = \tfrac{4}{5}m_0$

$\therefore$ (2) becomes $\tfrac{4}{5}m_0 = m_0 e^{30k}$

$$\Rightarrow \quad e^{30k} = \tfrac{4}{5}$$

$$\Rightarrow \quad e^k = \left(\tfrac{4}{5}\right)^{\frac{1}{30}}$$

Hence in (2), $m(t) = m_0 \left(\frac{4}{5}\right)^{\frac{t}{30}}$

Now when $m(t) = \frac{1}{2}m_0$,

$$m_0(0.8)^{\frac{t}{30}} = 0.5m_0$$

$$\Rightarrow \qquad (0.8)^{\frac{t}{30}} = 0.5$$

$$\Rightarrow \qquad \frac{t}{30} = \frac{\ln(0.5)}{\ln(0.8)}$$

$$\Rightarrow \qquad t \approx 93.2$$

It would take 93.2 days (approximately).

7 **a** $\dfrac{dy}{dx} = \dfrac{x-y}{x}$

Let $y = vx$, $\therefore \dfrac{dy}{dx} = \dfrac{dv}{dx}x + v$

Hence $x\dfrac{dv}{dx} + v = 1 - \dfrac{y}{x} = 1 - v$

$\therefore \quad x\dfrac{dv}{dx} = 1 - 2v$

$\therefore \quad \dfrac{1}{1-2v}\dfrac{dv}{dx} = \dfrac{1}{x}$

$\therefore \quad \displaystyle\int \dfrac{1}{1-2v}\,dv = \int \dfrac{1}{x}\,dx$

$\therefore \quad \dfrac{1}{-2}\ln|1-2v| = \ln|x| + c$

$\therefore \quad \ln\left|1 - \dfrac{2y}{x}\right| = -2\ln|x| - 2c$

$\therefore \quad \ln\left|\dfrac{x-2y}{x}\right| + \ln|x^2| = -2c$

$\therefore \quad \ln\left|\dfrac{x-2y}{x} \times x^2\right| = -2c$

$\therefore \quad \ln|x(x-2y)| = -2c$

$\therefore \quad |x^2 - 2xy| = e^{-2c}$

$\therefore \quad x^2 - 2xy = \pm e^{-2c}$

$\therefore \quad x^2 - 2xy = A$, a constant

b $\dfrac{dy}{dx} = \dfrac{x+y}{x-y}$

Let $y = vx$ $\therefore \dfrac{dy}{dx} = \dfrac{dv}{dx}x + v$

$\therefore \quad x\dfrac{dv}{dx} + v = \dfrac{x+vx}{x-vx} = \dfrac{1+v}{1-v}$

$\therefore \quad x\dfrac{dv}{dx} = \dfrac{1+v}{1-v} - v$

$\therefore \quad x\dfrac{dv}{dx} = \dfrac{1+v-v(1-v)}{1-v} = \dfrac{1+v^2}{1-v}$

Thus, $\dfrac{1-v}{1+v^2}\dfrac{dv}{dx} = \dfrac{1}{x}$

$\therefore \quad \displaystyle\int \left(\dfrac{1}{1+v^2} - \dfrac{v}{1+v^2}\right)\dfrac{dv}{dx}\,dx = \int \dfrac{1}{x}\,dx$

$\therefore \quad \displaystyle\int \dfrac{1}{1+v^2}\,dv - \dfrac{1}{2}\int \dfrac{2v}{1+v^2}\,dv = \int \dfrac{1}{x}\,dx$

$\therefore \quad \arctan v - \dfrac{1}{2}\ln\left|1+v^2\right| = \ln|x| + c$

Since $1 + v^2 > 0$ for all v,

$$\arctan v = \ln(1+v^2)^{\frac{1}{2}} + \ln|x| + c$$

$\therefore \quad \arctan\left(\dfrac{y}{x}\right) = \ln\left|x\sqrt{1+\dfrac{y^2}{x^2}}\right| + c$

$$= \ln\left|\sqrt{x^2+y^2}\right| + c$$

$$= \ln\sqrt{x^2+y^2} + c$$

c $\dfrac{dy}{dx} = \dfrac{y^2-x^2}{2xy}$

Let $y = vx$ $\therefore \dfrac{dy}{dx} = \dfrac{dv}{dx}x + v$

$\therefore \quad x\dfrac{dv}{dx} + v = \dfrac{v^2x^2-x^2}{2x(vx)} = \dfrac{v^2-1}{2v}$

$\therefore \quad x\dfrac{dv}{dx} = \dfrac{v^2-1}{2v} - v$

$\therefore \quad x\dfrac{dv}{dx} = \dfrac{v^2-1-2v^2}{2v} = \dfrac{-v^2-1}{2v}$

$\therefore \quad \dfrac{2v}{1+v^2}\dfrac{dv}{dx} = \dfrac{-1}{x}$

$\therefore \quad \displaystyle\int \dfrac{2v}{1+v^2}\dfrac{dv}{dx}\,dx = -\int \dfrac{1}{x}\,dx$

$\therefore \quad \ln\left|1+v^2\right| = -\ln|x| + c$

$\therefore \quad \ln\left|\left(1+\dfrac{y^2}{x^2}\right)x\right| = c$

$\therefore \quad x + \dfrac{y^2}{x} = \pm e^c = A$, say

$\therefore \quad x^2 + y^2 = Ax$, where A is a constant

8 **a** If $y = vx$, $\dfrac{dy}{dx} = \dfrac{dv}{dx}x + v$

$\therefore \quad \dfrac{dy}{dx} = \dfrac{y}{x} + f\left(\dfrac{y}{x}\right)g(x)$ becomes

$$x\dfrac{dv}{dx} + v = v + f(v)g(x)$$

$\therefore \quad x\dfrac{dv}{dx} = f(v)g(x)$

$\therefore \quad \dfrac{1}{f(v)}\dfrac{dv}{dx} = \dfrac{g(x)}{x}$ and so is separable.

b If $x\dfrac{dy}{dx} = y + e^{\frac{y}{x}}$ then

$$\dfrac{dy}{dx} = \dfrac{y}{x} + e^{\frac{y}{x}}\left(\dfrac{1}{x}\right)$$

So, by **a**, $\dfrac{1}{e^v}\dfrac{dv}{dx} = \dfrac{1}{x^2}$

$\therefore \quad \displaystyle\int \dfrac{1}{e^v}\,dv = \int x^{-2}\,dx$

$\therefore \quad \dfrac{1}{-1}e^{-v} = \dfrac{x^{-1}}{-1} + c$

$$\therefore \quad -e^{-\frac{y}{x}} = -\frac{1}{x} + c$$

$$\therefore \quad e^{-\frac{y}{x}} = \frac{1}{x} - c$$

$$-\frac{y}{x} = \ln\left[\frac{1}{x} - c\right]$$

$$\therefore \quad y = -x\ln\left[\frac{1 - cx}{x}\right]$$

$$\therefore \quad y = x\ln\left[\frac{1 - cx}{x}\right]^{-1}$$

$$\therefore \quad y = x\ln\left[\frac{x}{1 - cx}\right]$$

EXERCISE O

1 a $\dfrac{dy}{dx} + 4y = 12$ is of the form $\dfrac{dy}{dx} + P(x)y = Q(x)$

with $P(x) = 4$

$\therefore$ the integrating factor is $e^{\int 4\,dx} = e^{4x}$.

Multiplying the DE by e^{4x} gives

$$e^{4x}\frac{dy}{dx} + 4ye^{4x} = 12e^{4x}$$

$$\therefore \quad \frac{d}{dx}(ye^{4x}) = 12e^{4x}$$

$$\therefore \quad ye^{4x} = 12\left(\tfrac{1}{4}\right)e^{4x} + c$$

$$\therefore \quad y = 3 + ce^{-4x}$$

b $\dfrac{dy}{dx} - 3y = e^x$ has $I(x) = e^{\int -3\,dx} = e^{-3x}$

$$\therefore \quad e^{-3x}\frac{dy}{dx} - 3ye^{-3x} = e^x e^{-3x}$$

$$\therefore \quad \frac{d}{dx}(ye^{-3x}) = e^{-2x}$$

$$\therefore \quad ye^{-3x} = \left(\tfrac{1}{-2}\right)e^{-2x} + c$$

$$\therefore \quad y = -\tfrac{1}{2}e^{-2x+3x} + ce^{3x}$$

$$\therefore \quad y = -\tfrac{1}{2}e^x + ce^{3x}$$

But when $x = 0$, $y = 2$

$$\therefore \quad 2 = -\tfrac{1}{2} + c \;\Rightarrow\; c = \tfrac{5}{2}$$

Thus $y = -\dfrac{1}{2}e^x + \dfrac{5}{2}e^{3x}$.

c $\dfrac{dy}{dx} + y = x + e^x$ has $I(x) = e^{\int 1\,dx} = e^x$

$$\therefore \quad e^x\frac{dy}{dx} + e^x y = xe^x + e^{2x}$$

$$\therefore \quad \frac{d}{dx}(e^x y) = xe^x + e^{2x}$$

$$\therefore \quad e^x y = \int(xe^x + e^{2x})\,dx$$

$$= \int xe^x\,dx + \int e^{2x}\,dx$$

For $\int xe^x\,dx$ we integrate by parts with:

$$\begin{cases} u' = e^x & v = x \\ u = e^x & v' = 1 \end{cases}$$

$$\therefore \quad e^x y = xe^x - \int e^x\,dx + \int e^{2x}\,dx$$

$$= xe^x - e^x + \tfrac{1}{2}e^{2x} + c$$

$$\therefore \quad y = x - 1 + \tfrac{1}{2}e^x + ce^{-x}$$

But when $x = 1$, $y = 1 \;\Rightarrow\; 1 = 1 - 1 + \tfrac{1}{2}e + \dfrac{c}{e}$

$$\Rightarrow \quad 1 - \frac{e}{2} = \frac{c}{e}$$

$$\Rightarrow \quad c = e - \frac{e^2}{2}$$

$$\therefore \quad y = x - 1 + \tfrac{1}{2}e^x + e^{-x}(e - \tfrac{1}{2}e^2)$$

$$\therefore \quad y = x - 1 + \tfrac{1}{2}e^x + e^{1-x} - \tfrac{1}{2}e^{2-x}$$

d $x\dfrac{dy}{dx} + y = x\cos x$ .... (1)

$$\therefore \quad \frac{dy}{dx} + \left(\frac{1}{x}\right)y = \cos x \text{ which has } I(x) = e^{\int \frac{1}{x}\,dx}$$

$$= e^{\ln x}$$

$$= x$$

$$\therefore \quad x\frac{dy}{dx} + y = x\cos x \qquad \{\text{same as (1)}\}$$

$$\therefore \quad \frac{d}{dx}(xy) = x\cos x$$

$$\therefore \quad xy = \int x\cos x\,dx$$

We integrate by parts with: $\begin{cases} u' = \cos x & v = x \\ u = \sin x & v' = 1 \end{cases}$

$$\therefore \quad xy = x\sin x - \int \sin x\,dx$$

$$= x\sin x - (-\cos x) + c$$

$$\therefore \quad y = \sin x + \frac{\cos x}{x} + \frac{c}{x}$$

2 $$(x + 1)y + x\frac{dy}{dx} = x - x^2$$

$$\therefore \quad \frac{dy}{dx} + \left(\frac{x + 1}{x}\right)y = 1 - x \text{ where}$$

$$I(x) = e^{\int \left(1 + \frac{1}{x}\right)dx} = e^{x + \ln x} = e^x \times x$$

$$\therefore \quad xe^x\frac{dy}{dx} + xe^x\left(\frac{x + 1}{x}\right)y = e^x(x - x^2)$$

$$\therefore \quad xe^x\frac{dy}{dx} + e^x(x + 1)y = e^x(x - x^2)$$

$$\therefore \quad \frac{d}{dx}(xe^x y) = e^x(x - x^2)$$

$$\therefore \quad xe^x y = \int e^x(x - x^2)\,dx$$

We integrate by parts with: $\begin{cases} u' = e^x & v = x - x^2 \\ u = e^x & v' = 1 - 2x \end{cases}$

$$\therefore \quad xe^x y = e^x(x - x^2) - \int e^x(1 - 2x)\,dx$$

We integrate by parts with: $\begin{cases} u' = e^x & v = 1 - 2x \\ u = e^x & v' = -2 \end{cases}$

$$\therefore \quad xe^x y = e^x(x - x^2) - [e^x(1 - 2x) - \int(-2e^x)\,dx]$$

$\therefore\ xe^x y = e^x(x - x^2) - e^x(1 - 2x) - 2e^x + c$

$\therefore\ \ y = 1 - x - \dfrac{1 - 2x}{x} - \dfrac{2}{x} + \dfrac{c}{xe^x}$

$\qquad = 1 - x - \dfrac{1}{x} + 2 - \dfrac{2}{x} + \dfrac{c}{xe^x}$

$\qquad = 3 - x - \dfrac{3}{x} + \dfrac{c}{xe^x}$

EXERCISE P

1 a $\dfrac{dy}{dx} = \dfrac{e^{-y}}{3} - 1$

$\therefore\ \dfrac{d^2y}{dx^2} = \frac{1}{3}\left(-e^{-y}\dfrac{dy}{dx}\right)$

$\qquad = -\frac{1}{3}e^{-y}\dfrac{dy}{dx}$

$\dfrac{d^3y}{dx^3} = -\frac{1}{3}\left(-e^{-y}\left(\dfrac{dy}{dx}\right)^2 + e^{-y}\dfrac{d^2y}{dx^2}\right)$

$\qquad = \frac{1}{3}e^{-y}\left(\left(\dfrac{dy}{dx}\right)^2 - \dfrac{d^2y}{dx^2}\right)$

At $x = 0,\ y = 0,\quad \dfrac{dy}{dx} = \frac{1}{3} - 1 = -\frac{2}{3}$

$\qquad\qquad\qquad\quad \dfrac{d^2y}{dx^2} = -\frac{1}{3}\dfrac{dy}{dx} = \frac{2}{9}$

$\qquad\qquad\qquad\quad \dfrac{d^3y}{dx^3} = \frac{1}{3}\left(\frac{4}{9} - \frac{2}{9}\right) = \frac{2}{27}$

Now $T_3(x) = f(0) + f'(0)x + f''(0)\dfrac{x^2}{2!} + f'''(0)\dfrac{x^3}{3!}$

$\therefore\ T_3(x) = -\frac{2}{3}x + \frac{1}{9}x^2 + \frac{1}{81}x^3$

b If $y = \ln\left(\dfrac{1 + 2e^{-x}}{3}\right),\quad e^y = \frac{1}{3} + \frac{2}{3}e^{-x}$ .... (1)

$\therefore\ e^y\dfrac{dy}{dx} = -\frac{2}{3}e^{-x}$

$\therefore\ e^y\dfrac{dy}{dx} = \frac{1}{3} - e^y \qquad \{\text{from (1)}\}$

$\therefore\ \dfrac{dy}{dx} = \dfrac{1}{3e^y} - 1$

$\therefore\ \dfrac{dy}{dx} = \dfrac{e^{-y}}{3} - 1\ \checkmark$

2 a $\dfrac{dy}{dx} = 2x + \dfrac{y}{x}$

$\therefore\ x\dfrac{dy}{dx} = 2x^2 + y$

$\therefore\ 1\dfrac{\cancel{dy}}{\cancel{dx}} + x\dfrac{d^2y}{dx^2} = 4x + \dfrac{\cancel{dy}}{\cancel{dx}}$

$\therefore\ \dfrac{d^2y}{dx^2} = 4$

$\therefore\ \dfrac{d^3y}{dx^3} = 0,\ \text{etc}\quad \dfrac{d^{(n)}y}{dx^{(n)}} = 0$

$T_n(x) = y(1) + y'(1)(x - 1) + \dfrac{y''(1)(x-1)^2}{2!}$

$\{\text{as all other terms are zero}\}$

But $y'(x) = 2x + \dfrac{y}{x}\quad \Rightarrow\quad y'(1) = 2 + y$

$\qquad\qquad\qquad\qquad \Rightarrow\quad 1 = 2 + y$

$\qquad\qquad\qquad\qquad \Rightarrow\quad y = -1$

$\therefore\ T_n(x) = -1 + 1(x - 1) + \dfrac{4(x^2 - 2x + 1)}{2}$

$\therefore\ T_n(x) = -1 + x - 1 + 2x^2 - 4x + 2$

$\therefore\ T_n(x) = 2x^2 - 3x$

b $\dfrac{dy}{dx} - \left(\dfrac{1}{x}\right)y = 2x$ has $I(x) = e^{\int -\frac{1}{x}\,dx}$

$\qquad\qquad\qquad\qquad\qquad\qquad = e^{-\ln x}$

$\qquad\qquad\qquad\qquad\qquad\qquad = e^{\ln x^{-1}}$

$\qquad\qquad\qquad\qquad\qquad\qquad = \dfrac{1}{x}$

$\therefore\ \dfrac{1}{x}\dfrac{dy}{dx} - \dfrac{1}{x^2}y = 2$

$\therefore\ \dfrac{d}{dx}\left(\dfrac{y}{x}\right) = 2$

$\therefore\ \dfrac{y}{x} = \displaystyle\int 2\,dx = 2x + c$

$\qquad y = 2x^2 + cx$

But when $x = 1,\ y = -1\quad \Rightarrow\quad -1 = 2 + c$

$\qquad\qquad\qquad\qquad\qquad\quad \Rightarrow\qquad c = -3$

$\therefore\ y = 2x^2 - 3x$

Check: $\dfrac{dy}{dx} = 4x - 3 = 2x + (2x - 3) = 2x + \dfrac{y}{x}\ \checkmark$

3 a $\dfrac{dy}{dx} = \dfrac{3x - 2y}{x}$

$\therefore\ x\dfrac{dy}{dx} = 3x - 2y$

$\therefore\ 1\dfrac{dy}{dx} + x\dfrac{d^2y}{dx^2} = 3 - 2\dfrac{dy}{dx}$

$\therefore\ x\dfrac{d^2y}{dx^2} = 3 - 3\dfrac{dy}{dx}$

and differentiating again

$1\dfrac{d^2y}{dx^2} + x\dfrac{d^3y}{dx^3} = -3\dfrac{d^2y}{dx^2}$

$\therefore\ x\dfrac{d^3y}{dx^3} = -4\dfrac{d^2y}{dx^2}$

When $x = 1,\ y(1) = 0,\ y'(1) = 3,\ y''(1) = \dfrac{3 - 3(3)}{1}$

$\qquad\qquad\qquad\qquad\qquad\qquad\qquad\qquad = -6$

and $y'''(1) = \dfrac{-4(-6)}{1} = 24$

$T_3(x) = y(1) + y'(1)(x - 1) + \dfrac{y''(1)(x-1)^2}{2!}$

$\qquad\quad + \dfrac{y'''(1)(x-1)^3}{3!}$

$\qquad = 0 + 3(x - 1) - \dfrac{6(x-1)^2}{2} + \dfrac{24(x-1)^3}{6}$

$\qquad = 3(x - 1) - 3(x - 1)^2 + 4(x - 1)^3$

b As $\dfrac{dy}{dx} = \dfrac{3x - 2y}{x} = 3 - \dfrac{2}{x}y$ then $\dfrac{dy}{dx} + \dfrac{2}{x}y = 3$

where $I(x) = e^{\int \frac{2}{x}\,dx}$
$= e^{2\ln x}$
$= e^{\ln x^2}$
$= x^2$

$\therefore \ x^2\dfrac{dy}{dx} + 2xy = 3x^2$

$\therefore \ \dfrac{d}{dx}(x^2 y) = 3x^2$

$\therefore \ x^2 y = \displaystyle\int 3x^2\,dx = x^3 + c$

$\therefore \ y = x + \dfrac{c}{x^2}$

But when $x = 1$, $y = 0 \ \Rightarrow \ 0 = 1 + c$
$\Rightarrow \ c = -1$

$\therefore \ \ y = x - \dfrac{1}{x^2}$

4 a $\cos x\dfrac{dy}{dx} + y\sin x = 1,\ \ y(0) = 2$

Differentiating with respect to x gives

$-\sin x\dfrac{dy}{dx} + \cos x\dfrac{d^2y}{dx^2} + \dfrac{dy}{dx}\sin x + y\cos x = 0$

$\therefore \ \ \cos x\left(\dfrac{d^2y}{dx^2} + y\right) = 0 \ $ for all x

$\Rightarrow \ \dfrac{d^2y}{dx^2} = -y$

and $\dfrac{d^3y}{dx^3} = -\dfrac{dy}{dx}$

But when $x = 0$, $y = 2$

$\therefore \ \ \cos 0\dfrac{dy}{dx} + 2(0) = 1 \ \Rightarrow \ \dfrac{dy}{dx} = 1,$

$\dfrac{d^2y}{dx^2} = -2$

and $\dfrac{d^3y}{dx^3} = -1$

Now $T_3(x) = y(0) + y'(0)x + y''(0)\dfrac{x^2}{2!} + y'''(0)\dfrac{x^3}{3!}$

$\Rightarrow \ T_3(x) \approx 2 + x - x^2 - \tfrac{1}{6}x^3$

b $\cos x\dfrac{dy}{dx} + y\sin x = 1$

$\therefore \ \dfrac{dy}{dx} + \left(\dfrac{\sin x}{\cos x}\right)y = \dfrac{1}{\cos x}$

where $I(x) = e^{\int \frac{\sin x}{\cos x}\,dx}$
$= e^{-\int \frac{-\sin x}{\cos x}\,dx}$
$= e^{-\ln(\cos x)}$
$= \dfrac{1}{\cos x}$

$\therefore \ \dfrac{1}{\cos x}\dfrac{dy}{dx} + \dfrac{\sin x}{\cos^2 x}y = \dfrac{1}{\cos^2 x}$

$\therefore \ \dfrac{d}{dx}\left(\dfrac{y}{\cos x}\right) = \sec^2 x$

$\therefore \ \dfrac{y}{\cos x} = \displaystyle\int \sec^2 x\,dx = \tan x + c$

$\therefore \ \ y = \cos x\left(\dfrac{\sin x}{\cos x} + c\right)$

$\therefore \ \ y = \sin x + c\cos x$

But when $x = 0$, $y = 2 \ \Rightarrow \ 2 = 0 + c$
$\Rightarrow \ c = 2$

$\therefore \ \ y = \sin x + 2\cos x$

Note: $\sin x = x - \dfrac{x^3}{3!} + \dfrac{x^5}{5!} - \ ....$

$\cos x = 1 - \dfrac{x^2}{2!} + \dfrac{x^4}{4!} - \ ....$

$\therefore \ \ \sin x + 2\cos x$

$\approx x - \dfrac{x^3}{3!} + \dfrac{x^5}{5!} + 2 - \dfrac{2x^2}{2!} + \dfrac{2x^4}{4!} + \ ....$

$\approx 2 + x - x^2 - \tfrac{1}{6}x^3 + \tfrac{1}{12}x^4 + \ ....$

which checks with the answer in **a**.

5 a For $-1 < x < 1$,

$y = 1 + px + \dfrac{p(p-1)x^2}{2!} + \dfrac{p(p-1)(p-2)x^3}{3!} + \ ....$

$\therefore \ \dfrac{dy}{dx} = 0 + p + \dfrac{2p(p-1)x}{2!} + \dfrac{3p(p-1)(p-2)x^2}{3!} + \ ....$

$= p + p(p-1)x + \dfrac{p(p-1)(p-2)x^2}{2!} + \ ....$

$\therefore \ x\dfrac{dy}{dx} = px + p(p-1)x^2 + \dfrac{p(p-1)(p-2)x^3}{2!} + \ ....$

$\therefore \ (1+x)\dfrac{dy}{dx} = \dfrac{dy}{dx} + x\dfrac{dy}{dx},$

{a sum of two convergent series}
$= p + [p(p-1) + p]x$

$+ \left[\dfrac{p(p-1)(p-2)}{2!} + p(p-1)\right]x^2 + \ ....$

where the general term is:

$\left[\dfrac{p(p-1)\ ....\ (p-n)}{n!} + \dfrac{p(p-1)\ ....\ (p-n+1)}{(n-1)!}\right]x^n$

$= \dfrac{p(p-1)\ ....\ (p-n+1)}{n!}\,[(p-n) + n]x^n$

$= p\left[\dfrac{p(p-1)\ ....\ (p-n+1)}{n!}\,x^n\right]$

Hence

$(1+x)\dfrac{dy}{dx} = p + p\displaystyle\sum_{n=1}^{\infty}\dfrac{p(p-1)\ ....\ (p-n+1)x^n}{n!}$

$= py \ $ as required

b $(1+x)\dfrac{dy}{dx} = py$

$\dfrac{1}{y}\dfrac{dy}{dx} = \dfrac{p}{1+x}$

$\therefore \displaystyle\int \dfrac{1}{y}\,dy = \int \dfrac{p}{1+x}\,dx$

$\therefore \ \ln|y| = p\ln|1+x| + c$, where c is a constant

Since $|x| < 1$, we have $y = A(1+x)^p$, where $A = e^c$ is a constant.

c Since $y(x) = \displaystyle\sum_{n=0}^{\infty} \dfrac{p(p-1)\,....\,(p-n+1)x^n}{n!}$ is a

solution to the differential equation,

$y(x) = \displaystyle\sum_{n=0}^{\infty} \dfrac{p(p-1)\,....\,(p-n+1)x^n}{n!} = A(1+x)^p$

for some constant A.

Now $y(0) = 1$

$\therefore \ \ 1 = A(1+0)^p$

$\therefore \ \ A = 1$

Thus $y(x) = \displaystyle\sum_{n=0}^{\infty} \dfrac{p(p-1)\,....\,(p-n+1)x^n}{n!} = (1+x)^p$

for all $|x| < 1$, that is $x \in\,]-1,\,1[$.

REVIEW SET A

1 $\ln x$ and x are continuous for all $x > 0$

The limit has type $\frac{\infty}{\infty}$, so we can use l'Hôpital's Rule.

$\therefore \ \ \displaystyle\lim_{x\to\infty} \dfrac{\ln x}{x} = \lim_{x\to\infty} \dfrac{\frac{1}{x}}{x}$ {l'Hôpital's Rule}

$= 0$

2 As $x \to 0$, $e^x \sin x \to 0$ also

The limit has type $\frac{0}{0}$, so we can use l'Hôpital's Rule.

$\therefore \ \ \displaystyle\lim_{x\to 0} \dfrac{e^x \sin x}{x}$

$= \displaystyle\lim_{x\to 0} \dfrac{e^x \sin x + e^x \cos x}{1}$ {l'Hôpital's Rule}

$= 1(0) + 1(1)$

$= 1$

3 **a** $\displaystyle\lim_{n\to\infty} \dfrac{8 - 2n - 2n^2}{4 + 6n + 7n^2}$

$= \displaystyle\lim_{n\to\infty} \dfrac{\frac{8}{n^2} - \frac{2}{n} - 2}{\frac{4}{n^2} + \frac{6}{n} + 7}$

$= \dfrac{0 - 0 - 2}{0 + 0 + 7}$

$= -\frac{2}{7}$

b If n is even, $u_n = 3 + \dfrac{1}{n} + 2n$ which diverges as $n \to \infty$

$\therefore \ \ 3 + \dfrac{1}{n} + n[1 + (-1)^n]$ diverges

c $\displaystyle\lim_{n\to\infty} \dfrac{2n + 13}{\sqrt{6n^2 + 5n - 7}}$

$= \displaystyle\lim_{n\to\infty} \dfrac{2n + 13}{\sqrt{n^2\left(6 + \frac{5}{n} - \frac{7}{n^2}\right)}}$

$= \displaystyle\lim_{n\to\infty} \dfrac{2n + 13}{n\sqrt{6 + \frac{5}{n} - \frac{7}{n^2}}}$

$= \displaystyle\lim_{n\to\infty} \dfrac{2 + \frac{13}{n}}{\sqrt{6 + \frac{5}{n} - \frac{7}{n^2}}}$

$= \dfrac{2}{\sqrt{6}}$

$= \dfrac{\sqrt{6}}{3}$

d $\displaystyle\lim_{n\to\infty} \arctan n = \dfrac{\pi}{2}$

4 $\dfrac{1}{1^3 + 1} + \dfrac{2}{2^3 + 1} + \dfrac{3}{3^3 + 1} + \dfrac{4}{4^3 + 1} + \,....$

$= \displaystyle\sum_{n=1}^{\infty} \dfrac{n}{n^3 + 1}$ which is $\leqslant \displaystyle\sum_{n=1}^{\infty} \dfrac{n}{n^3} = \sum_{n=1}^{\infty} \dfrac{1}{n^2}$

But $\displaystyle\sum_{n=1}^{\infty} \dfrac{1}{n^2}$ converges   {p-series test}

$\Rightarrow \displaystyle\sum_{n=1}^{\infty} \dfrac{n}{n^3 + 1}$ converges   {Comparison test}

5 **a** $1 + \dfrac{3x}{x-2} + \left(\dfrac{3x}{x-2}\right)^2 + \left(\dfrac{3x}{x-2}\right)^3 + \,....$ is a geometric

series with $u_1 = 1$ and $r = \dfrac{3x}{x-2}$

$\therefore$ the series converges when $|r| = \left|\dfrac{3x}{x-2}\right| < 1$

$\Rightarrow$ $|3x| < |x-2|$

$\Rightarrow$ $|3x|^2 < |x-2|^2$

$\Rightarrow$ $9x^2 - (x-2)^2 < 0$

$\Rightarrow$ $(3x + x - 2)(3x - x + 2) < 0$

$\Rightarrow$ $(4x - 2)(2x + 2) < 0$

$\Rightarrow \ \ -1 < x < \frac{1}{2}$

Note: The ratio test could have also been used.

b $\displaystyle\sum_{n=0}^{\infty} \left(\dfrac{3x}{x-2}\right)^n = \dfrac{u_1}{1 - r}$

$= \dfrac{1}{1 - \frac{3x}{x-2}} \times \dfrac{x-2}{x-2}$

$= \dfrac{x-2}{x - 2 - 3x}$

$= \dfrac{x-2}{-2x - 2}$

$= \dfrac{2 - x}{2x + 2}$ {$-1 < x < \frac{1}{2}$}

c Differentiating the result in **b** with respect to x:

$$\frac{d}{dx}\sum_{n=0}^{\infty}\left(\frac{3x}{x-2}\right)^n = \frac{1}{2}\frac{d}{dx}\left(\frac{2-x}{x+1}\right)$$

$$\therefore \quad \sum_{n=0}^{\infty}\left(\frac{d}{dx}\left(\frac{3x}{x-2}\right)^n\right) = \frac{1}{2}\frac{d}{dx}\left(\frac{2-x}{x+1}\right)$$

$$\therefore \quad \sum_{n=0}^{\infty}n\left(\frac{3x}{x-2}\right)^{n-1}\left[\frac{3(x-2)-3x(1)}{(x-2)^2}\right]$$

$$= \frac{1}{2}\left[\frac{(-1)(x+1)-(2-x)1}{(x+1)^2}\right]$$

$$\therefore \quad \sum_{n=0}^{\infty}n\left(\frac{3x}{x-2}\right)^{n-1}\times\frac{-6}{(x-2)^2} = \frac{1}{2}\left[\frac{-3}{(x+1)^2}\right]$$

$$\therefore \quad \sum_{n=0}^{\infty}\frac{n(3x)^{n-1}}{(x-2)^{n+1}} = \frac{1}{4(x+1)^2}$$

6 $x + \dfrac{x^2}{1-x} + \dfrac{x^3}{(1-x)^2} + \ldots = \displaystyle\sum_{n=1}^{\infty}\frac{x^n}{(1-x)^{n-1}}$

The series is geometric with $u_1 = x$, $r = \dfrac{x}{1-x}$, but we will use the Ratio test.

If $a_n = \dfrac{x^n}{(1-x)^{n-1}}$, $\dfrac{a_{n+1}}{a_n} = \dfrac{x^{n+1}}{(1-x)^n}\times\dfrac{(1-x)^{n-1}}{x^n}$

$$= \frac{x}{1-x}$$

$\therefore \displaystyle\sum_{n=1}^{\infty} a_n$ converges for $\left|\dfrac{a_{n+1}}{a_n}\right| = \left|\dfrac{x}{1-x}\right| < 1$

$$\therefore \qquad |x| < |1-x|$$
$$\therefore \qquad |x|^2 < |1-x|^2$$
$$\therefore \qquad x^2 - (1-x)^2 < 0$$
$$\therefore \qquad (x+1-x)(x-1+x) < 0$$
$$\therefore \qquad 2x - 1 < 0$$
$$\therefore \qquad x < \tfrac{1}{2}$$

7 $\sin(x) = x - \dfrac{x^3}{3!} + \dfrac{x^5}{5!} - \dfrac{x^7}{7!} + \dfrac{x^9}{9!} - \ldots$

$\therefore \sin(x^2) = x^2 - \dfrac{x^6}{3!} + \dfrac{x^{10}}{5!} - \dfrac{x^{14}}{7!} + \dfrac{x^{18}}{9!} - \ldots$

$\therefore \displaystyle\int_0^1 \sin(x^2)\,dx = \left[\dfrac{x^3}{3} - \dfrac{x^7}{42} + \dfrac{x^{11}}{1320} - \dfrac{x^{15}}{75\,600} + \ldots\right]_0^1$

$$\approx \tfrac{1}{3} - \tfrac{1}{42} + \tfrac{1}{1320} - \tfrac{1}{75\,600}$$

$$\approx 0.310$$

Check: GDC gives $\approx 0.310\,268$

8 $P(X = x) = \dfrac{e^{-\lambda}\lambda^x}{x!}$ where $x = 0, 1, 2, 3, 4, \ldots$

$$\therefore \quad \sum_{x=0}^{\infty}\frac{e^{-\lambda}\lambda^x}{x!} = e^{-\lambda}\sum_{x=0}^{\infty}\frac{\lambda^x}{x!}$$

$$= e^{-\lambda}e^{\lambda}$$

$$\left\{\text{as } \sum_{x=0}^{\infty}\frac{\lambda^x}{x!} \text{ is the Maclaurin series for } e^{\lambda}\right\}$$

$$= e^0$$

$$= 1$$

9 a, b

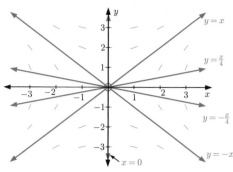

$\dfrac{dy}{dx} = \dfrac{x}{y} = k$ where $k = 0, \pm1, \pm4$

$\therefore$ we have isoclines $x = 0$, $y = \pm x$, $y = \pm\tfrac{1}{4}x$

10 $\dfrac{dy}{dx} = \dfrac{xy}{x-1}$

$$\therefore \quad \frac{1}{y}\frac{dy}{dx} = \frac{x}{x-1}$$

$$\therefore \quad \frac{1}{y}\frac{dy}{dx} = \frac{x-1+1}{x-1} = 1 + \frac{1}{x-1}$$

$$\therefore \quad \int \frac{1}{y}\frac{dy}{dx}\,dx = \int\left(1 + \frac{1}{x-1}\right)dx$$

$$\therefore \quad \ln|y| = x + \ln|x-1| + c$$

But, when $x = 2$, $y = 2$ $\Rightarrow$ $\ln 2 = 2 + c$

$$\Rightarrow \qquad c = \ln 2 - 2$$

$$\therefore \quad \ln|y| = x + \ln|x-1| + \ln 2 - 2$$

$\therefore$ $\ln|y| - \ln|2(x-1)| = x - 2$

$$\therefore \quad \ln\left|\frac{y}{2(x-1)}\right| = x - 2$$

$$\therefore \quad \left|\frac{y}{2(x-1)}\right| = e^{x-2}$$

$$\therefore \quad \frac{y}{2(x-1)} = \pm e^{x-2}$$

But $x = 2$, $y = 2$ does not satisfy the negative solution

$$\therefore \quad y = 2(x-1)e^{x-2}$$

11 $\dfrac{dy}{dx} - \left(\dfrac{1}{x}\right)y = \sqrt{x}$ has $I(x) = e^{\int -\frac{1}{x}\,dx}$

$$= e^{-\ln x}$$

$$= e^{\ln x^{-1}}$$

$$= \frac{1}{x}$$

$$\therefore \quad \frac{1}{x}\frac{dy}{dx} - \frac{1}{x^2}y = x^{-\frac{1}{2}}$$

$$\therefore \quad \frac{d}{dx}\left(\frac{y}{x}\right) = x^{-\frac{1}{2}}$$

$$\therefore \quad \frac{y}{x} = \int x^{-\frac{1}{2}}\,dx$$

$$\therefore \quad \frac{y}{x} = \frac{x^{\frac{1}{2}}}{\frac{1}{2}} + c$$

$$\therefore \quad y = 2x\sqrt{x} + cx$$

But when $x = 4$, $y = 0 \Rightarrow 0 = 16 + 4c$
$$\Rightarrow c = -4$$
Thus $y = 2x\sqrt{x} - 4x$

12

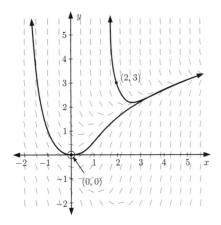

REVIEW SET B

1 a If n is even, $u_n = \dfrac{2n-1}{n} = 2 - \dfrac{1}{n}$

If n is odd, $u_n = \dfrac{-(2n-1)}{n} = -2 + \dfrac{1}{n}$

$\therefore$ $u_n \to 2$ if n is even and $u_n \to -2$ if n is odd

$\therefore$ $\{u_n\}$ is divergent   {has more than one limit}

b $u_n = \dfrac{(0.9)^n}{1 + (0.1)^n}$

But as $n \to \infty$, $a^n \to 0$ for $0 < a < 1$

$\therefore$ $\lim\limits_{n \to \infty} u_n = \dfrac{0}{1+0} = 0$

c $u_n = \left(\sqrt{n+5} - \sqrt{n-1}\right)\left(\dfrac{\sqrt{n+5} + \sqrt{n-1}}{\sqrt{n+5} + \sqrt{n-1}}\right)$

$= \dfrac{(n+5) - (n-1)}{\sqrt{n+5} + \sqrt{n-1}}$

$= \dfrac{6}{\sqrt{n+5} + \sqrt{n-1}}$

where $\sqrt{n+5}$ and $\sqrt{n-1} \to \infty$ as $n \to \infty$

$\therefore$ $\lim\limits_{n \to \infty} u_n = 0$

d $u_n = \dfrac{n^2}{3n+1} - \dfrac{2n^3}{6n^2+1}$

$= \dfrac{6n^4 + n^2 - 6n^4 - 2n^3}{(3n+1)(6n^2+1)}$

$= \dfrac{n^2 - 2n^3}{(3n+1)(6n^2+1)}$

$= \dfrac{\frac{1}{n} - 2}{\left(3 + \frac{1}{n}\right)\left(6 + \frac{1}{n^2}\right)}$

$\therefore$ $\lim\limits_{n \to \infty} u_n = \dfrac{-2}{3 \times 6} = -\dfrac{1}{9}$

2 $x + \dfrac{x^2}{2} + \dfrac{x^3}{3} + \dfrac{x^4}{4} + ... = \sum\limits_{n=1}^{\infty} \dfrac{x^n}{n}$

Now $\lim\limits_{n \to \infty} \left| \dfrac{a_{n+1}}{a_n} \right| = \lim\limits_{n \to \infty} \left| \dfrac{x^{n+1}}{n+1} \times \dfrac{n}{x^n} \right|$

$= \lim\limits_{n \to \infty} |x| \left(\dfrac{n}{n+1} \right)$

$= |x|$

Thus $\lim\limits_{n \to \infty} \left| \dfrac{a_{n+1}}{a_n} \right| < 1$ provided $|x| < 1$

$\therefore$ $\sum\limits_{n=1}^{\infty} \dfrac{x^n}{n}$ is absolutely convergent and hence convergent for

$-1 < x < 1$ and is divergent for $|x| > 1$.

When $x = 1$, $\sum\limits_{n=1}^{\infty} \dfrac{x^n}{n} = \sum\limits_{n=1}^{\infty} \dfrac{1}{n}$ which diverges

{p-series test}

When $x = -1$, $\sum\limits_{n=1}^{\infty} \dfrac{x^n}{n} = \sum\limits_{n=1}^{\infty} \dfrac{(-1)^n}{n}$, which is an

alternating series with $b_n = \dfrac{1}{n}$

Now $0 < b_{n+1} < b_n$ and $b_n \to 0$

$\therefore$ $\sum\limits_{n=1}^{\infty} \dfrac{(-1)^n}{n!}$ converges

{Alternating series test}

3 $\sum\limits_{k=1}^{\infty} \sin\left(\dfrac{(k-1)\pi}{2k} \right)$ has $a_k = \sin\left(\dfrac{(k-1)\pi}{2k} \right)$

$\therefore$ $a_k = \sin\left[\left(\dfrac{1}{2} - \dfrac{1}{2k} \right) \pi \right]$

$\therefore$ $\lim\limits_{k \to \infty} a_k = \sin\left(\dfrac{\pi}{2} \right) = 1$

Since $\lim\limits_{k \to \infty} a_k \neq 0$, $\sum\limits_{k=1}^{\infty} \sin\left(\dfrac{(k-1)\pi}{2k} \right)$ diverges.

{Test for divergence}

4 $\dfrac{r + r^2}{1 + r^2} \geqslant 1$ for all $r \geqslant 1$

$\therefore$ $\dfrac{1+r}{1+r^2} \geqslant \dfrac{1}{r}$

$\therefore$ $\sum\limits_{r=1}^{\infty} \dfrac{1+r}{1+r^2} \geqslant \sum\limits_{r=1}^{\infty} \dfrac{1}{r}$

But $\sum\limits_{r=1}^{\infty} \dfrac{1}{r}$ diverges   {p-series test}

$\therefore$ $\sum\limits_{r=1}^{\infty} \dfrac{1+r}{1+r^2}$ diverges   {Comparison test}

5 a $S_n = \sum\limits_{k=3}^{n} \dfrac{(-1)^{k+1}}{\ln(k-1)}$

Consider $b_k = \dfrac{1}{\ln(k-1)}$ where $k \geqslant 3$

Now $y = \ln x$ is an increasing function for all $x > 0$.

$\therefore$ $\dfrac{1}{\ln x}$ is decreasing for all $x > 0$

$\therefore$ b_k is decreasing for all $k \geqslant 3$

And, as $b_k > 0$ for all $k \geqslant 3$

$$S_n = \sum_{k=3}^{n} \dfrac{(-1)^{k+1}}{\ln(k-1)} \quad \text{converges} \quad \{\text{Alternating series test}\}$$

b Now $|S - S_{10}| \leqslant b_{11}$ when $S = \lim_{n \to \infty} S_n$

{Alternating Series Estimation Theorem}

$\therefore$ $|S - S_{10}| \leqslant \dfrac{1}{\ln 10}$

$\therefore$ $|S - S_{10}| \leqslant 0.4343$ {4 s.f.}

6 The Taylor series expansion of e^x is:

$$e^x = 1 + x + \dfrac{x^2}{2!} + \dfrac{x^3}{3!} + \dfrac{x^4}{4!} + \dots.$$

$$\therefore \ e^{x-1} = 1 + (x-1) + \dfrac{(x-1)^2}{2!} + \dfrac{(x-1)^3}{3!}$$

$$+ \dfrac{(x-1)^4}{4!} + \dots.$$

$\therefore$ $(x-1)e^{x-1} \approx (x-1) + (x-1)^2 + \tfrac{1}{2}(x-1)^3$

7 If $y = ax + b$ is a solution of $\dfrac{dy}{dx} = 4x - 2y$

then $a = 4x - 2(ax + b)$ for all x

$\therefore$ $a = (4 - 2a)x - 2b$ for all x

$\therefore$ $4 - 2a = 0$ and $a = -2b$

$\therefore$ $a = 2$ and $b = -1$

8

$$\dfrac{dy}{dx} = 2xy^2 - y^2 = (2x - 1)y^2$$

$\therefore$ $\dfrac{1}{y^2}\dfrac{dy}{dx} = 2x - 1$

$\therefore$ $\displaystyle\int y^{-2}\dfrac{dy}{dx}\,dx = \int (2x-1)\,dx$

$\therefore$ $\displaystyle\int y^{-2}\,dy = \int (2x-1)\,dx$

$\therefore$ $\dfrac{y^{-1}}{-1} = \dfrac{2x^2}{2} - x + c$

$\therefore$ $\dfrac{-1}{y} = x^2 - x + c$

$\therefore$ $y = \dfrac{-1}{x^2 - x + c}$

9

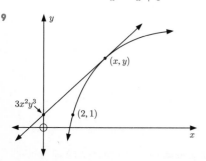

The equation of the tangent is $y = mx + c$

$\therefore$ $y = \dfrac{dy}{dx}x + 3x^2y^3$

$\therefore$ $x\dfrac{dy}{dx} = y - 3x^2y^3$ {see **Exercise N** question **8**}

Let $y = vx$,   so $\dfrac{dy}{dx} = \dfrac{dv}{dx}x + v$

Hence, $x^2\dfrac{dv}{dx} + vx = vx - 3x^2v^3x^3$

$\therefore$ $x^2\dfrac{dv}{dx} = -3x^2v^3x^3$

$\therefore$ $\dfrac{1}{v^3}\dfrac{dv}{dx} = -3x^3$

$\therefore$ $\displaystyle\int v^{-3}\dfrac{dv}{dx}\,dx = -3\int x^3\,dx$

$\therefore$ $\dfrac{v^{-2}}{-2} = \dfrac{-3x^4}{4} + c$

$\therefore$ $-\tfrac{1}{2}\left(\dfrac{x}{y}\right)^2 = -\tfrac{3}{4}x^4 + c$

But when $x = 2$, $y = 1$

$\therefore$ $-\tfrac{1}{2}(4) = -12 + c$

$\therefore$ $c = 10$

$\therefore$ $\left(\dfrac{x}{y}\right)^2 = \tfrac{3}{2}x^4 - 20$

$\therefore$ $\dfrac{x^2}{y^2} = \dfrac{3x^4 - 40}{2}$

$\therefore$ $y^2 = \dfrac{2x^2}{3x^4 - 40}$

$\therefore$ $y = \pm\sqrt{\dfrac{2x^2}{(3x^4 - 40)}}$

When $x = 2$, $y = \pm\sqrt{\tfrac{8}{8}} = \pm1$ indicates that the solution is

$$y = \sqrt{\dfrac{2x^2}{3x^4 - 40}}.$$

10 From equation **a**, $\dfrac{dy}{dx} = 1$ at $(0, 0)$

$\therefore$ **a** has slope field **B**.

From equation **b**, $\dfrac{dy}{dx} = 0$ at $(2, 2)$

$\therefore$ **b** has slope field **C**.

Consequently **c** has slope field **A**.

11   **a** $\dfrac{1}{P} + \dfrac{1}{400 - P} = \dfrac{400 - P + P}{P(400 - P)}$

$$= \dfrac{400}{P(400 - P)}$$

b Notice that as P is growing $\dfrac{dP}{dt} > 0$

$\therefore$ $0.2P\left(1 - \dfrac{P}{400}\right) > 0$

$\therefore \quad \dfrac{P(400-P)}{400} > 0$

$\therefore \quad P(400-P) > 0$

Sign diagram of $P(400-P)$ is:

$\therefore \quad 0 < P < 400 \quad .... \ (*)$

Now as $\dfrac{dP}{dt} = 0.2P\left(1 - \dfrac{P}{400}\right)$

$\therefore \quad \dfrac{dP}{dt} = \tfrac{1}{5}P\left(\dfrac{400-P}{400}\right)$

$\therefore \quad \dfrac{400}{P(400-P)}\dfrac{dP}{dt} = \tfrac{1}{5}$

$\therefore \quad \left(\dfrac{1}{P} + \dfrac{1}{400-P}\right)\dfrac{dP}{dt} = \tfrac{1}{5} \quad$ {from **a**}

$\therefore \quad \displaystyle\int \left(\dfrac{1}{P} + \dfrac{1}{400-P}\right)\dfrac{dP}{dt}\,dt = \int \tfrac{1}{5}\,dt$

$\therefore \quad \ln|P| + \tfrac{1}{-1}\ln|400-P| = \tfrac{1}{5}t + c$

But $P > 0$ and $400 - P > 0$ {from $*$}

$\therefore \quad \ln\left(\dfrac{P}{400-P}\right) = \dfrac{t}{5} + c$

$\therefore \quad \dfrac{P}{400-P} = e^{\frac{t}{5}+c}$

$\therefore \quad \dfrac{400-P}{P} = e^{-\frac{t}{5}-c}$

$\therefore \quad \dfrac{400}{P} - 1 = Ae^{-\frac{t}{5}}$

$\therefore \quad \dfrac{400}{P} = 1 + Ae^{-\frac{t}{5}}$

$\therefore \quad P = \dfrac{400}{1 + Ae^{-\frac{t}{5}}}$ people

But, when $t = 0$, $P = 154$

$\therefore \quad 154 = \dfrac{400}{1+A}$

$\therefore \quad 1 + A = \tfrac{400}{154}$

$\therefore \quad A = \tfrac{400}{154} - 1$

$\therefore \quad A = \tfrac{123}{77}$

$\therefore \quad P = \dfrac{400}{1 + \frac{123}{77}e^{-\frac{t}{5}}}$ people

c When $t = 20$, $P = \dfrac{400}{1 + \frac{123}{77}e^{-4}} \approx 389$ people

d As $t \to \infty$, $e^{-\frac{t}{5}} \to 0$

$\therefore \quad P \to 400$ people

12 a $f(x) = \displaystyle\sum_{i=1}^{\infty} \dfrac{x^2}{(1+x^2)^i}$

$\therefore \quad f(0) = \displaystyle\sum_{i=1}^{\infty} \dfrac{(0)^2}{(1+(0)^2)^i}$

$\qquad = \displaystyle\sum_{i=1}^{\infty} \dfrac{0}{1^i}$

$\qquad = 0$

b $\left(\dfrac{1+x^2}{x^2}\right)f(x)$

$= \dfrac{1+x^2}{x^2}\left[\dfrac{x^2}{1+x^2} + \dfrac{x^2}{(1+x^2)^2} + \dfrac{x^2}{(1+x^2)^3} + ...\right]$

$= \left(\dfrac{1+x^2}{x^2}\right)\left(\dfrac{x^2}{1+x^2}\right)\left[1 + \dfrac{1}{1+x^2} + \dfrac{1}{(1+x^2)^2} + ...\right]$

$= 1 + \dfrac{1}{1+x^2} + \dfrac{1}{(1+x^2)^2} + ...$

$= \displaystyle\sum_{i=0}^{\infty} \dfrac{1}{1+x^2}$

$= \displaystyle\sum_{i=0}^{\infty} r^i \quad$ where $\quad r = \dfrac{1}{1+x^2}$

c The geometric series is convergent if $\qquad |r| < 1$

$\therefore \quad \left|\dfrac{1}{1+x^2}\right| < 1$

$\therefore \quad 1 < \left|1+x^2\right|$

$\therefore \quad 1 < 1+x^2$

$\therefore \quad 0 < x^2$

$\therefore \quad x \neq 0$

$\therefore \quad f(x)$ is convergent for all $x \neq 0$ and by **a** $f(x)$ is convergent for $x = 0$.

$\therefore \quad f(x) = \dfrac{x^2}{1+x^2}\displaystyle\sum_{i=0}^{\infty} r^i$, $r = \dfrac{1}{1+x^2}$ is convergent for all $x \in \mathbb{R}$.

d For $x = 0$, $f(0) = 0$ from **a**.

For $x \neq 0$,

$f(x) = \dfrac{x^2}{1+x^2}\displaystyle\sum_{i=0}^{\infty} r^i$

$\qquad = \dfrac{x^2}{1+x^2}\left(\dfrac{1}{1-r}\right) \quad$ {Geometric series}

$\qquad = \dfrac{x^2}{1+x^2}\left(\dfrac{1}{1-\frac{1}{1+x^2}}\right)$

$\qquad = \dfrac{x^2}{1+x^2}\left(\dfrac{1+x^2}{1+x^2-1}\right)$

$\qquad = \dfrac{x^2}{1+x^2}\left(\dfrac{1+x^2}{x^2}\right)$

$\qquad = 1$

$\therefore \quad f(x) = \begin{cases} 1, & x \neq 0 \\ 0, & x = 0 \end{cases}$

e

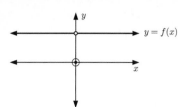

REVIEW SET C

1 a $n - \sqrt{n^2 + n} = \left(n - \sqrt{n^2 + n}\right)\left(\dfrac{n + \sqrt{n^2 + n}}{n + \sqrt{n^2 + n}}\right)$

$= \dfrac{n^2 - (n^2 + n)}{n + \sqrt{n^2 + n}}$

$= \dfrac{-n}{n\left[1 + \sqrt{1 + \frac{1}{n}}\right]}$

$\therefore \lim\limits_{n \to \infty} \left(n - \sqrt{n^2 + n}\right) = \lim\limits_{n \to \infty} \dfrac{-n}{n\left[1 + \sqrt{1 + \frac{1}{n}}\right]}$

$= \lim\limits_{n \to \infty} \dfrac{-1}{1 + \sqrt{1 + \frac{1}{n}}}$

$\{$since $n \neq 0\}$

$= \dfrac{-1}{1 + 1}$ $\{$since $\lim\limits_{n \to \infty} \frac{1}{n} = 0\}$

$= -\frac{1}{2}$

b Now $3^n \leqslant 3^n + 2^n \leqslant 3^n + 3^n$

$\therefore (3^n)^{\frac{1}{n}} \leqslant (3^n + 2^n)^{\frac{1}{n}} \leqslant (2 \times 3^n)^{\frac{1}{n}}$

$\therefore 3^1 \leqslant (3^n + 2^n)^{\frac{1}{n}} \leqslant 3 \times 2^{\frac{1}{n}}$

where $2^{\frac{1}{n}} \to 1$ as $n \to \infty$

Thus $\lim\limits_{n \to \infty} (3^n + 2^n)^{\frac{1}{n}} = 3$ $\{$Squeeze theorem$\}$

c As $\lim\limits_{n \to \infty} \dfrac{a^n}{n!} = 0$ for all $a > 0$ $\{$Theorem$\}$,

$\lim\limits_{n \to \infty} \dfrac{e^n}{n!} = 0$

d Let $u_n = (-1)^n n e^{-n} = (-1)^n \dfrac{n}{e^n}$

If n is even, $u_n = \dfrac{n}{e^n} \to 0^+$ as $n \to \infty$

If n is odd, $u_n = \dfrac{-n}{e^n} \to 0^-$ as $n \to \infty$

$\therefore \lim\limits_{n \to \infty} (-1)^n n e^{-n} = 0$

2 For $\sum\limits_{r=1}^{\infty} 3^{\frac{1}{r}}$ we let $a_r = 3^{\frac{1}{r}}$

Now $\lim\limits_{r \to \infty} a_r = 3^0 = 1 \neq 0$

$\therefore \sum\limits_{r=1}^{\infty} 3^{\frac{1}{r}}$ is not convergent $\{$Test of divergence$\}$

---

3 $\dfrac{1}{\ln(n^2)} = \dfrac{1}{2 \ln n}$

$\therefore \sum\limits_{n=2}^{\infty} \dfrac{1}{\ln(n^2)} = \frac{1}{2} \sum\limits_{n=2}^{\infty} \dfrac{1}{\ln n}$ .... $(*)$

But $n > \ln n$ for all $n \in \mathbb{Z}^+$

$\therefore \dfrac{1}{n} < \dfrac{1}{\ln n}$ for all $n \in \mathbb{Z}^+$

$\therefore \sum\limits_{n=2}^{\infty} \dfrac{1}{n} < \sum\limits_{n=2}^{\infty} \dfrac{1}{\ln n}$

But $\sum\limits_{n=2}^{\infty} \dfrac{1}{n}$ diverges $\{p$-series test$\}$

$\Rightarrow \sum\limits_{n=2}^{\infty} \dfrac{1}{\ln n}$ diverges $\{$Comparison test$\}$

Thus $\sum\limits_{n=2}^{\infty} \dfrac{1}{\ln(n^2)}$ diverges $\{$from $*\}$

4 a We use the Limit Comparison test which states:

"If $a_n > 0$ and $b_n > 0$ for all $n \in \mathbb{Z}^+$ and if

$\lim\limits_{n \to \infty} \dfrac{b_n}{a_n} = c$ where c is a real constant, then a_n and b_n

either converge or diverge together."

Suppose $\lim\limits_{n \to \infty} a_n = L$ and consider $b_n = a_n^2$

As $a_n > 0$ and $a_n^2 > 0$ and $\dfrac{b_n}{a_n} = a_n$

then $\lim\limits_{n \to \infty} \dfrac{b_n}{a_n} = \lim\limits_{n \to \infty} a_n = L$

$\Rightarrow$ both $\sum\limits_{n=1}^{\infty} a_n$ and $\sum\limits_{n=1}^{\infty} b_n$ converge

$\{$Limit Comparison test$\}$

$\Rightarrow \sum\limits_{n=1}^{\infty} a_n^2$ converges .... $(*)$

$\sum\limits_{n=1}^{\infty} \left(a_n - \dfrac{1}{n}\right)^2 = \sum\limits_{n=1}^{\infty} \left(a_n^2 - \dfrac{2a_n}{n} + \dfrac{1}{n^2}\right)$

$= \underbrace{\sum\limits_{n=1}^{\infty} a_n^2}_{(1)} - \underbrace{2\sum\limits_{n=1}^{\infty} \dfrac{a_n}{n}}_{(2)} + \underbrace{\sum\limits_{n=1}^{\infty} \dfrac{1}{n^2}}_{(3)}$

(1) is convergent $\{$from $*\}$

(2) is convergent as $\sum\limits_{n=1}^{\infty} \dfrac{a_n}{n} \leqslant \sum\limits_{n=1}^{\infty} a_n$ $\{$Comparison test$\}$

(3) is convergent $\{p$-series test$\}$

Thus $\sum\limits_{n=1}^{\infty} \left(a_n - \dfrac{1}{n}\right)^2$ converges.

b No, we can only apply the Limit Comparison test if $a_n \geqslant 0$ for all n.

For a counter example, consider $a_n = \dfrac{(-1)^n}{\sqrt{n}}$.

$\sum\limits_{n=1}^{\infty} a_n$ is convergent, but $\sum\limits_{n=1}^{\infty} a_n^2$ is divergent.

5 a $\dfrac{1}{x} - \dfrac{1}{x+1} = \dfrac{x+1-x}{x(x+1)}$

$= \dfrac{1}{x(x+1)}$

b Consider $f(x) = \dfrac{1}{x(x+1)}$.

If $x > 1$, $f(x)$ is > 0 and is continuous and

$$\int_1^\infty \frac{1}{x(x+1)}\,dx = \lim_{b\to\infty} \int_1^b \left(\frac{1}{x} - \frac{1}{x+1}\right) dx$$

$$= \lim_{b\to\infty} \Big[\ln x - \ln(x+1)\Big]_1^b$$

$$= \lim_{b\to\infty} \left[\ln\left(\frac{x}{x+1}\right)\right]_1^b$$

$$= \lim_{b\to\infty} \left(\ln\left(\frac{b}{b+1}\right) - \ln\left(\tfrac{1}{2}\right)\right)$$

$$= \lim_{b\to\infty} \left(\ln\left(\frac{1}{1+\frac{1}{b}}\right) + \ln 2\right)$$

$$= \ln 1 + \ln 2$$

$$= \ln 2$$

Hence, $\displaystyle\sum_{n=1}^\infty \frac{1}{n(n+1)}$ is convergent {Integral test}

c i S_n

$$= \sum_{i=1}^n \frac{1}{i(i+1)}$$

$$= \sum_{i=1}^n \frac{1}{i} - \frac{1}{i+1} \qquad \text{\{from \textbf{a}\}}$$

$$= \left(\tfrac{1}{1} + \frac{1}{1+1}\right) + \left(\tfrac{1}{2} - \frac{1}{2+1}\right) + \left(\tfrac{1}{3} - \frac{1}{3+1}\right)$$

$$+ \,.... + \left(\frac{1}{n-1} - \frac{1}{n-1+1}\right) + \left(\frac{1}{n} - \frac{1}{n+1}\right)$$

$$= 1 - \tfrac{1}{\cancel{2}} + \tfrac{1}{\cancel{2}} - \tfrac{1}{\cancel{3}} + \tfrac{1}{\cancel{3}} - \tfrac{1}{\cancel{4}} + /... + \frac{1}{\cancel{n-1}} - \frac{1}{\cancel{n}} + \frac{1}{\cancel{n}}$$

$$- \frac{1}{n+1}$$

$$= 1 - \frac{1}{n+1}$$

ii $\displaystyle\sum_{n=1}^\infty \frac{1}{n(n+1)} = \lim_{n\to\infty} S_n$

$$= \lim_{n\to\infty} \left(1 - \frac{1}{n+1}\right)$$

$$= 1, \quad \text{since } \lim_{n\to\infty} \frac{1}{n+1} = 0$$

6 $f(x) = \ln(1+x), \; 0 \leqslant x < 1$

$$\therefore \; f'(x) = \frac{1}{1+x} = (1+x)^{-1}$$

$$f''(x) = -1(1+x)^{-2}$$

$$f'''(x) = (-1)(-2)(1+x)^{-3}$$

$$f^{(4)}(x) = (-1)(-2)(-3)(1+x)^{-4}$$

$$\therefore \; f^{(n+1)}(x) = (-1)(-2)(-3)\,....\,(-n)(1+x)^{-n-1}$$

$$\therefore \; f^{(n+1)}(x) = \frac{(-1)^n n!}{(1+x)^{n+1}}$$

Thus $f^{(n+1)}(c) = \dfrac{(-1)^n n!}{(1+c)^{n+1}}$

Now $\ln(1+x) = T_n(x) + R_n(x : 0)$

$$\downarrow$$
$$\text{first } n \text{ terms}$$
$$\text{of Taylor series}$$

where $|R_n(x : 0)| = \left|\dfrac{f^{(n+1)}(c)x^{n+1}}{(n+1)!}\right|$

and c lies between 0 and 1 $\Rightarrow$ $1 < 1+c < 2$

Thus $|R_n(x : 0)| = \dfrac{n!}{(1+c)^{n+1}} \dfrac{|x|^{n+1}}{(n+1)!}$

$$= \left(\frac{x}{1+c}\right)^{n+1} \frac{1}{n+1}$$

But $0 \leqslant x < 1$ and $1 < 1+c < 2$

$$\Rightarrow \; 0 \leqslant \frac{x}{1+c} \leqslant 1$$

$$\therefore \; |R_n| \leqslant \frac{1}{n+1} \quad \left\{\text{as } \left(\frac{x}{1+c}\right)^{n+1} \to 0\right\}$$

7 $1 - x + x^2 - x^3 + x^4 - x^5 + \,....$ is a geometric series with $u_1 = 1$ and $r = -x$

So, its sum is $\dfrac{u_1}{1-r}$ for $|r| < 1$

$$= \frac{1}{1+x} \quad \text{for } |x| < 1$$

Thus $\displaystyle\sum_{n=0}^\infty (-x)^n = \frac{1}{1+x}$ for $-1 < x < 1$

$$\therefore \; \int_0^x \sum_{n=0}^\infty (-t)^n \, dt = \int_0^x \frac{1}{1+t} \, dt$$

$$\therefore \; \sum_{n=0}^\infty (-1)^n \int_0^x t^n \, dt = \Big[\ln(1+t)\Big]_0^x$$

$$\therefore \; \sum_{n=0}^\infty (-1)^n \left[\frac{t^{n+1}}{n+1}\right]_0^x = \ln(1+x) - \ln 1$$

$$\therefore \; \ln(1+x) = \sum_{n=0}^\infty \frac{(-1)^n x^{n+1}}{n+1}$$

$$= x - \frac{x^2}{2} + \frac{x^3}{3} - \frac{x^4}{4} + \frac{x^5}{5} - \,....$$

8 $\dfrac{dy}{dx} = x - 2y$ and when $x = 1$, $y = 2$

Now $x_{n+1} = x_n + 0.1$ and $y_{n+1} = y_n + 0.1 f(x_n, y_n)$
$$= y_n + 0.1(x_n - 2y_n)$$
$$= 0.1 x_n + 0.8 y_n$$

$x_0 = 1$	$y_0 = 2$
$x_1 = 1.1$	$y_1 = 1.7$
$x_2 = 1.2$	$y_2 = 1.47$
$x_3 = 1.3$	$y_3 = 1.296$
$x_4 = 1.4$	$y_4 = 1.1668$
$x_5 = 1.5$	$y_5 = 1.073\,44$
$x_6 = 1.6$	$y_6 = 1.008\,752$

$$\therefore \; y_6 \approx 1.009 \quad \text{\{to 4 s.f.\}}$$

9 **a** If V is the volume of water remaining then $4 - V$ has escaped.

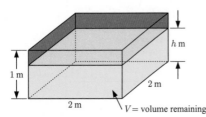

$V = $ volume remaining

$$\therefore \quad \frac{d}{dt}(4 - V) \propto \sqrt{h}$$

$$\therefore \quad -\frac{dV}{dt} = kh^{\frac{1}{2}}$$

$$\therefore \quad \frac{dV}{dt} = -kh^{\frac{1}{2}} \text{ m}^3/\text{min}$$

b But $V = 2 \times 2 \times h$ m^3

$$\therefore \quad V = 4h$$

$$\therefore \quad \frac{dV}{dt} = 4\frac{dh}{dt} = -kh^{\frac{1}{2}}$$

$$\therefore \quad \frac{dh}{dt} = -\frac{k}{4}h^{\frac{1}{2}}$$

c From **b**, $\dfrac{dt}{dh} = -\dfrac{4}{k}h^{-\frac{1}{2}}$

$$\therefore \quad t = -\frac{4}{k}\frac{h^{\frac{1}{2}}}{\frac{1}{2}} + c$$

$$\therefore \quad t = -\frac{8}{k}\sqrt{h} + c \quad .... \text{ (1)}$$

But when $t = 0$, $h = 1 \Rightarrow 0 = -\dfrac{8}{k} + c$

$$\Rightarrow \quad c = \frac{8}{k}$$

Thus $t = \dfrac{8}{k}(1 - \sqrt{h})$ .... (2) {in (1)}

and when $t = 2$, $h = 0.81 \Rightarrow 2 = \dfrac{8}{k}(0.1)$

$$\Rightarrow \quad \frac{8}{k} = 20$$

$$\therefore \quad t = 20(1 - \sqrt{h}) \quad \{\text{in (2)}\}$$

$$\therefore \quad \text{when } h = 0, \ t = 20 \text{ min}$$

10 $\dfrac{dy}{dx} = \dfrac{x}{y} + \dfrac{y}{x}$

Let $y = vx$, so $\dfrac{dy}{dx} = \dfrac{dv}{dx}x + v$

$$\therefore \quad \frac{dv}{dx}x + v = \frac{x}{vx} + \frac{vx}{x}$$

$$\therefore \quad \frac{dv}{dx}x + \not{v} = \frac{1}{v} + \not{v}$$

$$\therefore \quad v\frac{dv}{dx} = \frac{1}{x}$$

$$\therefore \quad \int v\frac{dv}{dx}\,dx = \int \frac{1}{x}\,dx$$

$$\therefore \quad \frac{v^2}{2} = \ln|x| + c$$

$$\therefore \quad \frac{y^2}{x^2} = 2\ln|x| + 2c$$

$$\therefore \quad y^2 = 2x^2(\ln|x| + c)$$

11 $\dfrac{dy}{dx} + (\cot x)y = \cos x$ has $I(x) = e^{\int \cot x\,dx}$

$$= e^{\int \frac{\cos x}{\sin x}\,dx}$$

$$= e^{\ln(\sin x)}$$

$$= \sin x$$

$$\therefore \quad \sin x\frac{dy}{dx} + \cos x \times y = \sin x\cos x$$

$$\therefore \quad \frac{d}{dx}(y\sin x) = \tfrac{1}{2}\sin 2x$$

$$\therefore \quad y\sin x = \tfrac{1}{2}\int \sin 2x\,dx$$

$$\therefore \quad y\sin x = \tfrac{1}{2}\left(\tfrac{1}{2}\right)(-\cos 2x) + c$$

$$\therefore \quad y\sin x = -\tfrac{1}{4}\cos 2x + c$$

But when $x = \frac{\pi}{2}$, $y = 0$

$$\therefore \quad 0 = -\tfrac{1}{4}\cos \pi + c$$

$$\therefore \quad c = \tfrac{1}{4}(-1) = -\tfrac{1}{4}$$

$$\therefore \quad y\sin x = -\tfrac{1}{4}(\cos 2x + 1)$$

$$\therefore \quad y = \frac{-\tfrac{1}{4}(2\cos^2 x)}{\sin x}$$

$$\therefore \quad y = -\frac{\cos^2 x}{2\sin x}$$

REVIEW SET D

1 **a** $u_n = \dfrac{3 \times 5 \times 7 \times .... \times (2n + 1)}{2 \times 5 \times 8 \times .... \times (3n - 1)}$

Consider $a_n = \dfrac{2n + 1}{3n - 1}$

$$\therefore \quad a_{n+1} - a_n = \frac{2(n + 1) + 1}{3(n + 1) - 1} - \frac{2n + 1}{3n - 1}$$

$$= \frac{2n + 3}{3n + 2} - \frac{2n + 1}{3n - 1}$$

$$= \frac{(2n + 3)(3n - 1) - (2n + 1)(3n + 2)}{(3n + 2)(3n - 1)}$$

$$= \frac{\not{6n^2} + \not{7n} - 3 - \not{6n^2} - \not{7n} - 2}{(3n + 2)(3n - 1)}$$

$$= \frac{-5}{(3n + 2)(3n - 1)}$$

$$\therefore \quad a_{n+1} - a_n < 0 \text{ for all } n$$

$$\therefore \quad a_{n+1} < a_n \text{ for all } n$$

$$\therefore \quad \{a_n\} \text{ is strictly decreasing}$$

$$\Rightarrow \quad \tfrac{7}{8}, \tfrac{9}{11}, \tfrac{11}{14}, ... \text{ decrease}$$

Hence, $u_n < \left(\frac{3}{2}\right)\left(\frac{7}{8}\right)^n$, for $n > 3$

In fact $0 < u_n < \left(\frac{3}{2}\right)\left(\frac{7}{8}\right)^n$

where $\left(\frac{7}{8}\right)^n \to 0$ as $n \to \infty$ $\{0 < c < 1 \Rightarrow c^n \to 0\}$

Thus $\lim\limits_{n \to \infty} u_n = 0$ {Squeeze theorem}

b

$u_n = n\left(2\cos\left(\frac{1}{n}\right) - \sin\left(\frac{1}{n}\right) - 2\right)$

$= n\left(2\left[1 - 2\sin^2\left(\frac{1}{2n}\right)\right] - \sin\left(\frac{1}{n}\right) - 2\right)$

$\{\cos 2\theta = 1 - 2\sin^2 \theta\}$

$= n\left(-4\sin^2\left(\frac{1}{2n}\right) - \sin\left(\frac{1}{n}\right)\right)$

$= -4n\left(\frac{\sin\left(\frac{1}{2n}\right)}{\left(\frac{1}{2n}\right)}\right)^2 \times \left(\frac{1}{2n}\right)^2 - n\left(\frac{\sin\left(\frac{1}{n}\right)}{\left(\frac{1}{n}\right)}\right) \times \frac{1}{n}$

$= -\frac{1}{n}\left(\frac{\sin\left(\frac{1}{2n}\right)}{\left(\frac{1}{2n}\right)}\right)^2 - \left(\frac{\sin\left(\frac{1}{n}\right)}{\frac{1}{n}}\right)$

Using $\lim\limits_{\theta \to 0} \frac{\sin\theta}{\theta} = 1$ with $\theta = \frac{1}{2n}$ and $\theta = \frac{1}{n}$,

$\lim\limits_{n \to \infty} u_n = 0(1)^2 - 1$

$= -1$

2 Consider $\displaystyle\int_2^\infty \frac{1}{x(\ln x)^2}\, dx$

$= \lim\limits_{b \to \infty} \left(\displaystyle\int_2^b \frac{1}{x(\ln x)^2}\, dx\right)$

$= \lim\limits_{b \to \infty} \left(\displaystyle\int_2^b \underbrace{(\ln x)^{-2}\left(\frac{1}{x}\right)}_{[f(x)]^n f'(x)}\, dx\right)$

$= \lim\limits_{b \to \infty} \left[\frac{(\ln x)^{-1}}{-1}\right]_2^b$

$= \lim\limits_{b \to \infty} \left[\frac{-1}{\ln x}\right]_2^b$

$= \lim\limits_{b \to \infty} \left(\frac{-1}{\ln b} + \frac{1}{\ln 2}\right)$

$= 0 + \frac{1}{\ln 2}$

$= \frac{1}{\ln 2}$

$\therefore \displaystyle\int_2^\infty \frac{1}{x(\ln x)^2}\, dx$ is convergent

$\Rightarrow \displaystyle\sum_{n=2}^\infty \frac{1}{n(\ln n)^2}$ is convergent   {Integral test}

3 $\displaystyle\sum_{n=1}^\infty \frac{(x-3)^n}{n^{\frac{3}{2}}}$ has $a_n = \frac{(x-3)^n}{n^{\frac{3}{2}}}$

$\therefore \lim\limits_{n \to \infty}\left|\frac{a_{n+1}}{a_n}\right| = \lim\limits_{n \to \infty}\left|\frac{(x-3)^{n+1}}{(n+1)^{\frac{3}{2}}} \times \frac{n^{\frac{3}{2}}}{(x-3)^n}\right|$

$= \lim\limits_{n \to \infty}\left|(x-3)\left(\frac{n}{n+1}\right)^{\frac{3}{2}}\right|$

Now as $n \to \infty$, $\left(\frac{n}{n+1}\right)^{\frac{3}{2}} \to 1^{\frac{3}{2}} = 1$

$\therefore \lim\limits_{n \to \infty}\left|\frac{a_{n+1}}{a_n}\right| = |x-3|$

Hence $\displaystyle\sum_{n=1}^\infty \frac{(x-3)^n}{n^{\frac{3}{2}}}$ is convergent for $|x-3| < 1$

$\Rightarrow -1 < x - 3 < 1$

$\Rightarrow 2 < x < 4$

<u>Case $x = 2$</u>

We have $\displaystyle\sum_{n=1}^\infty \frac{(-1)^n}{n^{\frac{3}{2}}}$ where $b_n = \frac{1}{n^{\frac{3}{2}}}$ is positive and

decreasing for all $n \in \mathbb{Z}^+$ and $\lim\limits_{n \to \infty} b_n = 0$

$\therefore \displaystyle\sum_{n=1}^\infty \frac{(-1)^n}{n^{\frac{3}{2}}}$ is convergent   {Alternating series test}

<u>Case $x = 4$</u>

We have $\displaystyle\sum_{n=1}^\infty \frac{1}{n^{1.5}}$ which converges as $p > 1$ {p-series test}

$\therefore \displaystyle\sum_{n=1}^\infty \frac{(x-3)^n}{n^{\frac{3}{2}}}$ is convergent on $2 \leqslant x \leqslant 4$

So, the radius of convergence is 1 and the interval of convergence is $x \in [2, 4]$.

4 $\displaystyle\sum_{n=0}^\infty \left(\frac{n}{n+5}\right)^n$ has $a_n = \left(\frac{n}{n+5}\right)^n = \left(\frac{1}{1 + \frac{5}{n}}\right)^n$

where $\lim\limits_{n \to \infty} a_n = \frac{1}{e^5} \neq 0$ $\left\{\lim\limits_{n \to \infty}\left(1 + \frac{k}{n}\right)^n = e^k\right\}$

$\therefore \displaystyle\sum_{n=0}^\infty \left(\frac{n}{n+5}\right)^n$ diverges   {Test for divergence}

5 The Taylor series for $f(x) = e^x$ is:

$e^x = f(0) + xf'(0) + \frac{x^2 f''(0)}{2!} + \dots + \frac{x^n f^{(n)}(0)}{n!}$

$\qquad + \frac{f^{(n+1)}(c)x^{n+1}}{(n+1)!}$

where $f^{(n)}(0) = e^0 = 1$ and $f^{(n+1)}(c) = e^c$

So, $e^x = 1 + x + \frac{x^2}{2!} + \frac{x^3}{3!} + \dots + \frac{x^n}{n!} + \frac{e^c x^{n+1}}{(n+1)!}$

where c lies between 0 and x.

Thus when $x = 0.3$,

$$e^{0.3} = 1 + 0.3 + \frac{(0.3)^2}{2!} + \frac{(0.3)^3}{3!} + \ldots + \frac{(0.3)^n}{n!}$$

$$+ \frac{e^c(0.3)^{n+1}}{(n+1)!} \quad \text{where} \ 0 < c < 0.3$$

So, we require $\dfrac{e^{0.3}(0.3)^{n+1}}{(n+1)!} < 0.0005$

$\{$giving e^c its maximum value$\}$

$$\Rightarrow \quad \frac{(0.3)^{n+1}}{(n+1)!} < 0.000\,37$$

If $n = 3$, $\dfrac{(0.3)^4}{4!} = 0.000\,34$ which is close to $0.000\,37$

But $\dfrac{(0.3)^3}{3!} = 0.0045$ so we use $n = 4$

Thus $e^{0.3} \approx 1 + 0.3 + \dfrac{(0.3)^2}{2!} + \dfrac{(0.3)^3}{3!} + \dfrac{(0.3)^4}{4!}$

$$\approx 1.350$$

6 $xy\dfrac{dy}{dx} = 1 + x + y^2$ where $y(1) = 0$

Let $y = vx$ $\quad \therefore \quad \dfrac{dy}{dx} = \dfrac{dv}{dx}x + v$

$\therefore \ x(vx)\left(\dfrac{dv}{dx}x + v\right) = 1 + x + v^2x^2$

$\therefore \ x^3 v \dfrac{dv}{dx} + x^2 v^2 = 1 + x + x^2 v^2$

$\therefore \quad v\dfrac{dv}{dx} = x^{-3} + x^{-2}$

$\therefore \ \displaystyle\int v\dfrac{dv}{dx}\,dx = \int (x^{-3} + x^{-2})\,dx$

$\therefore \ \displaystyle\int v\,dv = \dfrac{x^{-2}}{-2} + \dfrac{x^{-1}}{-1} + c$

$\therefore \quad \dfrac{v^2}{2} = \dfrac{-1}{2x^2} - \dfrac{1}{x} + c$

$\therefore \quad \dfrac{y^2}{2x^2} = \dfrac{-1}{2x^2} - \dfrac{1}{x} + c$

$\therefore \quad y^2 = -1 - 2x + 2cx^2$

But when $x = 1$, $y = 0$

$\therefore \quad 0 = -1 - 2 + 2c$

$\therefore \quad 2c = 3$

Thus $y^2 = 3x^2 - 2x - 1$

7 a The Taylor series for $f(x) = e^x$ is:

$$e^x = 1 + x + \frac{x^2}{2!} + \frac{x^3}{3!} + \ldots + \frac{x^n}{n!} + R_n(x : 0)$$

where $R_n(x : 0) = \dfrac{f^{(n+1)}(c)x^{n+1}}{(n+1)!} = \dfrac{e^c x^{n+1}}{(n+1)!}$

If we let $x = 1$,

$$e = 1 + 1 + \frac{1}{2!} + \frac{1}{3!} + \ldots + \frac{1}{n!} + \frac{e^c}{(n+1)!}$$

where c lies between 1 and 0.

$$\therefore \quad e = \sum_{k=0}^{n} \frac{1}{k!} + \frac{e^c}{(n+1)!}, \quad 0 < c < 1$$

$$\therefore \quad e - \sum_{k=0}^{n} \frac{1}{k!} = \frac{e^c}{(n+1)!}, \quad 0 < c < 1$$

b i From the result in **a**,

$$\frac{e^0}{(n+1)!} < e - \sum_{k=0}^{n} \frac{1}{k!} < \frac{e^1}{(n+1)!}$$

$$\therefore \quad \frac{1}{(n+1)!} < e - \sum_{k=0}^{n} \frac{1}{k!} < \frac{3}{(n+1)!}$$

ii Multiplying this inequality by $n!$ gives

$$\frac{1}{n+1} < e\,n! - \sum_{k=0}^{n} \frac{n!}{k!} < \frac{3}{n+1}$$

Now $n \geqslant 3 \ \Rightarrow \ n + 1 \geqslant 4$

$$\Rightarrow \quad \frac{3}{n+1} \leqslant \frac{3}{4}$$

$$\therefore \quad \frac{1}{n+1} < e\,n! - \sum_{k=0}^{n} \frac{n!}{k!} \leqslant \frac{3}{4}$$

c Suppose e is rational, that is, $e = \dfrac{p}{q}$ where p and q are positive integers.

$$\therefore \quad \frac{1}{n+1} < \frac{p}{q}\,n! - \sum_{k=0}^{n} \frac{n!}{k!} \leqslant \frac{3}{4}$$

We now choose n sufficiently large so that $n > q$.

$$\therefore \quad p\frac{n!}{q} \ \text{is an integer}$$

Also $\dfrac{n!}{k!}$ is an integer as $k \leqslant n$

Thus $\dfrac{p}{q}n! - \displaystyle\sum_{k=0}^{n} \frac{n!}{k!} \in \mathbb{Z}$

But $0 < \dfrac{1}{n+1} < \dfrac{p}{q}n! - \displaystyle\sum_{k=0}^{n} \frac{n!}{k!} \leqslant \dfrac{3}{4} < 1$ which is a contradiction as no integer lies between 0 and 1.

$\therefore$ the supposition that e is rational is false.

$\Rightarrow \ e$ is irrational.

8 $\dfrac{dy}{dx} + \left(\dfrac{3}{x}\right)y = 8x^4$, $y(1) = 0$ has $I(x) = e^{\int \frac{3}{x}\,dx}$

$$= e^{3\ln x}$$

$$= x^3$$

$\therefore \ x^3\dfrac{dy}{dx} + 3x^2 y = 8x^7$

$\therefore \ \dfrac{d}{dx}(x^3 y) = 8x^7$

$\therefore \ x^3 y = \displaystyle\int 8x^7$

$\therefore \ x^3 y = \dfrac{8x^8}{8} + c$

$\therefore \ y = x^5 + \dfrac{c}{x^3}$

But when $x = 1$, $y = 0 \ \Rightarrow \ 0 = 1 + c$

$$\Rightarrow \quad c = -1$$

Thus, $y = x^5 - \dfrac{1}{x^3}$

9 The gradient of the tangent at P is $\dfrac{dy}{dx}$.

But $(3x, 0)$ and $\left(0, \dfrac{3y}{2}\right)$ lie on the tangent.

$$\therefore \quad \frac{dy}{dx} = \frac{\frac{3y}{2} - 0}{0 - 3x} = -\frac{y}{2x}$$

$$\therefore \quad \frac{1}{y}\frac{dy}{dx} = -\frac{1}{2x}$$

$$\therefore \quad \int \frac{1}{y}\frac{dy}{dx}\,dx = -\tfrac{1}{2}\int \frac{1}{x}\,dx$$

$$\therefore \quad \ln|y| = -\tfrac{1}{2}\ln|x| + c$$

$$\therefore \quad 2\ln|y| + \ln|x| = 2c$$

$$\therefore \quad \ln(|y|^2\,|x|) = 2c$$

Now $(1, 5)$ lies on the curve

$$\therefore \quad \ln 25 = 2c$$

$$\therefore \quad |y^2|\,|x| = 25$$

$$\therefore \quad y^2 x = 25 \quad \{\text{since } x > 0\}$$

$$\therefore \quad y = \frac{5}{\sqrt{x}}$$

10

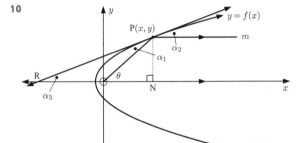

a
$$\alpha_1 = \alpha_2 \qquad \{\text{reflection property}\}$$
But $\alpha_1 = \alpha_3 \qquad \{\text{as [PM] is parallel to the } x\text{-axis}\}$
$$\therefore \quad \alpha_2 = \alpha_3$$
But $\theta = \alpha_1 + \alpha_3 \qquad \{\text{exterior angle of } \triangle \text{ theorem}\}$
$$\therefore \quad \theta = 2\alpha$$

b The gradient of the tangent at P is $\dfrac{dy}{dx}$.

$$\therefore \quad \frac{dy}{dx} = \tan\alpha \text{ as the tangent makes an angle of } \alpha \text{ with}$$

the x-axis, and $\tan\alpha = \dfrac{PN}{RN}$.

c
$$\tan(2\alpha) = \frac{2\tan\alpha}{1 - \tan^2\alpha} = \frac{y}{x} \quad \{\text{in } \triangle OPN\}$$

$$\therefore \quad 2x\tan\alpha = y - y\tan^2\alpha$$

$$\therefore \quad y\tan^2\alpha + 2x\tan\alpha - y = 0$$

$$\therefore \quad \tan\alpha = \frac{-2x \pm \sqrt{4x^2 - 4y(-y)}}{2y}$$

$$= \frac{-2x \pm 2\sqrt{x^2 + y^2}}{2y}$$

$$= \frac{\sqrt{x^2 + y^2} - x}{y} \quad \{\text{since } \tan\alpha > 0\}$$

d Let $r^2 = x^2 + y^2$, so $2r\dfrac{dr}{dx} = 2x + 2y\dfrac{dy}{dx}$

$$\therefore \quad y\frac{dy}{dx} = r\frac{dr}{dx} - x$$

But from **c**, $\tan\alpha = \dfrac{dy}{dx} = \dfrac{r - x}{y}$

$$\therefore \quad r\frac{dr}{dx} - x = r - x$$

$$\therefore \quad \frac{dr}{dx} = 1$$

$$\therefore \quad r = x + c$$

Thus $x^2 + y^2 = x^2 + 2cx + c^2$

$$\therefore \quad y^2 = 2cx + c^2$$

e $y = f(x)$ is half of a parabola since $x = \dfrac{1}{2c}y^2 - \dfrac{c}{2}$ where x is a quadratic in y.

11 a
$$\frac{dy}{dx} = y\ln x, \quad y(1) = 1$$

$$\therefore \quad \frac{d^2y}{dx^2} = \frac{dy}{dx}\ln x + y\left(\frac{1}{x}\right) = y(\ln x)^2 + \frac{y}{x}$$

$$\frac{d^3y}{dx^3} = \frac{dy}{dx}(\ln x)^2 + y\,2(\ln x)^1\frac{1}{x} + \frac{\frac{dy}{dx}x - y}{x^2}$$

$$= y(\ln x)^3 + \frac{2y\ln x}{x} + \frac{xy\ln x - y}{x^2}$$

$$\therefore \quad y(1) = 1, \ y'(1) = 0, \ y''(1) = 1, \ y'''(1) = -1$$

$$\therefore \quad T_3(x) = y(1) + y'(1)(x - 1) + \frac{y''(1)(x - 1)^2}{2!}$$

$$+ \frac{y'''(1)(x - 1)^3}{3!}$$

$$\therefore \quad T_3(x) = 1 + \frac{(x - 1)^2}{2!} - \frac{(x - 1)^3}{3!}$$

b Hence, $y \approx 1 + \tfrac{1}{2}(x - 1)^2 - \tfrac{1}{6}(x - 1)^3$

$$\therefore \quad y \approx \tfrac{5}{3} - \tfrac{3}{2}x + x^2 - \tfrac{1}{6}x^3$$

c
$$\frac{1}{y}\frac{dy}{dx} = \ln x$$

$$\therefore \quad \int \frac{1}{y}\frac{dy}{dx}\,dx = \int \ln x\,dx$$

$$\therefore \quad \int \frac{1}{y}\,dy = \int \ln x\,dx$$

$$\therefore \quad \ln|y| = x\ln x - x + c$$

But when $x = 1, \ y = 1 \ \Rightarrow \ 0 = 0 - 1 + c$
$$\Rightarrow \ c = 1$$

$$\therefore \quad \ln|y| - \ln x^x = 1 - x$$

$$\therefore \quad \ln\left(\frac{|y|}{x^x}\right) = 1 - x$$

$$\therefore \quad \frac{|y|}{x^x} = e^{1-x}$$

$$\therefore \quad y = x^x e^{1-x} \text{ as } y > 0$$

Check: When $x = 1.2$, from **b**, $y \approx 1.0187$
from **c**, $y \approx 1.0190$ ✓

INDEX